INSTRUCTOR'S MANUAL
WITH TEST ITEM FILE

Stanley C. Hatfield
Southwestern Illinois College

ESSENTIALS OF
GEOLOGY

TENTH EDITION

Frederick K. Lutgens | Edward J. Tarbuck | Dennis Tasa

PEARSON

Prentice Hall

Upper Saddle River, NJ 07458

Assistant Editor: Sean Hale
Project Manager: Crissy Dudonis
Acquisitions Editor: Drusilla Peters
Publisher, Geosciences: Dan Kaveney
Editor-in-Chief, Science: Nicole Folchetti
Assistant Managing Editor, Science: Gina M. Cheselka
Project Manager, Science: Ashley M. Booth
Supplement Cover Manager: Paul Gourhan
Supplement Cover Designer: Victoria Colotta
Operations Specialist: Amanda A. Smith
Director of Operations: Barbara Kittle

© 2009 Pearson Education, Inc.
Pearson Prentice Hall
Pearson Education, Inc.
Upper Saddle River, NJ 07458

All rights reserved. No part of this book may be reproduced, in any form or by any means, without permission in writing from the publisher.

Pearson Prentice Hall™ is a trademark of Pearson Education, Inc.

The author and publisher of this book have used their best efforts in preparing this book. These efforts include the development, research, and testing of the theories and programs to determine their effectiveness. The author and publisher make no warranty of any kind, expressed or implied, with regard to these programs or the documentation contained in this book. The author and publisher shall not be liable in any event for incidental or consequential damages in connection with, or arising out of, the furnishing, performance, or use of these programs.

This work is protected by United States copyright laws and is provided solely for the use of instructors in teaching their courses and assessing student learning. Dissemination or sale of any part of this work (including on the World Wide Web) will destroy the integrity of the work and is not permitted. The work and materials from it should never be made available to students except by instructors using the accompanying text in their classes. All recipients of this work are expected to abide by these restrictions and to honor the intended pedagogical purposes and the needs of other instructors who rely on these materials.

Printed in the United States of America

10   9   8   7   6   5   4   3   2

ISBN-13:   978-0-13-604910-4

ISBN-10:   0-13-604910-9

Pearson Education Ltd., *London*
Pearson Education Australia Pty. Ltd., *Sydney*
Pearson Education Singapore, Pte. Ltd.
Pearson Education North Asia Ltd., *Hong Kong*
Pearson Education Canada, Inc., *Toronto*
Pearson Educación de Mexico, S.A. de C.V.
Pearson Education—Japan, *Tokyo*
Pearson Education Malaysia, Pte. Ltd.

Instructor's Manual Table of Contents

An Introduction to Geology

An Introduction to Geology begins with a discussion of the science of geology, including an explanation of the difference between physical geology and historical geology. Following an explanation of catastrophism and uniformitarianism is a brief overview of geologic time. The nature of scientific inquiry is presented, as well as a description of the major spheres of Earth's physical environment. The concept of Earth system science is followed by a discussion of the rock cycle and the nebular hypothesis. The chapter closes with an examination of the internal structure of Earth and an overview of plate tectonics.

Learning Objectives

After reading, studying, and discussing the chapter, students should be able to:

- Briefly define geology as a science.
- Explain the relationship between geology, people, and the environment.
- Discuss the history of geology, including the concepts of uniformitarianism and catastrophism.
- Briefly explain relative dating of geologic events and the geologic timescale.
- Briefly discuss the nature of scientific inquiry and scientific methods.
- Define and briefly discuss the major "spheres" of Earth.
- Explain Earth system science and the changes involved in natural systems.
- Discuss Earth as a system.
- Explain the concept of the rock cycle.
- Briefly discuss the formation of the solar system in the nebular hypothesis.
- Compare and contrast the layers of Earth that are defined by composition with those defined by physical properties.
- Discuss the theory of plate tectonics and list the three types of plate boundaries.

Chapter Outline

I. The science of geology
   A. Geology is the science that pursues an understanding of planet Earth
      1. Two broad areas of geology
         a. Physical geology—examines the materials composing Earth and seeks to understand the many processes that operate beneath and upon its surface
         b. Historical geology—seeks an understanding of the origin of Earth and its development through time

      2. Understanding Earth is challenging because it is a dynamic body with many interacting parts
   B. Historical notes about geology
      1. The nature of Earth has been a focus of study for centuries
         a. Early Greeks wrote about such topics as fossils, gems, earthquakes, and volcanoes more than 2,300 years ago
         b. Aristotle—the most influential Greek philosopher

© 2008 Pearson Education, Inc., Upper Saddle River, NJ. All rights reserved. This material is protected under all copyright laws as they currently exist. No portion of this material may be reproduced, in any form or by any means, without permission in writing from the publisher.

2. Catastrophism
   a. Archbishop James Ussher
      1. Mid-1600s
      2. Constructed a chronology of human and Earth history
      3. Earth was only a few thousand years old (created in 4004 B.C.)
   b. During the seventeenth and eighteenth century, the doctrine of catastrophism strongly influenced people's thinking about Earth
      1. Catastrophists believed that Earth's landscape had been shaped primarily by great catastrophes
      2. Features such as mountains and canyons were produced by sudden and often worldwide disasters
3. The birth of modern geology
   a. Modern geology began in the late 1700s with James Hutton
      1. Published *Theory of the Earth*
      2. Uniformitarianism
         a. Fundamental principle of geology
         b. The physical, chemical, and biological laws that operate today also operated in the geologic past
         c. Acceptance means the acceptance of a very long history for Earth
   b. Prior to Hutton, no one effectively demonstrated that geological processes occur over extremely long periods of time

II. Geologic time
   A. Geologists are now able to assign fairly accurate dates to events in Earth history
   B. Relative dating and the geologic timescale
      1. Relative dating means that dates are placed in their proper sequence or order without knowing their age in years
      2. Principles of relative dating include
         a. Law of superposition
         b. Principle of fossil succession

III. The nature of scientific inquiry
   A. Science assumes the natural world is
      1. Consistent and
      2. Predictable
   B. Goal of science is to
      1. Discover the underlying patterns in nature, and
         a. Use the knowledge to make predictions
   C. Scientists collect "facts" through observation and measurements
   D. How or why things happen are explained using a
      1. Hypothesis—a tentative (or untested) explanation
      2. Theory—a well-tested and widely accepted view that the scientific community agrees best explains certain observable facts
         a. A hypothesis that has survived extensive scrutiny
         b. Paradigm—a theory that is held with a very high degree of confidence because it explains a large number of interrelated aspects of the natural world
   E. Scientific methods
      1. Scientific method involves
         a. Gathering facts through observations and
         b. Formulate
            1. Hypotheses and
            2. Theories
      2. There is no fixed path that scientists follow that leads to scientific knowledge
      3. Many scientific investigations involve
         a. Collecting scientific facts through observation and measurement

© 2008 Pearson Education, Inc., Upper Saddle River, NJ. All rights reserved. This material is protected under all copyright laws as they currently exist. No portion of this material may be reproduced, in any form or by any means, without permission in writing from the publisher.

b. Developing one or more working hypotheses or models
c. Development of observations and experiments to test the hypothesis
d. Reexamine the hypothesis and either
   1. Accept
   2. Modify or
   3. Reject the model
4. Still other scientific discoveries result from
   a. Purely theoretical ideas that stand up to extensive examination
   b. Totally unexpected occurrences during an experiment

IV. A view of Earth
A. Earth is a planet that is
   1. Small
   2. Self-contained
   3. In some ways even fragile
B. Earth's four spheres
   1. Hydrosphere
      a. Water more than anything else makes Earth unique
      b. Global ocean—the most prominent feature of the hydrosphere
         1. Nearly 71% of Earth's surface
         2. About 97% of Earth's water
      c. Also includes the water found in streams, lakes, and glaciers
         1. Sources of fresh water
         2. Responsible for sculpting and creating many of Earth's varied landforms
   2. Atmosphere
      a. The life-giving gaseous envelope that surrounds Earth
      b. Without an atmosphere many of the processes that shape Earth's surface could not operate
   3. Biosphere
      a. Includes all life on Earth
      b. Influences the makeup and nature of the other three spheres

4. Geosphere
   a. Extends from the surface to the center of the planet
   b. Largest of Earth's four spheres

V. Earth as a system
A. Earth is a dynamic planet with many interacting parts or spheres
   1. This complex and continuously interacting whole is referred to as the Earth system
   2. System—a group of interacting, or independent, parts that form a complex whole
      a. e.g., Weather system
      b. e.g., Solar system
B. Parts of the Earth system are linked so that a change in one part can produce changes in any or all other parts
C. Characterized by processes that
   1. Vary on spatial scales from fractions of millimeter to thousands of kilometers
   2. Have timescales that range from milliseconds to billions of years
D. The Earth system is powered by energy from
   1. Sun—drives external processes that occur in the
      a. The atmosphere
      b. The hydrosphere, and
      c. At Earth's surface
   2. Earth's interior—heat remaining from the formation and heat that is continuously generated by radioactive decay powers the internal processes that produce
      a. Volcanoes
      b. Earthquakes, and
      c. Mountains
E. Humans are part of the Earth system

VI. The rock cycle: part of the Earth system
A. The loop that involves the processes by which one rock changes to another
B. Basic cycle ( ) denotes processes

© 2008 Pearson Education, Inc., Upper Saddle River, NJ. All rights reserved. This material is protected under all copyright laws as they currently exist. No portion of this material may be reproduced, in any form or by any means, without permission in writing from the publisher.

An Introduction to Geology

1. Magma
2. (Crystallization)
3. Igneous rock
4. (Weathering)
5. (Transportation)
6. (Deposition)
7. Sediment
8. (Lithification—convert into rock)
9. Sedimentary rock
10. (Heat and pressure)
11. Metamorphic rock
12. (Melting)
13. Magma
   C. Alternate paths
   1. e.g., Igneous rocks become metamorphic rocks
   2. e.g., Metamorphic and sedimentary rocks become sediment

VII. Early evolution of Earth
   A. Origin of Earth
      1. Most researchers believe that Earth and the other planets formed at essentially the same time from the same primordial material as the Sun
      2. Nebular hypothesis
         a. Solar system evolved from an enormous rotating cloud called the solar nebula
         b. Nebula was composed mostly of hydrogen and helium
         c. About 5 billion years ago, the nebula began to contract
         d. Assumes a flat, disk shape with the protosun (pre-Sun) at the center
         e. Inner planets begin to form from metallic and rocky clumps of substances with high melting points
         f. Larger outer planets began forming from fragments with a high percentage of ices—water, carbon dioxide, ammonia, and methane

   B. Formation of Earth's layered structure

1. As Earth formed, the decay of radioactive elements and heat from high-velocity impacts caused the temperature to increase
   a. Iron and nickel began to melt and sink toward the center
   b. Lighter rocky components floated outward, toward the surface
2. Gaseous material escaped from Earth's interior to produce the primitive atmosphere

VIII. Earth's internal structure
   A. Earth's internal layers can be defined by
      1. Chemical composition, and/or
      2. Physical properties
   B. Layers defined by composition
      1. Crust
         a. Thin, rocky outer skin
         b. Two divisions
            1. Oceanic crust
               a. Seven kilometers (5 miles thick)
               b. Composed of dark igneous rocks called basalt
            2. Continental crust
               a. Averages 35–40 kilometers (25 miles) thick
               b. Composition consists of many rock types
                  1. Upper crust has an average composition of a granitic rock
                  2. Lower crust is more akin to basalt
               c. Continental crust rocks are less dense and older than oceanic crust rocks
      2. Mantle
         a. Over 82% of Earth's volume
         b. Solid, rocky shell
         c. Extends to a depth of 2900 kilometers (1800 miles)
         d. Dominant rock in the uppermost mantle is peridotite

© 2008 Pearson Education, Inc., Upper Saddle River, NJ. All rights reserved. This material is protected under all copyright laws as they currently exist. No portion of this material may be reproduced, in any form or by any means, without permission in writing from the publisher.

3. Core
   a. Thought to be composed of an iron-nickel alloy with minor amounts of oxygen, silicon, and sulfur
   b. Due to the extreme pressure found in the core, the density is nearly 11 g/cm^3

C. Layers defined by physical properties
   1. Temperature, pressure, and density gradually increase with depth in Earth's interior
   2. Changes in temperature and pressure affect the physical properties and hence the mechanical behavior of Earth materials
   3. Five main layers of Earth based on physical properties and hence mechanical strength
      a. Lithosphere
         1. Consists of
            a. The crust and
            b. Uppermost mantle
         2. Relatively cool, rigid shell
         3. Averages about 100 kilometers in thickness, but may be 250 kilometers or more thick below the older portions of the continents
         4. Within the ocean basins it is only a few kilometers thick
      b. Asthenosphere ("weak sphere")
         1. Beneath the lithosphere, in the upper mantle
         2. Melting in the top portion
         3. Lithosphere is mechanically detached and is able to move independently of the asthenosphere
      c. Mesosphere (or lower mantle)
         1. Between 660 and 2900 kilometers
         2. Rocks are rigid but capable of very gradual flow
      d. Core
         1. Outer core

a. A liquid layer
b. Convective flow of metallic iron generates Earth's magnetic field
   2. Inner core
      a. Strong due to high pressure
      b. Solid

IX. Dynamic Earth
   A. The theory of plate tectonics
      1. Involves understanding the workings of our dynamic planet
      2. Began in the early part of the twentieth century with a proposal called continental drift – the idea that continents moved about the face of the planet
      3. Theory, called plate tectonics, has now emerged that provides geologists with the first comprehensive model of Earth's internal workings
         a. Earth's rigid outer shell (lithosphere) is divided into numerous slabs called plates
         b. The lithospheric plates move relative to each other at a very slow but continuous rate that averages about 5 centimeters (2 inches) a year
         c. The grinding movements of the plates
            1. Generates earthquakes
            2. Creates volcanoes, and
            3. Deforms large masses of rock into mountains
   B. Plate boundaries
      1. All major interactions among individual plates occurs along their boundaries
      2. Types of plate boundaries
         a. Divergent boundary – two plates move apart, resulting in upwelling of material from the mantle to create new seafloor
            1. Occurs mainly at the mid-ocean ridge

© 2008 Pearson Education, Inc., Upper Saddle River, NJ. All rights reserved. This material is protected under all copyright laws as they currently exist. No portion of this material may be reproduced, in any form or by any means, without permission in writing from the publisher.

2. Mechanism, called seafloor spreading, has created the floor of the Atlantic Ocean during the past 160 million years
3. Along divergent boundaries the oceanic lithosphere is elevated and forms a ridge because it is hot and occupies more volume than cooler rocks
   b. Convergent boundary—two plates move together
      1. Older oceanic plates return to the mantle along these boundaries
      2. Descending plates produce ocean trenches
      3. Subduction zones are plate margins where oceanic crust is being consumed
      4. Whenever continental lithosphere moves toward an adjacent slab of oceanic lithosphere, the less dense continental plate remains "floating" while the denser oceanic lithosphere sinks into the asthenosphere
      5. Where one oceanic plate is thrust beneath another, a chain of volcanic structures may eventually emerge from the sea as a volcanic island arc
      6. Collisions of continental lithosphere are responsible for the formation of major mountain belts such as the Himalayas, Alps, and Appalachians
   c. Transform fault boundaries
      1. Located where plates grind past each other without either generating new lithosphere or consuming old lithosphere
      2. Most are located along mid-ocean ridges
   d. Changing boundaries
      1. Individual plates may grow or diminish in area depending on the distribution of convergent and divergent boundaries
      2. New plate boundaries are created in response to changes in the forces acting on the lithosphere
      3. As long as Earth's internal heat engine is operating, the positions and shapes of the continents and ocean basins will change

Answers to the Review Questions

1. The science of geology is traditionally divided into two broad areas: physical and historical. Physical geology examines Earth's rocks and minerals and seeks to understand the processes that operate beneath and upon its surface. On the other hand, the aim of historical geology is to understand Earth's origin and how the planet changed through time. Historical geology strives to establish the chronology of physical and biological changes of the past 4.6 billion years.

2. Volcanoes, floods, earthquakes, and landslides are all examples of potential geologic hazards.

3. Aristotle's explanations of the natural world were not based on keen observations and experimentation, as modern science is. Instead, they were his opinions, based on the limited knowledge of his day. Unfortunately, many of his wrong interpretations continued to be believed for many centuries, thus thwarting the acceptance of better ideas based on observations.

© 2008 Pearson Education, Inc., Upper Saddle River, NJ. All rights reserved. This material is protected under all copyright laws as they currently exist. No portion of this material may be reproduced, in any form or by any means, without permission in writing from the publisher.

4. Catastrophists believed that Earth was a young planet and that its landscape was shaped by great catastrophes.

5. Uniformitarianism, a fundamental concept in modern geology, states that the physical, chemical, and biological laws that operate today have also operated in the geologic past. The uniformitarian view is one of a very old Earth, modified by processes that have been at work for a very long time.

6. The currently accepted age of the Earth is 4.5 to 4.6 billion years, based on meticulous experimental measurements of lead isotopes on meteoritic and terrestrial samples. The basic assumptions and results are supported by rubidium-strontium isotopic age determinations on meteorite samples. The oldest rocks yet dated formed about 4 billion years ago. Because Earth is a dynamic planet, most rocks we see formed much later during Earth's history and thus are much younger than the age of the Earth.

7. The principles used to establish the geologic timescale include the law of superposition—which establishes the sequence of rock layers, and the principle of fossil succession—fossil organisms succeed one another in a definite and determinable order, and, therefore, any time period can be recognized by its fossil content. These concepts enable geologists to correlate similar-age rocks anywhere in the world and to place them in their proper chronological order and position in the timescale.

8. A scientific hypothesis is a preliminary, untested explanation. On the other hand, a scientific theory is a well tested and widely accepted view that scientists agree best explains observable facts.

9. The four major spheres of our living environment are: (1) the atmosphere—the gaseous envelope surrounding our planet; (2) the hydrosphere—those environments (oceans, rivers, lakes, ice, groundwater, and water vapor in the atmosphere) involved in the hydrologic cycle; (3) the biosphere—the diverse, surficial, and near-surface environments that include all living organisms and their habitats; and (4) the solid earth—the soils, regolith, and crustal bedrock layers of Earth; it hosts most of the hydrosphere, forms the inorganic substrate for the biosphere, and interacts extensively with the atmosphere.

10. In an open system both energy and matter flow into and out of the system. Closed systems, however, are self-contained with regard to matter.

11. Positive-feedback mechanisms tend to enhance or drive changes in a system. By contrast, negative-feedback mechanisms work to maintain a system as it is (e.g., maintain the status quo).

12. The Earth system is driven by energy from two sources. The Sun provides the energy that drives the external processes that occur in the atmosphere and on Earth's surface. Internal processes, such as plate tectonics and volcanism, are driven by energy from Earth's interior. This internal energy is the result of leftover heat from the origin of Earth and also heat from the decay of radioactive elements.

13. Sedimentary rocks are composed of constituents derived from the disintegration and decomposition of other rocks (igneous, metamorphic, or sedimentary). Metamorphic rocks were once igneous, sedimentary, or metamorphic rocks that have since changed in texture and/or mineral composition in response to elevated temperatures, or elevated temperatures and pressures (deep burial). Igneous rocks form by cooling and crystallization of magmas; magmas form by melting of other igneous, sedimentary, or metamorphic rocks. Therefore, all rocks are the result of various processes acting upon preexisting rocks.

© 2008 Pearson Education, Inc., Upper Saddle River, NJ. All rights reserved. This material is protected under all copyright laws as they currently exist. No portion of this material may be reproduced, in any form or by any means, without permission in writing from the publisher.

14. About 5 billion years ago, a huge cloud of gases and minute rocky fragments began to contract under its own gravitational influence. As it contracted, the rotation of this nebular cloud caused it to assume a disk-like shape, with the protosun located at the center. Within the rotating disk, small eddy-like contractions formed the nuclei from which the planets would eventually develop. As the temperature began to drop, materials in the disk began to condense into small rocky and icy fragments. These fragments in turn were swept up by the protoplanets. Because of higher temperatures in the inner solar system, the innermost planets are made mostly of rocky material and lack the gases and ices, which are the main constituents of the outer planets.

15. Earth's compositional layers include (1) the crust, Earth's comparatively thin outer skin; (2) the mantle, a solid rocky shell that extends to a depth of about 2900 kilometers (1800 miles); and (3) the core, which can be further divided into the outer core, a molten metallic layer, and inner core, a solid iron-rich sphere.

16. The lithosphere, which averages about 100 kilometers in thickness, is the rigid outer layer of Earth, which includes the crust and part of the upper mantle. Beneath the lithosphere (to a depth of about 660 kilometers) lies a soft, relatively weak layer located in the upper mantle known as the asthenosphere.

17. Earth's youngest mountains tend to occur in two major zones. The first zone is the circum-Pacific belt, which includes the mountains of the western Americas and volcanic island arcs of the western Pacific. The second zone extends eastward from the Alps through Iran into the Himalayas. Note that the younger mountain belts on Earth generally occur as long, topographic features at the margins of continents.

18. Shields are relatively flat expanses of metamorphic rocks and associated igneous plutons found near the center or cores of the continents. The crystalline rocks in shields are typically Precambrian in age and highly deformed. Stable platforms are areas of the stable interior where the highly deformed rocks of the shield are covered by a thin veneer of sedimentary rocks. The sedimentary rocks are nearly horizontal except where they have been deformed to form large basins or domes.

19. Divergent boundaries: where plates are moving apart.

    Convergent boundaries: where plates are moving together.

    Transform boundaries: where plates slide past one another along faults.

20. Subduction zone—convergent boundary; San Andreas Fault—transform fault boundary; seafloor spreading—divergent boundary; Mount St. Helens—convergent boundary

Lecture outline, art-only, and animation PowerPoint presentations for each chapter of *Essentials of Geology* are available on the IRC DVD (ISBN 0-13-604914-1).

© 2008 Pearson Education, Inc., Upper Saddle River, NJ. All rights reserved. This material is protected under all copyright laws as they currently exist. No portion of this material may be reproduced, in any form or by any means, without permission in writing from the publisher.

<table>
<tr><td>Chapter</td><td rowspan="2"></td></tr>
</table>

Chapter 2
Minerals: Building Blocks of Rocks

Minerals: Building Blocks of Rocks begins by formally defining a mineral followed by an explanation of the difference between a mineral and a rock. Mineral composition is discussed along with atomic structure, which includes an explanation of elements, atoms, compounds, ions, and atomic bonding. Also investigated are isotopes and radioactivity. Following descriptions of the properties used in mineral identification, the silicate and nonsilicate mineral groups are examined. The chapter concludes with a discussion of mineral resources, reserves, and ores.

Learning Objectives

After reading, studying, and discussing the chapter, students should be able to:

- List the definitive characteristics that qualify certain Earth materials as minerals.
- Explain the difference between a mineral and a rock.
- Discuss the basic concepts of atomic structure as it relates to minerals.
- Compare and contrast the different types of chemical bonding.
- Explain what an isotope is and how it relates to radioactive decay.
- List and discuss in some detail the various physical properties of minerals.
- Explain the structure and importance of silicate minerals.
- List the common rock-forming silicate minerals and briefly discuss their physical properties.
- List other mineral groups and give an example of the important nonsilicate minerals.
- List the economic use of some nonsilicate minerals.
- Distinguish between mineral resources, reserves, and ores.

Chapter Outline

I. Minerals: The building blocks of rocks
  A. Mineral: definition
    1. Naturally occurring
    2. Inorganic
    3. Solid
    4. Orderly internal structure
    5. Definite chemical structure
  B. Rock: a solid, natural mass of mineral, or mineral-like, matter

II. Composition of minerals
  A. Elements
    1. Basic building blocks of minerals
    2. Over 100 are known (92 naturally occurring)
  B. Atoms

    1. Smallest particles of matter
    2. Retains all the characteristics of an element
  C. Atomic structure
    1. Nucleus, which contains
      a. Protons—positive electrical charges
      b. Neutrons—neutral electrical charges
    2. Electrons
      a. Surround nucleus
      b. Negatively charged zones called energy levels, or shells
    3. Atomic number is the number of protons in an atom's nucleus

© 2008 Pearson Education, Inc., Upper Saddle River, NJ. All rights reserved. This material is protected under all copyright laws as they currently exist. No portion of this material may be reproduced, in any form or by any means, without permission in writing from the publisher.

D. Bonding
   1. Forms a compound with two or more elements
   2. Ionic bonds
      a. Atoms give up or gain valence electrons to form ions
         1. Anion—negatively charged due to a gain of an electron(s)
         2. Cation—positively charged due to a loss of an electron(s)
      b. Ionic compounds consist of an orderly arrangement of oppositely charged ions
   3. Covalent bonds
      a. Atoms share electrons
      b. e.g., The gaseous elements oxygen (O_2) and hydrogen (H_2)
   4. Other bonds
      a. Both ionic and covalent bonds may occur in the same compound
      b. Metallic bonding—valence electrons are free to migrate
E. Isotopes and radioactive decay
   1. Mass number—the sum of the neutrons plus protons in an atom's nucleus
   2. Isotope—variants of the same element with more than one mass number
   3. Some isotopes have unstable nuclei and emit particles and energy in a process called radioactive decay

III. Physical properties of minerals
   A. Crystal form
      1. External expression of the orderly internal arrangement of atoms
      2. Crystal growth is often interrupted because of competition for space
   B. Luster
      1. Appearance of reflected light
      2. Two basic types
         a. Metallic
         b. Nonmetallic
   C. Color
      1. Often an unreliable diagnostic property
      2. Varieties of colors
         a. Exotic coloration
         b. Inherent coloration
   D. Streak

   1. Color of a mineral in its powdered form
   2. Helps to distinguish metallic luster
E. Hardness
   1. Resistance of a mineral to abrasion or scratching
   2. Mohs scale of hardness
F. Cleavage
   1. Tendency to break along planes of weak bonding
   2. Described by
      a. Number of planes
      b. Angles at which the planes meet
G. Fracture
   1. Absence of cleavage when broken
   2. Types
      a. Irregular
      b. Conchoidal
H. Specific gravity
   1. Ratio of the weight of a mineral to the weight of an equal volume of water
   2. Can be estimated by hefting the mineral
I. Other properties
   1. Taste
   2. Smell
   3. Elasticity
   4. Malleability
   5. Feel
   6. Magnetism
   7. Double refraction
   8. Reaction to hydrochloric acid

IV. Mineral groups
   A. General characteristics
      1. Nearly 4000 minerals have been named
      2. Rock-forming minerals
         a. No more than a few dozen
         b. Make up most of the rocks of Earth's crust
         c. Composed essentially of the eight elements that represent over 98% (by weight) of the continental crust
            1. Oxygen (O) (46.6% by weight)
            2. Silicon (Si) (27.7% by weight)
            3. Aluminum (Al)
            4. Iron (Fe)
            5. Calcium (Ca)
            6. Sodium (Na)

© 2008 Pearson Education, Inc., Upper Saddle River, NJ. All rights reserved. This material is protected under all copyright laws as they currently exist. No portion of this material may be reproduced, in any form or by any means, without permission in writing from the publisher.

7. Potassium (K)
8. Magnesium (Mg)

B. Silicates
   1. Most common mineral group
   2. Contain silicon-oxygen tetrahedron
      a. Four oxygen ions surrounding a much smaller silicon ion
      b. Complex ion with a negative four (–4) charge
   3. Other silicate structures
      a. Tetrahedra join to form
         1. Single chains
         2. Double chains
         3. Sheets, etc.
      b. Negative structures are neutralized by the inclusion of metallic cations that bond them together
         1. Ions of about the same size are able to substitute freely
         2. In some cases, ions that interchange do not have the same electrical charge
   4. Common silicate minerals
      a. Ferromagnesian (dark) silicates
         1. Olivine
            a. High-temperature silicate
            b. Forms small, rounded crystals
            c. Individual tetrahedron bonded together by a mixture of iron and magnesium ions
            d. No cleavage
         2. Pyroxene group
            a. Most common member— augite
            b. Tetrahedra are arranged in single chains bonded by iron and magnesium ions
            c. Cleavage present
         3. Amphibole group
            a. Most common member— hornblende
            b. Tetrahedra are arranged in double chains
            c. Cleavage present
         4. Biotite mica
            a. Tetrahedra are arranged in sheets
            b. Excellent cleavage in one direction
      b. Nonferromagnesian (light) silicates
         1. Muscovite mica
            a. Light color
            b. Excellent cleavage
         2. Feldspar
            a. Most common mineral group
            b. Two planes of cleavage
            c. Three-dimensional framework of tetrahedron
            d. Two different varieties of feldspar
               1. Potassium feldspar
               2. Plagioclase (sodium and calcium) feldspar
         3. Quartz
            a. Composed entirely of silicon and oxygen
            b. Three-dimensional framework of tetrahedron
         4. Clay
            a. Sheet structure
            b. Term used to describe a variety of complex minerals
            c. Most originate as products of chemical weathering

C. Important nonsilicate minerals
   1. Major groups
      a. Oxides
      b. Sulfides
      c. Sulfates
      d. Native elements
      e. Carbonates
      f. Hydroxides
      g. Phosphates
   2. Carbonates
      a. Two most common carbonate minerals
         1. Calcite (calcium carbonate)
         2. Dolomite (calcium/magnesium carbonate)
      b. Primary constituents in the sedimentary rocks limestone and dolostone
   3. Halite and gypsum
      a. Evaporite minerals
      b. Important nonmetallic resources
   4. Many other nonsilicate minerals have economic value
      a. Hematite (iron ore)
      b. Sphalerite (zinc ore)

© 2008 Pearson Education, Inc., Upper Saddle River, NJ. All rights reserved. This material is protected under all copyright laws as they currently exist. No portion of this material may be reproduced, in any form or by any means, without permission in writing from the publisher.

c. Galena (lead ore)

V. Mineral resources
  A. The endowment of useful minerals ultimately available commercially
  B. Mineral resources include
    1. Reserves – already identified deposits
    2. Known deposits that are not yet economically or technologically recoverable
  C. Ore
    1. A useful metallic mineral that can be mined at a profit
    2. Must be concentrated above its average crustal abundance
    3. Profitability may change because of economic changes
  D. The mechanisms that generate igneous, sedimentary, and metamorphic rocks play a major role in producing concentrated accumulations of useful elements

Answers to the Review Questions

1. In order to be considered a mineral, a substance must exhibit the following characteristics: (1) naturally occurring, (2) solid, (3) an orderly crystalline structure, (4) definite chemical composition, and (5) generally inorganic.

2. A rock is a more or less hardened (lithified) aggregate of minerals and/or amorphous solids such as natural glass and organic matter.

3. The particles are electrons, protons, and neutrons. The latter two are heavy particles found in the nucleus of an atom. Electrons are tiny, very lightweight particles that form a "cloud" surrounding the nucleus. The mass and charge data are as follows:
   proton—one atomic mass unit, 1+ electrical charge
   neutron—one atomic mass unit, electrically neutral
   electron—tiny fraction of one atomic mass unit, 1– electrical charge

4. (a) The number of protons—A neutral atom with 35 electrons has 35 protons. (b) The atomic number—The atomic number is 35, equal to the number of protons in the nucleus. (c) The number of neutrons—The mass number (80) is the sum of protons (35) and neutrons. Thus the nucleus contains 45 (80 – 35) neutrons.

5. They are the electrons of an atom that are involved in bonding.

6. In an ionic bond one or more valence electrons are transferred from one atom to another. However, in a covalent bond there is a sharing of valence electrons.

7. One or more valence electrons are simultaneously gained and lost by atoms participating in a chemical reaction. The atoms that gain electrons are negative ions; those that lose electrons are positive ions.

8. Isotopes of an element have varying numbers of neutrons in the nucleus and, hence, different atomic weights.

9. Usually crystal growth is interrupted because of competition for space. The result is an intergrown mass of small, closely spaced crystals, none of which exhibits its crystal form.

© 2008 Pearson Education, Inc., Upper Saddle River, NJ. All rights reserved. This material is protected under all copyright laws as they currently exist. No portion of this material may be reproduced, in any form or by any means, without permission in writing from the publisher.

10. Impurities often cause the same mineral to have many colors. For example, fluorite can be purple, clear, yellow, etc., while quartz can be practically any color.

11. The hardness test might help you make a determination.

12. Any mineral listed in Mohs scale, corundum for example, will scratch softer minerals (those with lower hardness values) and will not scratch harder minerals. Corundum would scratch virtually all other minerals, diamond being the lone exception. Thus corundum is widely used in abrasives and polishing compounds.

13. The specific gravity of water is 1 by definition. Thus equal volumes of water and gold would have their weights in the ratio 1:20. Since the 5 gallons of water weigh 40 pounds, the 5 gallons of gold will weigh about 800 pounds (25 liters × 20 kg/l = 500 kg).

14. The two most common elements in Earth's crust are oxygen and silicon.

15. "Ferromagnesian" is a word derived from the chemical elements magnesium and iron (ferro, ferrous, ferric, etc.). The term refers to rock-forming, silicate minerals that contain some iron (Fe) and/or magnesium (Mg) in addition to silicon and oxygen. Additional elements such as aluminum, sodium, and calcium may be present without changing the designation. Ferromagnesian minerals comprise most of the dark-colored (dark green and black) mineral grains in igneous rocks.

16. They are both micas with layered (sheet-silicate), internal, crystalline structures and one direction of perfect cleavage. Muscovite is the light-colored, potassium aluminum (K and Al) mica; biotite is the darker-colored, ferromagnesian mica (contains Mg and Fe).

17. No, because they both have similar colors. The best means of physically distinguishing between the two types of feldspars is to look for fine lines, called striations. Striations are found on some cleavage planes of plagioclase feldspar, but are not present on orthoclase feldspar.

18. (a) hornblende, (b) muscovite, (c) quartz, (d) olivine, (e) plagioclase feldspar, (f) carbonate minerals (calcite), halite, and/or gypsum

19. Both minerals are carbonates. Calcite reacts vigorously with diluted acids such as hydrochloric (HCl), with the formation of carbon dioxide (CO_2) gas bubbles. In contrast, dolomite must first be finely powdered before reacting vigorously enough with the same dilute acid to produce visible bubbling.

20. Mineral reserves are identified deposits from which minerals can be extracted profitably. The concept of a mineral resource has a broader meaning. In addition to including reserves, it also includes known deposits that are not yet economically or technologically recoverable, as well as deposits that are inferred to exist but not yet discovered.

© 2008 Pearson Education, Inc., Upper Saddle River, NJ. All rights reserved. This material is protected under all copyright laws as they currently exist. No portion of this material may be reproduced, in any form or by any means, without permission in writing from the publisher.

21. One way a mineral deposit could become profitable to extract is through an economic change; e.g., the demand for a metal may increase and cause a price increase. Also, if a technological advance allows the metal to be extracted at a lower cost, it may become profitable to extract and thus be reclassified as an ore.

Lecture outline, art-only, and animation PowerPoint presentations for each chapter of *Essentials of Geology* are available on the IRC DVD (ISBN 0-13-604914-1).

NOTES:

© 2008 Pearson Education, Inc., Upper Saddle River, NJ. All rights reserved. This material is protected under all copyright laws as they currently exist. No portion of this material may be reproduced, in any form or by any means, without permission in writing from the publisher.

Igneous Rocks

Igneous Rocks begins with a discussion of the crystallization of magma, followed by an examination of igneous rock textures and compositions. The discussion of igneous rock compositions includes examinations of Bowen's reaction series, magmatic differentiation, assimilation, and magma mixing. Granitic, andesitic, basaltic, and pyroclastic rocks are presented in detail. The chapter closes with a review of mineral resources and igneous processes.

Learning Objectives

After reading, studying, and discussing the chapter, students should be able to:

- Describe how igneous rocks form.
- Explain the difference between magma and lava.
- List the two criteria that are used to classify igneous rocks.
- Describe how the rate of cooling of magma influences the crystal size of igneous rocks.
- Relate the mineral makeup of an igneous rock to Bowen's reaction series.
- Describe the characteristics of basaltic and granitic rocks.
- Explain how economic deposits of gold, silver, and many other metals form.

Chapter Outline

I. Magma: The parent material of igneous rocks
  A. Igneous rocks form as molten rock cools and solidifies
  B. General characteristics of magma
    1. Parent material of igneous rocks
    2. Forms by a process called partial melting inside the Earth
    3. Magma that reaches the surface is called lava
    4. Rocks formed from magma at the surface are classified as extrusive, or volcanic rocks
    5. Rocks formed from magma that crystallizes at depth are termed intrusive, or plutonic
  C. The nature of magma
    1. Completely or partly molten material that cools and solidifies to form igneous rock
    2. Consists of three parts:
      a. A liquid portion, called melt, composed of mobile ions

      b. Solids, if any, are silicate minerals that have already crystallized from the melt
      c. Volatiles, gaseous components dissolved within the melt
        1. Water vapor (H_2O)
        2. Carbon dioxide (CO_2)
        3. Sulfur dioxide (SO_2)
  D. Crystallization of magma
    1. Generates various silicate minerals
    2. Cooling results in the ions arranging into orderly patterns and various minerals
    3. Size and arrangement of the mineral grains give an igneous rock its texture
    4. Igneous rocks are most often classified by their
      a. Texture, and
      b. Mineral composition

© 2008 Pearson Education, Inc., Upper Saddle River, NJ. All rights reserved. This material is protected under all copyright laws as they currently exist. No portion of this material may be reproduced, in any form or by any means, without permission in writing from the publisher.

II. Igneous textures
  A. Used to describe the overall appearance of a rock based on the size, shape, and arrangement of its interlocking mineral crystals
  B. Factors affecting crystal size
    1. Rate of cooling of the magma
       a. Slow rate promotes the growth of fewer but larger crystals
       b. Fast rate forms many small crystals
       c. Very fast rate forms glass
    2. Amount of silica present
    3. Amount of dissolved gases
  C. Types of igneous textures
    1. Aphanitic (fine-grained) texture
       a. Rapid rate of cooling of lava or magma
       b. Microscopic crystals
       c. May contain vesicles (voids)
    2. Phaneritic (coarse-grained) texture
       a. Slow cooling
       b. Crystals can be identified without a microscope
    3. Porphyritic texture
       a. Minerals form at different temperatures as well as differing rates
       b. Large crystals, called phenocrysts, embedded in a matrix of smaller crystals, called the groundmass
    4. Glassy texture
       a. Rapid cooling of molten rock
       b. e.g., obsidian
       c. Mainly from viscous (granitic) magma
    5. Pyroclastic texture
       a. Fragments ejected during a violent eruption
       b. Textures appear to be more similar to sedimentary rocks
    6. Pegmatitic texture
       a. Exceptionally coarse grained
       b. Form in the late stages of crystallization
       c. Most have compositions similar to granite

III. Igneous compositions
  A. Mainly silicate minerals
    1. Dark (or ferromagnesian) silicates
       a. Olivine
       b. Pyroxene
       c. Amphibole
       d. Biotite mica
    2. Light (or nonferromagnesian) silicates
       a. Quartz
       b. Muscovite mica
       c. Feldspars
  B. Granitic versus basaltic compositions
    1. Granitic composition
       a. Composed of light-colored silicates
       b. Referred to as being felsic (*f*eldspar and *si*lica)
       c. Rich in silica
       d. Major constituents of the continental crust
    2. Basaltic composition
       a. Composed of dark silicates and calcium-rich feldspar
       b. Referred to as being mafic (*m*agnesium and *f*errum, for iron)
       c. Darker and denser than granitic rocks
       d. Make up the ocean floor as well as many volcanic islands
  C. Other compositional groups
    1. Intermediate (or andesitic) composition
       a. Contain at least 25% dark silicate minerals
       b. Associated with volcanic activity
    2. Ultramafic
       a. e.g., peridotite
       b. Rare
  D. Silica content as an indicator of composition
    1. Silica content in crustal rocks ranges from
       a. A low of about 45% in ultramafic rocks to
       b. Over 70% in felsic rocks
    2. Influences a magma's behavior
       a. Granitic magma
          1. High silica content
          2. Viscous
          3. Liquid at temperatures as low as 700°C
       b. Basaltic magma
          1. Low in silica
          2. Fluid

© 2008 Pearson Education, Inc., Upper Saddle River, NJ. All rights reserved. This material is protected under all copyright laws as they currently exist. No portion of this material may be reproduced, in any form or by any means, without permission in writing from the publisher.

3. Crystallize at higher temperature
E. Naming igneous rocks
    1. Felsic (granitic) rocks
        a. Granite
            1. Phaneritic
            2. Twenty-five% quartz, about 65% feldspar
            3. May have a porphyritic texture
            4. Often by-products of mountain building
            5. Very abundant
            6. The term *granite* can cover rocks having a wide range of mineral compositions
        b. Rhyolite
            1. Extrusive equivalent of granite
            2. May contain glass fragments and voids
            3. Aphanitic
            4. Less common and less voluminous than granite
        c. Obsidian
            1. Dark-colored
            2. Glassy
        d. Pumice
            1. Volcanic
            2. Glassy texture
            3. Frothy mass
    2. Intermediate (andesitic) igneous rocks
        a. Andesite
            1. Fine-grained
            2. Volcanic origin
            3. Often resembles rhyolite
        b. Diorite
            1. Plutonic equivalent of andesite
            2. Coarse grained
            3. Intrusive
            4. Primarily sodium-rich plagioclase feldspar and amphibole
    3. Mafic (basaltic) igneous rocks
        a. Basalt
            1. Fine-grained
            2. Volcanic
            3. Composed primarily of pyroxene and calcium-rich plagioclase feldspar
            4. Most common extrusive igneous rock
        b. Gabbro
            1. Intrusive equivalent of basalt
            2. Composed primarily of pyroxene and calcium-rich plagioclase feldspar
            3. Makes up a significant percentage of the oceanic crust
    4. Pyroclastic rocks
        a. Fragments ejected during a volcanic eruption
        b. Varieties
            1. Tuff—ash-sized fragments
            2. Volcanic breccia—particles larger than ash

IV. Origin of magma
    A. Controversial topic
    B. Generating magma from solid rock
        1. Produced when essentially solid rock in the crust and upper mantle melts
        2. Role of heat
            a. The temperature increase within Earth's upper crust (called the geothermal gradient) averages between 20°C and 30°C per kilometer
            b. Rocks in the lower crust and upper mantle are near their melting points, additional heat to melt the rocks comes from
                1. Friction at subduction zones
                2. Heating as the rocks descend into the mantle
                3. Heat from rising hot mantle rocks
        3. Role of pressure
            a. An increase in confining pressure causes an increase in a rock's melting temperature; conversely, reducing the pressure lowers the melting temperature
            b. When confining pressure drops, decompression melting occurs
        4. Role of volatiles
            a. Volatiles (primarily water) cause rock to melt at lower temperatures
            b. Important where oceanic lithosphere descends into the mantle

© 2008 Pearson Education, Inc., Upper Saddle River, NJ. All rights reserved. This material is protected under all copyright laws as they currently exist. No portion of this material may be reproduced, in any form or by any means, without permission in writing from the publisher.

V. How magmas evolve
  A. A single volcano may extrude lavas exhibiting quite different compositions
  B. Bowen's reaction series and the composition of igneous rocks
    1. N.L. Bowen demonstrated that as a basaltic magma cools, minerals tend to crystallize in a systematic fashion based on their melting points
    2. During crystallization, the composition of the liquid portion of the magma continually changes
      a. Removal of elements by earlier-forming minerals
      b. Silica component of the melt becomes enriched as the magma evolves
      c. Minerals that remain in the melt can chemically react and change
    3. Ways that magma's composition changes
      a. Magmatic differentiation
        1. Minerals crystallize from magma in a systematic fashion
        2. Crystal settling causes a separation of the solid and liquid components
        3. Remaining melt will form a rock with a different chemical composition
        4. The formation of a secondary magma from a single parent magma is called magmatic differentiation
      b. Assimilation
        1. Changing a magma's composition by the incorporation of foreign matter
        2. May operate in a near-surface environment where rocks are brittle
      c. Magma mixing

    1. One magma body intrudes another
    2. May occur during the ascent of two chemically distinct magma bodies
  C. Partial melting and magma formation
    1. Incomplete melting of rocks is known as partial melting
    2. Rocks with a granitic composition are composed of minerals with the lowest melting (crystallization) temperatures—namely quartz and potassium feldspar
    3. Partial melting of rock separates the ions from minerals with lower melting temperatures from those with higher melting temperatures

VI. Mineral resources and igneous processes
  A. Many important accumulations of metals are produced by igneous processes
  B. Igneous mineral resources can form from
    1. Magmatic segregation
      a. Heavy minerals that crystallize early in a magma body settle to the lower portion of the magma chamber
      b. Crystallization in the late stages of the magmatic process may produce pegmatites
    2. Hydrothermal solutions
      a. Originate from hot, metal-rich fluids that are remnants of the late-stage magmatic process
      b. Cool and produce vein deposits
        1. Gold
        2. Silver
        3. Mercury
      c. May form disseminated deposits where minute quantities are spread throughout an entire rock mass

Answers to the Review Questions

1. Magma is molten rock material found within Earth. It generally includes some solid mineral grains and/or dissolved gases in addition to the rock melt. Lava is magma that has reached Earth's surface.

© 2008 Pearson Education, Inc., Upper Saddle River, NJ. All rights reserved. This material is protected under all copyright laws as they currently exist. No portion of this material may be reproduced, in any form or by any means, without permission in writing from the publisher.

2. Magma is a general term that refers to any molten-rock melt on or beneath Earth's surface. Magmas usually include some solid mineral grains and/or dissolved gases in addition to the molten liquid. Lava is a much more restricted term to describe magma extruded on the surface. Thus all rock melts are magmas, but only those extruded at the surface are lavas.

3. Slow cooling allows ions time to migrate over relatively great distances, which results in the formation of rather large crystals. On the other hand, when cooling occurs rapidly, the ions quickly lose their motion and readily combine into large numbers of nuclei, and hence a mass of small intergrown crystals.

4. In addition to the rate of cooling, the mineral composition of a magma and the amount of volatile material influence the crystallization process.

5. The two criteria are (1) texture, which describes the sizes, shapes, and arrangements of the mineral grains, and (2) the mineral composition.

6. (a) vesicles (b) glassy (not crystalline) (c) porphyritic (d) aphanitic texture (e) porphyritic texture (f) phaneritic texture (g) pegmatite

7. Very large silicate mineral grains (crystals) indicate extremely fast, in-melt transport of the mineral constituents (atoms and molecules) to the growing crystals. We know that pegmatite magmas are small-volume, relatively low-temperature melts that are extremely rich in water and other dissolved volatiles (gases). The volatiles promote very fast rates of molecular transfer, thus accounting for rapid growth of very large crystals.

8. Since crystal size is related to the rate of cooling of magma, two different crystal sizes in the same igneous rock (a porphyritic texture) usually indicates two different rates of cooling. For example, a magma begins cooling within Earth and large crystals form, and then the material is erupted onto the surface where the remaining magma cools quickly.

9. Both are igneous rocks with quartz and potassium feldspar as major minerals. Granite is the phaneritic-textured rock crystallized slowly at depth from intrusive, granitic magma. Rhyolite is the aphanitic, rapidly cooled, volcanic rock that forms when granitic magma is extruded during a volcanic eruption. Both have similar chemical and mineralogical compositions. All granites have phaneritic textures, whereas rhyolites may have glassy textures (obsidian), fragmental textures (tuffs and welded tuffs), and aphanitic textures.

10. (a) Granite and diorite—both are phaneritic igneous rocks. Granite has quartz and potassium feldspar as dominant minerals and is light in color. Diorite has plagioclase (sub-equal amounts of sodium and calcium) as the definitive mineral and is darker than granite in color. Biotite, hornblende, and augite are ferromagnesian minerals that are commonly found in diorite.

(b) Basalt and gabbro—both rocks are dark in color and have the same mineral compositions. Calcium-rich plagioclase is the definitive feldspar and quartz is absent. Olivine and augite are the main ferromagnesian minerals in both rocks. Basalt is an aphanitic volcanic rock, and gabbro has a phaneritic texture, reflecting its origin at depth from a slow-cooling intrusive magma.

© 2008 Pearson Education, Inc., Upper Saddle River, NJ. All rights reserved. This material is protected under all copyright laws as they currently exist. No portion of this material may be reproduced, in any form or by any means, without permission in writing from the publisher.

(c) Andesite and rhyolite—both are aphanitic-textured rocks, usually of volcanic origin. Rhyolite has the same dominant minerals (quartz and potassium feldspar) as granite, while andesite has the same mineral composition as diorite. Typically, rhyolites are light in color and andesites are somewhat darker. Whereas biotite is the only common ferromagnesian mineral in rhyolite, andesite often contains hornblende or augite in addition to biotite.

11. Tuff is a pyroclastic rock formed from fragments ejected during a volcanic eruption. Granite and basalt are crystalline rocks.

12. General knowledge gained from deep mines and drill holes tells us that rock temperatures gradually increase with depth below a relatively shallow zone wherein rock temperatures are dominated by circulating groundwaters and surface climatic conditions. The change in rock temperature with increasing depth in the earth is called the geothermal gradient. The average geothermal gradient in stable crustal areas of Earth is approximately 30°C/km.

13. Melting temperature ranges for silicate rocks are most strongly affected by three factors: total pressure (depth), chemical composition, and fluid pressures (essentially the quantity of water involved in the partial melting process). Melting temperatures increase with increasing pressure and as compositions change from felsic to ultramafic. Increased fluid pressures significantly decrease melting temperature ranges for most silicate rocks. Water released by dehydration of sinking, subducted oceanic crustal slabs can move upward and promote partial melting in overlying mantle rocks where temperatures are too low for dry-rock melting but high enough for "wet-rock" partial melting.

14. Magmas contain many different chemical constituents. Minerals that crystallize from magma almost always have different compositions from the magma; and, during any given portion of the crystallization history, only a fraction of the magma crystallizes into minerals. Physical separation of melt and crystals can produce rocks enriched in the early-formed minerals and a magma enriched in those components excluded from the early-formed minerals. Rocks different in composition from the original parent magma can then crystallize from the remaining, compositionally changed (compositionally differentiated) magma. This process, known as magmatic differentiation, operates throughout the crystallization history of a parent magma and later derivative magmas. Thus accumulations of early-formed minerals and crystallization of later-stage derivative magmas can result in different igneous rocks being derived from a single batch of an original parent magma.

15. Bowen's reaction series depicts the order in which major minerals crystallize at low (crustal) pressures from a hot, basaltic magma and how that magma changes composition (differentiates) as it gradually cools. In terms of rock classification, the reaction series predicts that Ca-rich plagioclase, olivine, and pyroxene will crystallize first (basalt or gabbro), followed by hornblende and plagioclase with Na-to-Ca ratios of about one (diorite and andesite). At lower temperatures, quartz and potassium feldspar (granite and rhyolite) crystallize from fractionated magmas strongly enriched in silica and potassium.

16. Partial melting denotes the fusion behavior of multi-component solids (rocks are mixtures of minerals of different compositions) that melt over a range of temperatures. Melt fractions produced at lower temperatures are enriched in the more fusible components, and unmelted, residual solids are enriched in refractory components. Just think of the reverse of Bowen's Reaction Series. Low temperature, small volume, partial melts of basaltic rocks would be enriched in K- and Na-rich feldspar components and

© 2008 Pearson Education, Inc., Upper Saddle River, NJ. All rights reserved. This material is protected under all copyright laws as they currently exist. No portion of this material may be reproduced, in any form or by any means, without permission in writing from the publisher.

silica. At higher temperatures, pyroxenes and olivine would be the last minerals to melt. In general, the compositions of partial melt fractions are more felsic than the solid parent, and the residual solid rocks are more mafic. Partial melt liquid fractions and residual, unmelted solid fractions are generally different in composition from the parental solid rock.

17. As a generalization, partial melts are enriched in chemical components from minerals with lower melting temperature ranges and depleted in components from the more refractory minerals. Thus basalt partial melts are enriched in alkalis and silica and depleted in magnesium compared to the parental mantle peridotite. Partial melting of mafic rocks in the lower crust is expected to yield more felsic liquids such as andesite and rhyolite, depending on the extent or degree to which the basaltic parent is melted. The smaller the percentage of the parent rock that melts, the more felsic the derived liquid. Of course, complete melting without any fractionation produces a liquid with the same composition as the solid rock.

18. Hydrothermal solutions can deposit metals as (1) vein deposits in fractures or (2) as disseminated deposits distributed as minute masses throughout an entire rock body.

Lecture outline, art-only, and animation PowerPoint presentations for each chapter of *Essentials of Geology* are available on the IRC DVD (ISBN 0-13-604914-1).

NOTES:

© 2008 Pearson Education, Inc., Upper Saddle River, NJ. All rights reserved. This material is protected under all copyright laws as they currently exist. No portion of this material may be reproduced, in any form or by any means, without permission in writing from the publisher.

Volcanoes and Other Igneous Activity

Volcanoes and Other Igneous Activity begins with a description of the nature of volcanic eruptions and how the composition, temperature, and volatiles affect the viscosity of magma. Following a discussion of the materials extruded during an eruption and the types of volcanic cones, various volcanic landforms are presented. The discussion of intrusive igneous activity includes descriptions of the various intrusive igneous bodies. After examining the origin of magma, the chapter concludes with presentations on the relation between igneous activity and plate tectonics and the global distribution of igneous activity.

Learning Objectives

After reading, studying, and discussing the chapter, students should be able to:

- Discuss the differences between explosive and relatively mild volcanic activity.
- Discuss viscosity, silica content, volatiles, and temperature as each relates to magma composition.
- List the various materials erupted from volcanoes.
- Compare and contrast shield volcanoes, stratovolcanoes, and cinder cones.
- Discuss the hazards and features associated with explosive volcanic eruptions.
- Explain the origin of other landforms including calderas, necks, lava domes, and lava plateaus.
- List and describe the various types of plutonic igneous bodies.
- Discuss igneous activity at divergent margins, subduction zones, and intraplate regions.

Chapter Outline

I. Volcanic eruptions
   A. Factors that determine the violence of an eruption
      1. Composition of the magma
      2. Temperature of the magma
      3. Dissolved gases in the magma
   B. Viscosity of magma
      1. Viscosity is a measure of a material's resistance to flow
      2. Factors affecting viscosity
         a. Temperature (hotter magmas are less viscous)
         b. Composition (silica content)
            1. High silica = high viscosity (e.g., felsic lava)
            2. Low silica = more fluid (e.g., mafic lava)
         c. Dissolved gases

      1. Gas content affects magma mobility
      2. Gases expand near the surface and extrude lava
      3. Violence of an eruption is related to how easily gases escape from magma
         a. Fluid basaltic lavas are generally quiescent
         b. Highly viscous magmas produce explosive eruptions

II. Materials extruded during an eruption
   A. Lava flows
      1. Basaltic lavas are more fluid
      2. Types of basaltic lava
         a. Pahoehoe lava (resembles braids in ropes)
         b. Aa lava (rough, jagged blocks)

© 2008 Pearson Education, Inc., Upper Saddle River, NJ. All rights reserved. This material is protected under all copyright laws as they currently exist. No portion of this material may be reproduced, in any form or by any means, without permission in writing from the publisher.

B. Gases
1. One to 6% of magma by weight
2. Mainly water vapor and carbon dioxide
C. Pyroclastic materials
1. "Fire fragments"
2. Types of pyroclastic material
a. Ash and dust—fine, glassy fragments
b. Pumice—from "frothy" lava
c. Lapilli—walnut size
d. Cinders— pea size
e. Particles larger than lapilli
1. Blocks—hardened lava
2. Bombs—ejected as hot lava

III. Volcanoes
A. General features
1. Opening at summit
a. Crater (steep-walled depression at the summit)
b. Caldera (a summit depression greater than 1 km diameter)
2. Vent (connected to the magma chamber via a pipe)
B. Types of volcanoes
1. Shield volcano
a. Broad, slightly domed
b. Primarily made of basaltic (fluid) lava
c. Generally large
d. Generally produce a large volume of lava
e. e.g., Mauna Loa in Hawaii
2. Cinder cone
a. Built from ejected lava fragments
b. Steep slope angle
c. Rather small size
d. Frequently occur in groups
3. Composite cone (or stratovolcano)
a. Most are adjacent to the Pacific Ocean (e.g., Fujiyama, Mt. Shasta)
b. Large size
c. Interbedded lavas and pyroclastics
d. Most violent type of activity (e.g., Vesuvius)
e. Often produce nuée ardente
1. Fiery pyroclastic flow made of hot gases infused with ash
2. Flows down sides of a volcano at speeds up to 200 km per hour

f. May produce a lahar, a type of volcanic mudflow

IV. Other volcanic landforms
A. Calderas
1. Steep walled depression at the summit
2. Size exceeds 1 kilometer in diameter
3. Types of calderas
a. Crater Lake type
b. Hawaiian type
c. Yellowstone type
B. Fissure eruptions and lava plateaus
1. Fluid basaltic lava extruded from crustal fractures called fissures
2. Produces flood basalts
3. e.g., Columbia Plateau
C. Volcanic pipes and necks
1. Pipes are short conduits that connect a magma chamber to the surface
2. Volcanic necks (e.g., Ship Rock, New Mexico) are resistant vents left standing after erosion has removed the volcanic cone

V. Intrusive igneous activity
A. Most magma is emplaced at depth
B. An underground igneous body is called a pluton
C. Plutons are classified according to
1. Shape
a. Tabular (sheetlike)
b. Massive
2. Orientation with respect to the host (surrounding) rock
a. Discordant—cuts across sedimentary beds
b. Concordant—parallel to sedimentary beds
D. Types of igneous intrusive features
1. Dike, a tabular, discordant pluton
2. Sill, a tabular, concordant pluton (e.g., Palisades Sill, NY)
3. Laccolith
a. Similar to a sill
b. Lens-shaped mass
c. Arches overlying strata upward
4. Batholith
a. Largest intrusive body
b. Surface exposure 100+ square kilometers (smaller bodies are termed stocks)

© 2008 Pearson Education, Inc., Upper Saddle River, NJ. All rights reserved. This material is protected under all copyright laws as they currently exist. No portion of this material may be reproduced, in any form or by any means, without permission in writing from the publisher.

      c. Frequently form the cores of
        mountains

VI. Plate tectonics and igneous activity
  A. Global distribution of igneous activity is not random
    1. Most volcanoes are located along the margins of ocean basins
    2. Other general locations include
      a. Deep ocean basins
      b. Interiors of the continents
    3. Plate motions provide the mechanism by which mantle rocks melt to generate magma
  B. Igneous activity at convergent plate boundaries
    1. Oceanic crust descends into the mantle, generating an oceanic trench
    2. Descending plate partially melts
    3. Magma slowly rises upward
    4. Rising magma can form
      a. Volcanic island arc in an ocean
      b. Andesitic to granitic volcanoes in a continental volcanic arc

    5. Most of the activity is associated with the rim of the Pacific Basin, called the Ring of Fire
  C. Igneous activity at divergent plate boundaries
    1. The greatest volume of magma is produced along the oceanic ridge system
      a. Lithosphere pulls apart
      b. Less confining pressure on underlying rocks
      c. Partial melting of mantle rock occurs
      d. Large quantities of basaltic magma are produced
    2. Not all spreading centers are located along the axis of an oceanic ridge
  D. Intraplate igneous activity
    1. Activity within a rigid plate
    2. Plumes of hot mantle material ascend toward the surface
      a. Form localized volcanic regions called hot spots
      b. Associated with the Hawaiian Islands

Answers to the Review Questions

1. An earthquake with a 5.1 Richter magnitude caused the north face of Mount St. Helens to flow downslope. This landslide removed the overburden that had trapped the magma below.

2. The nature of a volcanic eruption is determined by the composition of the magma, the temperature of the magma, and the quantity of dissolved gases contained in the magma. The composition and temperature of the magma influence the viscosity of this material. The viscosity, in turn, helps determine whether the eruption will be violent or quiet. The viscosity is least for very hot magmas with relatively low silica content. The gases dissolved in the molten material provide the force to propel the liquid rock from the volcano. The quantity of gases present and the ease with which they can escape (dependent upon viscosity) determines the nature of the eruption.

3. When magma migrates to a near-surface environment, the gases that were dissolved at great depth begin to rise and expand. The viscosity of the lava determines the ease with which these gases can escape. Highly viscous magma inhibits the escape of gas, which may then accumulate to the point where the lava is violently ejected from the volcano.

4. These terms describe basaltic lava flows with different surface and flow-front characteristics. Aa flows are relatively thick with high, steep, flow fronts; their surfaces are covered with angular, congealed, lava rubble. Pahoehoe flows are thinner, the flow fronts are more gently sloping, and the surface is smooth or rippled (ropy). As the pahoehoe flow advances, small lava prongs break out, forming rippled areas that move a short distance beyond the main flow front. When pahoehoe lava congeals, the smooth, rippled surfaces are preserved.

© 2008 Pearson Education, Inc., Upper Saddle River, NJ. All rights reserved. This material is protected under all copyright laws as they currently exist. No portion of this material may be reproduced, in any form or by any means, without permission in writing from the publisher.

5. Water (H_2O) is generally the dominant gas; carbon dioxide (CO_2) is typically the second most-abundant gas in Hawaiian eruptions, but it can be dominant at specific volcanoes, such as Mt. Vesuvius. In other eruptions, such as El Chichon (Mexico) and Pinatubo (Philippines), sulfur dioxide (SO_2) was the dominant volatile. Nitrogen (N_2), hydrogen (H_2), argon (Ar), hydrogen chloride (HCI), and hydrogen fluoride (HF) may also be released to the atmosphere during eruptions and fumarolic activity. Dissolved gases are important in volcanism because the large volume expansion that accompanies their dissolution from the melt pushes magma upward toward the surface and generates explosive overpressures in silicic magma chambers.

6. Both are pebble-sized or larger pyroclastic fragments. Bombs are cooled from ejected magma blobs. They typically have very fine-grained, chilled margins, are vesicular, exhibit surface patterns characteristic of solidified liquid, have rounded, twisted shapes produced in flight, and may be flattened and cracked on impact. Essentially all bombs are vesicular to a greater or lesser extent. Blocks are lithic clasts broken from preexisting rock. They are typically angular and show none of the morphological features associated with impacts, in-flight movements, and solidification of liquid or partly liquid magma masses. Blocks may or may not be vesicular.

7. A volcanic crater is a relatively small depression marking the vent or exit site of erupting lava or pyroclastic material. A crater is excavated by the boring or drilling action of the erupting magma and gases. A caldera is a much larger volcanic depression that forms during or following a large outpouring of lava or pyroclastic debris. Extremely rapid emission of huge quantities of magma, such as occurs during a powerful explosive eruption, evacuates upper portions of the former magma chamber. Thus, the rocks above the chamber fail and a large, circular to elliptical volcanic depression is formed by collapse and subsidence.

8. Shield volcanoes are among the largest on Earth. These gently sloping domes are associated with relatively quiet eruptions of fluid basaltic lava. They contain very little pyroclastic material. Cinder cones are composed almost exclusively of pyroclastics, are steep-sided, and are the smallest of the volcanoes. Composite cones, as the name suggests, are composed of alternating layers of lava (usually andesitic or rhyolitic in composition) and pyroclastic debris. Their slopes are steeper than those of a shield volcano, but gentler than a cinder cone. Composite cones are associated with violent periods of volcanic activity.

9. The volcanoes composing the island of Hawaii serve as excellent examples of shield volcanoes. Paricutin, as well as many small cones on the Colorado Plateau north of Flagstaff, Arizona, are good examples of cinder cones. Mt. Fuji, in Japan, and Mt. Shasta, in California, as well as the many volcanoes of the Cascade Range, are examples of composite cones.

10. Paricutin is a small, basaltic cinder cone that formed in a cornfield in southern Mexico during a few years of eruptive activity in the 1940s. During the cone-forming phase, mainly pyroclastic materials (bombs, cinders, and ash) were erupted; later in the eruptive cycle, lava flows broke out from the base of the cinder cone and spread over the surrounding countryside. After a few years of continuing activity, the eruptive episode ended as abruptly as it had started.

© 2008 Pearson Education, Inc., Upper Saddle River, NJ. All rights reserved. This material is protected under all copyright laws as they currently exist. No portion of this material may be reproduced, in any form or by any means, without permission in writing from the publisher.

Kilauea is the most active volcano on Hawaii, the largest of the Hawaiian Islands, and is part of a massive, basaltic, shield volcano complex that forms the island. Eruptions are mainly fluid, basaltic lava flows and minor pyroclastic activity. The volcanic activity began millions of years ago when submarine lava flows were erupted on the ocean floor. With continued activity, a massive, mound-shaped seamount was constructed; eventually it grew above sea level, forming the present-day island of Hawaii. Kilauea is the youngest, southeastern most, sub-aerial volcano on the island but has yet to reach the elevation and size of the much larger shield volcanoes, Mauna Loa and Mauna Kea.

11. A nueé ardente generated by the 1902 explosive eruption of Mt. Pelé devastated the city of St. Pierre. The nueé ardente was evolved from a massive, pyroclastic flow that sped to the sea along a stream valley outside the city. However, at a fairly sharp curve in the valley, the nueé ardente portion of the flow jumped a low ridge and bore on straight toward the city. It was all over in a few minutes. The hot, violently turbulent dust-and-ash cloud, moving at hurricane speeds, flattened buildings and suffocated all living beings in its path. Only a few centimeters of hot, very-fine size ash were deposited over the ruined city.

Pompeii and its sister city of Herculaneum were buried over a three- to four-day, cataclysmic phase of the 79 A.D. eruption of Mount Vesuvius. Pompeii was buried by 20–30 feet of airfall pumice and ash. Written accounts and archeological excavations suggest that many people escaped during the early phase of the eruption, and others managed to survive a day or two before succumbing to thirst and suffocation. Herculaneum was evidently buried suddenly by mudflows or pyroclastic flows unleashed simultaneously with, or shortly following, the phase of the eruption that buried Pompeii.

12. Crater Lake (Oregon) caldera is about six miles in diameter. It formed following a major eruption of ash and pyroclastic flows about 7000 years ago. Glacial valleys cutting through the caldera rim and other geologic evidence prove that a complex, composite volcano once existed above the site of the present-day caldera. In contrast, the summit caldera block of Kilauea is about three miles in diameter and acts somewhat like a floating cork, rising when magma is accumulating and sinking after an eruption. The rising and sinking movements are gradual as contrasted with the catastrophic collapse that follows large-volume pyroclastic flow eruptions.

13. The largest volcanic structures on Earth are the Yellowstone-type calderas that occur in continental regions. They are not associated with a composite volcano, such as Crater Lake in Oregon. Instead, they occur as very large (tens of miles in diameter) depressions in volcanic terrains dominated by explosive rhyolitic and andesitic magmas. Good examples include Yellowstone National Park in Wyoming, Long Valley Caldera in California, and the Valles Caldera in New Mexico.

14. Shiprock, a well-known landmark in northwestern New Mexico, marks the subsurface "plumbing" system of a former volcano. The igneous rock is much harder than surrounding sedimentary strata. As erosion gradually cut into the bedrock, spires and sharp ridges of igneous rock were left towering above the more easily eroded sedimentary rocks. Shiprock itself is the central magma pipe that once fed magma upward to the volcano. The sharp ridges extending outward from the central spire are dikes representing radial cracks filled with magma injected outward from the central pipe.

© 2008 Pearson Education, Inc., Upper Saddle River, NJ. All rights reserved. This material is protected under all copyright laws as they currently exist. No portion of this material may be reproduced, in any form or by any means, without permission in writing from the publisher.

15. Large, voluminous, volcanic edifices such as Mts. Rainier, Washington, and Shasta, California, are composite cones (stratovolcanoes). They are built by repeated, central-vent eruptions over time spans ranging up to a million years or more, interspersed with eruptions from flank fissures and satellite centers. Higher viscosity magmas (andesite to rhyolite) erupt explosively or form thick, stubby lava flows that, unless the lava is unusually hot, move only short distances from the vent.

    The Columbia Plateau is an eroded, uplifted flood basalt province of mid-Tertiary age. Elsewhere, flood basalts comprise the most voluminous, volcanic accumulations on Earth (Deccan basalts, India, and the Siberian traps, for example). Over a million years or more, basaltic lava flows are erupted repeatedly from fissure vents. The lavas collect as pools in topographically low areas and solidify to sheets of basalt. At first only low areas are buried; eventually, the lava stack thickens and higher parts of the former land surface are buried. Later flows rest exclusively on earlier ones, and the lava pile attains a relatively flat upper surface.

16. Voluminous, pyroclastic flow deposits are always accompanied by collapse of the rock above the evacuated part of the magma chamber, forming a caldera. The large magma volumes and high extrusion rates make collapse inevitable. Caldera collapse is often simultaneous with pyroclastic flow emission, as shown by the tremendous thickness of ash-flow tuff deposited in large Tertiary calderas in Nevada, Utah, and the San Juan Mountain region in southwestern Colorado.

17. Dikes are tabular, sheetlike igneous rock bodies emplaced into fractures and fissures cutting through the wall rock. Most dikes are steeply dipping to vertical, but some low-angle dikes are recognized. Dikes are generally discordant in that they usually cross cut bedding and other structures in the wall rocks. Sills are tabular, sheetlike igneous rock bodies emplaced parallel to bedding in enclosing strata or intruded as sub-horizontal sheets into older igneous and metamorphic basement rocks. The Palisades Sill, a Triassic, mafic rock body exposed along the west side of the Hudson River valley near New York City, is a well-studied example. Laccoliths are relatively small-volume, intrusive igneous rock bodies. The typical laccolith is emplaced into sub-horizontal sedimentary strata as a sill that simultaneously spreads laterally and inflates vertically, producing a magma body with dome-shaped upper contact and more-or-less horizontal, planar lower contact. Wall rock strata above the laccolith bend upward and stretch to conform to the upper contact of the magma body. Laccoliths are intruded at shallow depths; they represent intrusion in a sub-volcanic environment. Batholiths, generally granitic in composition, are the largest plutons. They are massive and discordant; they occur as extensive, linear arrays of separate plutons, many of which are large enough (>100 square miles in cross-sectional area) to individually qualify as batholiths. The Sierra Nevada batholith is one of many mid-Mesozoic to early Cenozoic regional batholiths intruded along the then-convergent, western margin of North America.

18. Laccoliths are known to be emplaced at shallow depths. Domed strata above a laccolith may be exposed at the surface before erosion cuts down far enough to expose the igneous rock. Thus the domed strata may suggest that the top of a laccolith lies a short distance below the surface.

19. The largest of all intrusive igneous rock bodies are batholiths. They are massive, possibly teardrop shaped, and discordant. By definition, their surface exposure exceeds 100 square kilometers.

© 2008 Pearson Education, Inc., Upper Saddle River, NJ. All rights reserved. This material is protected under all copyright laws as they currently exist. No portion of this material may be reproduced, in any form or by any means, without permission in writing from the publisher.

Volcanoes and Other Igneous Activity

20. Divergent boundaries lie above slowly rising, largely solid mantle plumes that turn laterally as they near the surface, carrying the diverging plates in opposite directions. Melting temperatures of rock-forming minerals increase with higher pressure and decrease with lower pressure. As the plume rises, pressures and melting temperatures are lowered, but the plume loses very little of its heat; thus rock temperatures stay constant. Eventually, temperatures exceed the melting range, and partial melting occurs. More melting ensues as the plume rises closer to the surface. Basaltic magma is the most common partial melt formed in a rising mantle-rock plume.

21. The Ring of Fire refers to the volcanic mountains ranges and islands that surround much of the Pacific Ocean. Many of the active volcanoes on Earth today are located on the Ring of Fire.

22. The volcanoes on the Ring of Fire lie above subduction zones, where plates that make up the Pacific Ocean floor are sinking beneath other oceanic plates or beneath plates carrying continents.

23. Very large composite volcanoes (stratovolcanoes), like those on the Ring of Fire, typically erupt explosively. The 1991 eruption of Pinatubo in the Philippines was the second most powerful eruption of the twentieth century, being surpassed only by the 1902 eruption of Santa Maria in Guatemala. The 1980 eruption of Mount St. Helens is another good example.

24. Magma generation along convergent plate boundaries is associated with subduction zones. Partial melting along a subducting slab seems to begin at depths around 100 km. Fluids released from the slab promote melting of hot peridotite in the overlying lithosphere. Also, materials at the top of the slab, such as sediments, hydrated volcanic rocks, and continental-rock slivers are in contact with hot, non-slab peridotite and may undergo partial melting. As the slab tip penetrates to deeper levels, upward, counter flows of hot peridotite are set in motion, resulting in decompression melting and production of basaltic magma. If the slab is cool and dense enough at the start of subduction, it may sink, unmelted, to depths as great as 700 km, as indicated by the deepest-known earthquake foci.

25. The source of magma for intraplate volcanism appears to be localized areas of increased thermal energy known as hot spots. Hot spots may occur at plate boundaries (such as Iceland on a divergent boundary), but generally they are randomly distributed with respect to tectonic plates.

26. Hot spot volcanism refers to the volcanic activity produced at localized areas not related to tectonic plate boundaries. Hot spots are thought to be the result of large heat plumes in the mantle that induce melting in the overriding lithospheric plate. Yellowstone National Park in Wyoming and the island of Hawaii are good examples of hot spot volcanism.

27. Aside from the obvious presence of volcanic activity, hot spots are identified by two other means. Hot spots are generally elevated relative to the surrounding land surface due to the rising of warm, lower density material. Measuring heat flow, which is much higher than the normal values found in the lithosphere, also identifies hot spots.

© 2008 Pearson Education, Inc., Upper Saddle River, NJ. All rights reserved. This material is protected under all copyright laws as they currently exist. No portion of this material may be reproduced, in any form or by any means, without permission in writing from the publisher.

28. Both Yellowstone and the Hawaiian Islands are associated with hot spot volcanism, as evidenced by the track of volcanic activity and the lack of a plate boundary at both locations. The Cascade Range is a volcanic arc produced at a convergent plate boundary where oceanic crust is being subducted under the North American continental plate. Flood basalt provinces, such as the Columbia Plateau and the Deccan Traps in India, are also the result of hot spot volcanism. The mantle plumes responsible for such vast outpourings of lava are perhaps much larger than those responsible for Hawaii and Yellowstone.

Lecture outline, art-only, and animation PowerPoint presentations for each chapter of *Essentials of Geology* **are available on the IRC DVD (ISBN 0-13-604914-1).**

NOTES:

© 2008 Pearson Education, Inc., Upper Saddle River, NJ. All rights reserved. This material is protected under all copyright laws as they currently exist. No portion of this material may be reproduced, in any form or by any means, without permission in writing from the publisher.

Weathering and Soils

Weathering and Soils begins with a brief examination of the external processes of weathering, mass wasting, and erosion. The two forms of weathering, mechanical and chemical, are investigated in detail, including the types, conditions, rates, and net effect of each. The soils section of the chapter begins with a description of the general composition and structure of soil. After examining the factors that influence soil formation, development, and classification, soil erosion, as well as some ore deposits produced by weathering, are presented.

Learning Objectives

After reading, studying, and discussing the chapter, students should be able to:

- Explain the difference between Earth's external and internal processes.
- Discuss the various processes involved in physical weathering.
- Discuss the various processes involved in chemical weathering.
- List and briefly explain those factors that control rates of weathering.
- Define soil and explain the difference between soil and regolith.
- Discuss soil formation, including those factors that control soil formation.
- Explain the concept of the soil profile and how it relates to soil formation.
- Discuss the characteristics of the soil horizons in a typical soil profile.
- Briefly explain soil classification.
- Briefly discuss soil erosion.
- Relate the process of weathering to the formation of some ore deposits.

Chapter Outline

I. Earth's external processes
   A. Weathering—the physical breakdown (disintegration) and chemical alteration (decomposition) of rock at or near Earth's surface
   B. Mass wasting—the transfer of rock and soil downslope under the influence of gravity
   C. Erosion—the physical removal of material by mobile agents such as water, wind, or ice

II. Weathering
   A. Two types of weathering
      1. Mechanical weathering
         a. Breaking of rocks into smaller pieces
         b. Four processes

1. Frost wedging
2. Unloading
3. Thermal expansion
4. Biological activity
      2. Chemical weathering
         a. Breaks down rock components and internal structures of minerals
         b. Most important agent is water
         c. Major processes
            1. Dissolution
               a. Aided by small amount of acid in the water
               b. Soluble ions are retained in the underground water supply
            2. Oxidation

© 2008 Pearson Education, Inc., Upper Saddle River, NJ. All rights reserved. This material is protected under all copyright laws as they currently exist. No portion of this material may be reproduced, in any form or by any means, without permission in writing from the publisher.

a. Any chemical reaction in which a compound or radical loses electrons
b. Important in decomposing ferromagnesian minerals
3. Hydrolysis
   a. The reaction of any substance with water
   b. Hydrogen ion attacks and replaces other positive ions
d. Alterations caused by chemical weathering
   1. Decomposition of unstable minerals
   2. Generation or retention of materials that are stable
   3. Physical changes such as the rounding of corners or edges
B. Rates of weathering
   1. Advanced mechanical weathering aids chemical weathering by increasing the surface area
   2. Other important factors include
      a. Rock characteristics
         1. Marble (calcite) readily dissolves in weakly acidic solutions
         2. Silicate minerals weather in the same order as their order of crystallization
      b. Climate
         1. Temperature and moisture are the most crucial factors
         2. Chemical weathering is most effective in areas of warm temperatures and abundant moisture
   3. Differential weathering
      a. Masses of rock do not weather uniformly
      b. Creates many unusual and spectacular rock formations and landforms

III. Soil
A. A combination of mineral and organic matter, water, and air—that portion of the regolith (rock and mineral fragments produced by weathering) that supports the growth of plants
B. Controls of soil formation
   1. Parent material

a. Residual soil—parent material is the bedrock
b. Transported soil—form in place on parent material that has been carried from elsewhere and deposited
2. Time
   a. Important in all geologic processes
   b. Amount of time to evolve varies for different soils
3. Climate
   a. Most influential control of soil formation
   b. Temperature and precipitation are the elements that exert the strongest impact on soil formation
4. Plants and animals
   a. Organisms influence the soil's physical and chemical properties
   b. Furnish organic matter to the soil
5. Slope
   a. Steep slopes often have poorly developed soils
   b. Optimum terrain is a flat-to-undulating upland surface
   c. Slope orientation is also important
C. The soil profile
   1. Soil-forming processes operate from the surface downward
   2. Vertical differences are called horizons—zones or layers of soil
      a. Horizons in temperate regions
         1. *O*—organic matter
         2. *A*—organic and mineral matter
            a. High biological activity
            b. Together the *O* and *A* horizons make up the topsoil
         3. *E*—little organic matter
            a. Eluviation
            b. Leaching
         4. *B*—zone of accumulation
         5. *C*—partially altered parent material
      b. *O*, *A*, *E*, and *B* together called the solum, or "true soil"
D. Classifying soils
   1. Variations in soil formation over time and distances has led to a great variety of recognized soil types
   2. Groups have been established using common characteristics to facilitate analysis and better understanding

© 2008 Pearson Education, Inc., Upper Saddle River, NJ. All rights reserved. This material is protected under all copyright laws as they currently exist. No portion of this material may be reproduced, in any form or by any means, without permission in writing from the publisher.

3. In the United States a system is used called the soil taxonomy
    a. Emphasis is placed on physical and chemical properties of the soil profile
    b. Six hierarchical categories ranging from order, the broadest category, to series, the most specific
    c. Names are descriptive using syllables derived from Latin or Greek
    d. 12 basic soil orders are recognized in the soil taxonomy
E. Soil erosion
    1. Recycling of Earth materials
    2. Natural rates of soil erosion depend on
        a. Soil characteristics
        b. Climate
        c. Slope
        d. Type of vegetation
    3. In many regions, the rate of soil erosion is significantly greater than the rate of soil formation
    4. Sedimentation and chemical pollution
        a. Related to excessive soil erosion

    b. Occasionally soil particles are contaminated with pesticides

IV. Weathering and ore deposits
    A. Secondary enrichment—concentrating metals into economically valuable concentrations
        1. By downward-percolating water removing undesirable materials
        2. By carrying desirable elements to lower zones and concentrating them
    B. Bauxite
        1. Principal ore of aluminum
        2. Forms in rainy tropical climates from chemical weathering and the removal of undesirable elements by leaching
    C. Other deposits, such as many copper and silver deposits, result when weathering concentrates metals that are deposited through a low-grade primary ore

Answers to the Review Questions

1. Weathering, mass wasting, and erosion are all integral processes involved in the rock cycle because of their relationship to the formation of sedimentary rocks. In the rock cycle, the first step in the formation of sedimentary rocks involves the derivation of sediment from preexisting igneous, metamorphic, or sedimentary rocks. Solid rock is transformed into sediment by the collective processes of weathering, mass wasting, and erosion. Therefore, the external processes provide the important first step toward the formation of sedimentary rocks.

2. A rock exposed to mechanical weathering would be broken into smaller and smaller pieces. Therefore, the same rock following mechanical weathering would look identical to the original rock, only in smaller fragments or pieces. Chemical weathering involves various processes that convert the minerals in a rock into new minerals or release them to the surrounding environment. Because of these chemical changes, the same identical rock above, having been chemically weathered, will most likely look considerably different from the mechanically weathered rock.

3. Reduction in particle size produces an enormous increase in surface area of the material being weathered. For very small particles, water, oxygen, and other important chemical-weathering agents have direct access to nearly the entire grain, while uncracked interiors of coarser particles are protected, at least temporarily, from contact with the main chemical-weathering agents.

4. Exfoliation domes form when the reduction in pressure that accompanies unloading leads to sheeting. Fractures typically develop parallel to the surface and give these exhumed granite masses a domed shape. Continued weathering causes the slabs produced by sheeting to separate and spall off. Examples include

© 2008 Pearson Education, Inc., Upper Saddle River, NJ. All rights reserved. This material is protected under all copyright laws as they currently exist. No portion of this material may be reproduced, in any form or by any means, without permission in writing from the publisher.

Stone Mountain, Georgia, and Half Dome and Liberty Cap in Yosemite National Park.

5. (a) Moisture and warm temperatures accelerate rates of chemical reactions, thus chemical weathering will predominate. Also, mechanical weathering processes dependent on freezing and thawing will not be operative.

   (b) Basalt would probably weather more rapidly. Ferromagnesian minerals would be rapidly oxidized and decomposed under these conditions, and basalts have much larger percentages of these minerals than granite.

6. In general, high temperatures do raise chemical weathering reaction rates, but most of these reactions take place in an aqueous (watery) media or on the moist surfaces of rock and soil particles. Reaction rates decrease drastically under very dry conditions.

7. Carbonic acid is a very weak acid formed by the solution of carbon dioxide (CO_2) in water. Carbon dioxide is a minor component of the atmosphere but is often enriched in soil gases by the oxidation of organic matter. The common cations of feldspars ($K = +1$, $Na = +1$, and $Ca = +2$) are fairly soluble in acidic solutions, so reaction of carbonic acid with potassium feldspar causes the feldspar to chemically decompose. Potassium, sodium, and calcium are then released to the soil and precipitated as minerals.

8. Soil is an interface where different parts of the Earth system interact. It forms where the solid Earth, the atmosphere, the hydrosphere, and the biosphere meet. Over time, the material of soil develops in response to complex environmental interactions among the different parts of the Earth system.

9. Different soils are likely to form from the same parent material if the climates are different. Other factors, which would contribute to differences, include the nature of the vegetation, the slopes, and the length of time the soils have been forming. Similar soils from different parent materials would result if the above-named factors were essentially the same in each situation.

10. Climate is the most important factor in soil formation. Temperature and moisture abundance largely control most of the other weathering variables mentioned in Review Question 11. Time, however, is obviously independent of the climatic variable.

11. Slope greatly influences drainage and the amount of erosion that will occur. Because of accelerated erosion on steep slopes, soils are thin. Conversely, in flat bottomlands, soils are often waterlogged. Optimum conditions for soil development are flat to undulating upland surfaces. Here erosion is at a minimum and drainage is good. Slope orientation refers to the amount of sunlight received. This affects the soil temperature and moisture conditions that in turn influence the nature of the vegetation and the character of the soil.

© 2008 Pearson Education, Inc., Upper Saddle River, NJ. All rights reserved. This material is protected under all copyright laws as they currently exist. No portion of this material may be reproduced, in any form or by any means, without permission in writing from the publisher.

Weathering and Soils

12. O—This is a dark, surface layer of decaying plant matter (humus).

   A—The A horizon (just below the O horizon) consists of humus mixed with very tough, chemically resistant mineral grains such as quartz that have survived the processes of disintegration, chemical weathering, and leaching associated with the soil-forming process.

   E—This is a light-colored horizon of resistant mineral grains as in horizon A, but depleted in silt and clay-sized particles that have been transported downward (eluviated) to the B horizon; humus is sparse or absent.

   B—The B horizon is often called the zone of accumulation. Small size soil particles eluviated downward from higher horizons accumulate in the B horizon, and chemical constituents leached from the A horizon are precipitated there as well. These include the most insoluble minerals formed in soils such as the iron oxides and hydroxides and clays. This zone is usually red, yellow, or brown, depending on the nature of the finely divided iron oxides in the soil.

   C—The C horizon is the zone of partly weathered bedrock. Weathered fragments and chips of rock found here are evidence of the unweathered parent rock material at depth.

   The solum includes all the horizons above the top of the C horizon. Recently exposed regolith lacks distinctive soil horizons because the soil-forming process is still in its infancy, and horizons have not had enough time to develop. A newly deposited floodplain sediment is a good example of regolith.

13. Soil erosion is a natural process; it is part of the constant recycling of Earth materials that we call the rock cycle. However, soil erosion is a growing problem as human activities expand and disturb more and more of Earth's surface.

14. Soil erosion contributes excess sediment loads to reservoirs, streams, and rivers, thus degrading water quality and adversely affecting aquatic and riparian habitats. It also diminishes the quality of outdoor recreational activities and raises the cost of maintaining navigational channels and hydroelectric power generation facilities. Blowing dust can seriously degrade air quality, causing health problems and premature failure of machinery and electronics equipment.

15. Bauxite is the primary ore of aluminum. Bauxite results when intense and prolonged chemical weathering leaches most of the soluble elements, leaving the highly insoluble aluminum concentrated in the soil.

Lecture outline, art-only, and animation PowerPoint presentations for each chapter of *Essentials of Geology* are available on the IRC DVD (ISBN 0-13-604914-1).

NOTES:

© 2008 Pearson Education, Inc., Upper Saddle River, NJ. All rights reserved. This material is protected under all copyright laws as they currently exist. No portion of this material may be reproduced, in any form or by any means, without permission in writing from the publisher.

Sedimentary Rocks

Sedimentary Rocks begins with a detailed examination of the various detrital and chemical sedimentary rocks, including shale, sandstone, conglomerate, limestone, dolostone, chert, and coal, as well as several evaporites. Having examined the types of rocks, the ways that sediment becomes rock are investigated. Following a look at the classification of sedimentary rocks and sedimentary structures, the chapter concludes with a discussion of the mineral and energy resources that are associated with these rocks.

Learning Objectives

After reading, studying, and discussing the chapter, students should be able to:

- Briefly discuss how sediment is turned into sedimentary rock.
- Explain and briefly define the major types of detrital sedimentary rocks.
- Explain and briefly define the major types of chemical sedimentary rocks.
- List and briefly discuss the major sedimentary depositional environments.
- Discuss the single most common characteristic feature of sedimentary rocks.
- Describe the two broad groups of nonmetallic mineral resources.
- List the energy resources that are associated with sedimentary rocks.

Chapter Outline

I. What is a sedimentary rock?
   A. Products of mechanical and chemical weathering
   B. Account for about 5% (by volume) of Earth's outer 16 km (10 miles)
   C. Contain evidence of past environments
      1. Provide information about sediment transport
      2. Often contain fossil
   D. Economic importance
      1. Coal
      2. Petroleum and natural gas
      3. Sources of iron, aluminum, and manganese

II. Turning sediment into sedimentary rock
   A. A great deal of change can occur to sediment after it is deposited
   B. Diagenesis—all chemical, physical, and biological changes that take place after sediments are deposited

      1. Occurs within the upper few kilometers of Earth's crust
      2. Includes:
         a. Recrystallization—development of more stable minerals from less stable ones
         b. Lithification—unconsolidated sediments are transformed into solid sedimentary rocks by
            1. Compaction
            2. Cementation by the materials
               a. Calcite and/or
               b. Silica
               c. Iron oxide

III. Types of sedimentary rocks
   A. Material originates from mechanical and/or chemical weathering
   B. Rock types are based on the source of the material
      1. Detrital rocks—material is solid particles

© 2008 Pearson Education, Inc., Upper Saddle River, NJ. All rights reserved. This material is protected under all copyright laws as they currently exist. No portion of this material may be reproduced, in any form or by any means, without permission in writing from the publisher.

2. Chemical rocks—material that was once in solution

IV. Detrital sedimentary rocks
   A. Chief constituents
      1. Clay minerals
      2. Quartz
      3. Others
         a. Feldspars
         b. Micas
   B. Particle size is used to distinguish among the various types of detrital rocks
   C. Common detrital sedimentary rocks (in order of increasing particle size)
      1. Shale
         a. Thin layers (lamina)
         b. Most common sedimentary rock
      2. Sandstone
         a. Form in a variety of environments
         b. Sorting, shape, and composition of the grains can be used to interpret the rock's history
         c. Quartz is the most predominant mineral
      3. Conglomerate and breccia
         a. Conglomerate consists largely of rounded gravels
         b. Breccia composed mainly of large angular particles

V. Chemical sedimentary rocks
   A. Consist of precipitated material that was once in solution
   B. Precipitation of material occurs in two ways
      1. Inorganic processes
      2. Organic processes (biochemical origin)
   C. Common chemical sedimentary rocks
      1. Limestone
         a. Most abundant chemical rock
         b. Composed chiefly of the mineral calcite
         c. Marine biochemical limestones
            1. Coral reefs
            2. Coquina
            3. Chalk
         d. Inorganic limestones
            1. Travertine
            2. Oolitic limestone
      2. Dolostone
      3. Chert

a. Made of microcrystalline quartz
b. Forms
   1. Flint
   2. Jasper (banded form called agate)
4. Evaporites
   a. Evaporation triggers deposition of chemical precipitates
   b. Examples
      1. Rock salt
      2. Rock gypsum
5. Coal
   a. Different from other rocks—made of organic material
   b. Stages in coal formation
      1. Plant material
      2. Peat
      3. Lignite
      4. Bituminous

VI. Classification of sedimentary rocks
   A. Classified according to the type of material
   B. Two major groups
      1. Detrital
      2. Chemical
   C. Two major textures used in the classification of sedimentary rocks
      1. Clastic
         a. Discrete fragments and particles
         b. All detrital rocks have a clastic texture
      2. Nonclastic
         a. Pattern of interlocking crystals
         b. May resemble igneous rocks

VII. Sedimentary environments
   A. A geographic setting where sediment is accumulating
   B. Determines the nature of the sediments that accumulate
   C. Types of sedimentary environments
      1. Continental
      2. Marine
      3. Transitional (shoreline)

VIII. Sedimentary structures
   A. Provide information useful in the interpretation of Earth history
   B. Types

© 2008 Pearson Education, Inc., Upper Saddle River, NJ. All rights reserved. This material is protected under all copyright laws as they currently exist. No portion of this material may be reproduced, in any form or by any means, without permission in writing from the publisher.

1. Strata or beds (most characteristic feature of sedimentary rocks)
2. Bedding planes that separate strata
3. Cross-bedding
4. Graded beds
5. Ripple marks
6. Mud cracks
7. Fossils

IX. Nonmetallic mineral resources from sedimentary rocks
   A. Use of the word "mineral" is very broad
   B. Two common groups
      1. Building materials
         a. Natural aggregate (crushed stone, sand, and gravel)
         b. Gypsum (plaster and wallboard)
         c. Clay (tile, bricks, and cement)
      2. Industrial minerals
         a. Corundum
         b. Garnet

X. Energy resources from sedimentary rocks
   A. Coal
      1. Formed mostly from plant material
      2. Along with oil and natural gas, coal is commonly called a fossil fuel
      3. The major fuel used in power plants to generate electricity
      4. Problems with coal use
         a. Environmental damage from mining
         b. Air pollution
   B. Oil and natural gas
      1. Oil and natural gas, consisting of various hydrocarbon compounds, are found in similar environments
      2. Derived from the remains of marine plants and animals
      3. Formation is complex and not completely understood
      4. A geologic environment that allows for economically significant amounts of oil and gas to accumulate underground is termed an oil trap
         a. Two basic conditions for an oil trap
            1. Porous, permeable reservoir rock
            2. Impermeable cap rock, such as shale
         b. Cap rock keeps the mobile oil and gas from escaping at the surface

Answers to the Review Questions

1. In Earth's crust, igneous rocks exceed sedimentary rocks in volume. Neither rock type is evenly distributed. In the interiors of continents, sedimentary rocks occur as thin veneers covering over much larger volumes of igneous and metamorphic rocks deeper in the crust. Ocean basin rocks are mainly igneous with very thin covers of sediments. Sedimentary strata many kilometers in thickness accumulate only in relatively restricted basins along the edges of continents or in deep rift basins where continental blocks are splitting apart.

2. The three basic categories of sedimentary rocks are detrital, chemical, and organic. Detrital sedimentary rocks originate from the weathering, transportation, and deposition of solid particles (preexisting earth materials). Chemical sedimentary rocks are formed from soluble material that is produced mainly by chemical weathering. The ions in solution are then precipitated by either inorganic or biologic processes to form various chemical rocks. Organic sedimentary rocks owe their origin to the accumulation of undecayed plant material that constitutes the "sediment" in such rocks. Coal, formed from the remains of plants that accumulated in ancient terrestrial swamps, is the primary example of an organic sedimentary rock.

3. The most common minerals in sedimentary rocks are clay minerals and quartz. Clay minerals are the most abundant product of the chemical weathering of silicate minerals, especially feldspar. Quartz is abundant because it is extremely durable and very resistant to chemical weathering.

© 2008 Pearson Education, Inc., Upper Saddle River, NJ. All rights reserved. This material is protected under all copyright laws as they currently exist. No portion of this material may be reproduced, in any form or by any means, without permission in writing from the publisher.

Sedimentary Rocks

4. Particle size is the primary basis for distinguishing among various detrital sedimentary rocks.

5. Shale is made of very thin laminae and often is weak because it is poorly cemented and not well lithified. As a consequence, shale usually crumbles quite easily.

6. A sand grain, regardless of initial shape, is gradually rounded during transport. Sharp corners and edges are preferentially abraded, resulting in rounded but not necessarily spherical grains. Well-sorted sands are deposited in aqueous and terrestrial environments characterized by vigorous current activity. Finer particles are winnowed out and carried elsewhere; coarser, gravel-sized clasts have already been deposited or abraded and broken into smaller particles. The currents are highly selective, and although finer particles may be available, only sand grains of roughly equal size are deposited, such as in a sand dune or on a beach. Generally, well-sorted sands are also well-rounded, the grains having been extensively transported prior to deposition.

7. Conglomerate consists largely of rounded gravel particles. If the large particles are angular rather than rounded, the rock is called breccia. The degree of rounding of the large particles is related to the distance that they have been transported.

8. The two different categories of chemical sedimentary rocks are defined on the basis of the mechanism of formation of the material. Inorganic processes, such as evaporation and chemical activity, can produce chemical sediments. On the other hand, organic (life) processes of water-dwelling organisms also form chemical sediments, said to be of biochemical origin.

9. Evaporite deposits are chemical sedimentary rocks formed as water becomes chemically saturated and salt deposition begins. Common evaporites include rock salt and rock gypsum.

10. Bituminous coal has higher carbon content, generates more heat, and is more compact than lignite. Anthracite coal is a metamorphic rock with a higher carbon content than bituminous coal. It is a very hard, shiny black, clean-burning fuel.

11. (a) gypsum; (b) mudstone; (c) graywacke; (d) limestone; (e) chert; (f) oolitic limestone

12. Some chemical sedimentary rocks are clastic, for example, coquina. The non-clastic chemical rocks are either made of large crystals that formed as water evaporated (rock salt and rock gypsum) or shell fragments that were subsequently obliterated or obscured as the particles recrystallized when they were consolidated into limestone or chert.

13. Diagenesis refers to the collective chemical, physical, and biological changes that take place following deposition and during and after lithification of sediments. Typically, diagenesis occurs within the upper few kilometers of Earth's crust at temperatures below 200°C. An example of diagenesis is recrystallization, which involves the formation of more stable minerals from less stable ones.

14. Compaction is most important as a diagenetic process in fine-grained sedimentary rocks such as shales or mudstones. Sand and other coarse sediments are much less compressible so that compaction is not as significant as it is in finer sediments.

© 2008 Pearson Education, Inc., Upper Saddle River, NJ. All rights reserved. This material is protected under all copyright laws as they currently exist. No portion of this material may be reproduced, in any form or by any means, without permission in writing from the publisher.

15. The three common cementing agents for sedimentary rocks are calcite, silica (quartz), and iron oxide. They are relatively easy to distinguish from one another by their physical or chemical properties. Calcite will readily effervesce with dilute hydrochloric acid, silica is much harder than the other two, and a distinctive orange to dark red color normally identifies iron oxide.

16. Rocks that display a clastic texture consist of discrete fragments and particles that are cemented or compacted together. Non-clastic rocks consist of intergrown crystals. A clastic texture is common to all detrital sedimentary rocks.

17. The single most characteristic feature of sedimentary rocks are layers, called strata, or beds.

18. Cross-bedding, most characteristic of sand dunes, is when a bed of sedimentary rock contains layers within it that are inclined to the horizontal. Graded bedding is a special type of bedding where the particles within a single sedimentary layer gradually change from coarse at the bottom to fine at the top.

19. The two broad groups of nonmetallic resources are building materials (limestone, aggregate, gypsum for plaster and wallboard, and clay for tile and bricks) and industrial minerals (fluorite, limestone, corundum, garnet, and sylvite).

20. Coal mining is hazardous work, with its associated roof falls, gas explosions, and working with heavy equipment. Furthermore, air pollution is a major problem associated with the burning of coal because of the release of carbon dioxide, sulfur, and other materials during combustion.

21. Oil traps are confined porous and permeable zones, usually in sedimentary rocks that trap and retain natural gas and petroleum. All have two conditions in common; a porous, permeable reservoir rock, and a cap rock that is virtually impermeable to oil and gas.

Lecture outline, art-only, and animation PowerPoint presentations for each chapter of *Essentials of Geology* are available on the IRC DVD (ISBN 0-13-604914-1).

NOTES:

© 2008 Pearson Education, Inc., Upper Saddle River, NJ. All rights reserved. This material is protected under all copyright laws as they currently exist. No portion of this material may be reproduced, in any form or by any means, without permission in writing from the publisher.

Metamorphic Rocks

Metamorphic Rocks begins with an examination of the process of metamorphism, including a discussion of the agents of metamorphism—heat, pressure, and chemical activity. After presenting how metamorphism alters the texture and mineralogy of a rock, the most common foliated and nonfoliated rocks are examined. The chapter closes with an investigation of contact and regional metamorphism, along with a discussion of how the texture and mineralogy of a rock reflect the intensity or degree of metamorphism.

Learning Objectives

After reading, studying, and discussing the chapter, students should be able to:

- Briefly discuss the concept of metamorphism and metamorphic rocks.
- List and discuss the agents of metamorphism, including heat, pressure, and chemical fluids.
- Briefly discuss the importance and origin of metamorphic textures.
- Compare and contrast the various types of foliated and nonfoliated metamorphic textures.
- List and briefly define the common metamorphic rocks, both foliated and nonfoliated.
- Briefly discuss the various metamorphic environments found on Earth.
- Explain the concept of metamorphic zones, including index minerals and metamorphic grade.

Chapter Outline

I. Metamorphism
 A. The transformation of one rock into another by temperatures and/or pressures unlike those in which it formed
 B. Metamorphic rocks are produced from
  1. Igneous rocks
  2. Sedimentary rocks
  3. Other metamorphic rocks
 C. Progresses incrementally from low-grade to high-grade
 D. During metamorphism the rock must remain essentially solid
 E. Metamorphic settings
  1. Contact or thermal metamorphism—driven by a rise in temperature within the host rock
  2. Hydrothermal metamorphism—chemical alterations from hot, ion-rich water
  3. Regional metamorphism
   a. Occurs during mountain building

 b. Produces the greatest volume of metamorphic rock
 c. Rocks usually display zones of contact and/or hydrothermal metamorphism

II. Agents of Metamorphism
 A. Heat
  1. The most important agent
  2. Recrystallization results in new, stable minerals
  3. Two sources of heat
   a. Contact metamorphism—when the rocks are intruded by magma from below
   b. An increase in temperature due to the geothermal gradient as the rocks are transported to greater depths
 B. Pressure (stress)
  1. Increases with depth

© 2008 Pearson Education, Inc., Upper Saddle River, NJ. All rights reserved. This material is protected under all copyright laws as they currently exist. No portion of this material may be reproduced, in any form or by any means, without permission in writing from the publisher.

2. Confining pressure applies forces equally in all directions
3. Rocks may also be subjected to differential stress, which is unequal in different directions

C. Chemically active fluids
   1. Mainly water with other volatile components
   2. Enhance ion migration
   3. Aid in recrystallization, which causes minerals to grow longer in a direction perpendicular to compressional stresses
   4. Sources
      a. Pore spaces of sedimentary rocks
      b. Fractures in igneous rocks
      c. Hydrated minerals such as clays and micas

D. The importance of parent rock
   1. Most metamorphic rocks have the same overall chemical composition as the parent rock from which they formed, except for the possible loss or acquisition of volatiles
   2. Mineral makeup determines, to a large extent, the degree to which each metamorphic agent will cause change

III. Metamorphic textures
   A. Texture is used to describe the size, shape, and arrangement of grains within a rock
   B. Foliation
      1. Any planar (nearly flat) arrangement of mineral grains or structural features within a rock
         a. Examples
            1. Parallel alignment of platy and/or elongated minerals
            2. Parallel alignment of flattened mineral grains and pebbles
            3. Compositional banding
            4. Slaty cleavage where rocks can be easily split into thin, tabular sheets
         b. Types of foliation can form from
            1. Rotation of platy and/or elongated minerals
            2. Recrystallization of minerals in the direction of preferred orientation
         3. Changing the shape of equidimensional grains into elongated shapes that are aligned
      2. Foliated textures
         a. Rock or slaty cleavage
            1. Closely spaced planar surfaces along which rocks split
            2. Can develop in a number of ways depending on the metamorphic environment and the composition of the parent rock
         b. Schistosity
            1. Platy minerals are discernible with the unaided eye and exhibit a planar or layered structure
            2. Rocks having this texture are referred to as schist
         c. Gneissic
            1. During high-grade metamorphism, ion migration results in the segregation of minerals
            2. Banded appearance
   C. Other metamorphic textures
      1. Those metamorphic rocks that do not exhibit a foliated texture are referred to as nonfoliated
         a. Develop in environments where deformation is minimal and are composed of minerals that exhibit equidimensional crystals
         b. e.g., marble
      2. Porphyroblastic textures
         a. Large grains, called porphyroblasts, surrounded by a fine-grained matrix of other minerals
         b. Porphyroblasts may be garnet, staurolite, and/or andalusite

IV. Common metamorphic rocks
   A. Foliated rocks
      1. Slate
         a. Very fine-grained
         b. Excellent rock cleavage
         c. Most often generated from low-grade metamorphism of shale, mudstone, or siltstone

© 2008 Pearson Education, Inc., Upper Saddle River, NJ. All rights reserved. This material is protected under all copyright laws as they currently exist. No portion of this material may be reproduced, in any form or by any means, without permission in writing from the publisher.

2. Phyllite
   a. Gradation in the degree of metamorphism between slate and schist
   b. Platy minerals not large enough to be identified with the unaided eye
   c. Glossy sheen and wavy surface
   d. Exhibits rock cleavage
   e. Composed mainly of fine crystals of either muscovite, chlorite, or both
3. Schist
   a. Medium- to coarse-grained
   b. Platy minerals predominate
   c. Commonly include the micas
   d. Term *schist* describes the texture
   e. To indicate composition, mineral names are used
   f. e.g., mica schist
4. Gneiss
   a. Medium- to coarse-grained
   b. Banded
   c. High-grade metamorphism
   d. Often composed of white or reddish feldspar-rich zones and layers of dark ferromagnesian minerals

B. Nonfoliated rocks
   1. Marble
      a. Coarse, crystalline
      b. Parent rock was limestone or dolostone
      c. Composed essentially of calcite crystals
      d. Used to create monuments and statues
      e. Exhibits a variety of colors
   2. Quartzite
      a. Formed from quartz sandstone
      b. Quartz grains are fused

V. Metamorphic environments
   A. Contact or thermal metamorphism
      1. Occurs due to a rise in temperature when magma invades a host rock
      2. Zone of alteration called an aureole forms in the rock that surrounds the emplaced magma
         a. Mineral composition of the host rock and the availability of water

affect the size of the aureole produced
         b. Large aureoles often consist of distinct zones of metamorphism
      3. Most easily recognized when it occurs at the surface, or in a near-surface environment
   B. Hydrothermal metamorphism
      1. Chemical alteration caused when hot, ion-rich fluids, called hydrothermal solutions, circulate through fissures and cracks that develop in rock
      2. Most widespread along the axis of the mid-ocean ridge system
   C. Regional metamorphism
      1. Produces the greatest quantity of metamorphic rock
      2. Associated with mountain building
   D. Other metamorphic environments
      1. Burial metamorphism
         a. Associated with very thick accumulations of sedimentary strata
         b. Required depth varies from one location to another, depending on the prevailing geothermal gradient
      2. Metamorphism along fault zones
         a. Occurs at great depth and at high temperatures
         b. Preexisting minerals deform by ductile flow
      3. Impact metamorphism
         a. Occurs when high speed projectiles called meteorites strike Earth's surface

VI. Metamorphic zones
   A. Systematic variations in the mineralogy and often the textures of rocks related to the variations in the degree of metamorphism
   B. Index minerals and metamorphic grade
      1. Changes in mineralogy from regions of low-grade metamorphism to regions of high-grade metamorphism
      2. Certain minerals, called index minerals, are good indicators of the metamorphic environment in which they form

© 2008 Pearson Education, Inc., Upper Saddle River, NJ. All rights reserved. This material is protected under all copyright laws as they currently exist. No portion of this material may be reproduced, in any form or by any means, without permission in writing from the publisher.

a. Low-grade environments
   indicated by rocks containing
   chlorite
b. High-grade environments often
   produce rocks containing the
   mineral sillimanite
3. Migmatites

a. Most extreme environments
b. Contain light bands of igneous, or
   igneous-appearing, components,
   along with dark bands consisting
   of unmelted metamorphic rock

Answers to the Review Questions

1. Metamorphism is a change in mineral composition and/or texture in a rock in response to changing conditions. The agents responsible for such changes are heat, pressure (stress), and chemically active fluids (water-dominated solutions at elevated temperatures and pressures that contain dissolved, silicate mineral components). Metamorphism also accompanies localized, mechanical fragmentation, and melting such as occur due to fault-zone shearing and impacts of meteorites.

2. Heat is the most important agent of metamorphism because it provides the energy that drives the chemical reactions responsible for mineral and textural changes during metamorphism. An increase in temperature results in increased ionic movement that allows crystalline structures to achieve a more stable configuration. Also, the rate of most chemical reactions approximately doubles for every 10°C increase in temperature. Therefore, heat is primarily responsible for the recrystallization and growth of new minerals that accompanies metamorphism.

3. Confining pressure refers to the forces applied to rocks as they are buried deeper in the earth, much like the increase in water pressure as you go deeper in the ocean. Because confining pressure is caused by the thickness of the overlying rocks, it is applied equally in all directions.

   Differential stress refers to those directed forces that result from the collision of tectonic plates. Unlike confining pressure, which is applied equally in all directions, differential stress is applied mainly in one plane. As a result, rocks subjected to differential stress are shortened in the direction the force is applied and elongated in the direction perpendicular to that force.

4. Chemically active fluids in metamorphism serve to facilitate the movement of ions during metamorphic reactions. Metamorphism involves changes in the solid state, and diffusion rates in solids are extremely slow. Therefore, fluids provide a transporting mechanism for ions that are involved in recrystallization of existing minerals, dissolution and redistribution of ions to form new, more stable minerals, and longer-distance transport between adjacent rock units that results in an overall change in chemical composition.

5. Parent material or parent rock refers to an original rock prior to metamorphism. The parent material affects the metamorphic process because the resulting metamorphic rock has essentially the same overall composition as the original parent. Some volatiles, such as H_2O or CO_2, may be lost or gained during metamorphism and new minerals may appear, but the overall chemical composition is determined by the parent material. Also, the mineral content of the original rock determines, to a large extent, the amount of change that will occur because of each metamorphic agent. Certain minerals, such as quartz, are relatively nonreactive and will change very little during metamorphism. Other minerals, such as calcite, are highly reactive and may result in various chemical changes in the resulting metamorphic rock.

© 2008 Pearson Education, Inc., Upper Saddle River, NJ. All rights reserved. This material is protected under all copyright laws as they currently exist. No portion of this material may be reproduced, in any form or by any means, without permission in writing from the publisher.

Metamorphic Rocks

6. Foliation describes a preferred orientation of parallel to sub-parallel aligned sheetlike (platy) mineral grains, mainly micas and chlorite, in a metamorphic rock. This parallel orientation of platy mineral grains is responsible for the development of slaty (rock) cleavage, schistosity, and gneissic texture. The strong tendency of slate to split along parallel cracks, forming plate-shaped fragments with a dull, surface luster, is called slaty or rock cleavage. The cracks open parallel to the plane of the tiny, aligned mica and chlorite grains. Thus in some areas, slate is still used as roofing material. The strong foliation in metamorphic rocks imparted by concentrations of visible, aligned mica and/or chlorite grains is called schistosity, because it characterizes virtually all schists. The key point here is that the aligned minerals in schistosity are clearly visible, unlike those in a slaty texture. In a gneissic texture, ions migrate into segregated bands or layers of different minerals. The distinctive banded or layered appearance of gneisses is generally indicative of higher grades of metamorphism.

7. The preferred orientation of mineral grains in foliated metamorphic rocks generally results from one of three mechanisms. Existing platy or elongated minerals may be rotated into a new orientation by directed forces during metamorphism. Also, recrystallization may result in new mineral grains that are elongated in the direction of preferred orientation. Finally, original, equidimensional grains may be elongated or flattened by ductile deformation or by dissolution of a mineral from a highly stressed region and precipitation in a lower-stressed position on the same mineral grain.

8. Mineral grain size often increases with metamorphic recrystallization, as in the change of limestone into marble. Overall, the mineralogy in a rock may also change as a result of metamorphism as certain minerals decompose and new ones grow (crystallize). The growth of these new minerals can result in not only a change in mineral composition, but also in the texture of the rock. Finally, longer-distance transport of ions during metamorphism may result in an overall change in bulk composition of the metamorphic rock as compared to the parent material.

9. Both slate and phyllite are derived from the regional metamorphism of shale or mudstone. Slate forms at lower temperatures and often exhibits well-developed rock cleavage. The aligned mica and chlorite grains are far too small to be visible to the naked eye, and the fracture cleavage surfaces show, at most, a dull sheen. Phyllite develops at somewhat higher temperatures. Therefore, the mica and chlorite are fine-grained but usually visible to the naked eye, sometimes with difficulty. The foliation surfaces exhibit a bright sheen caused by light reflecting from the aligned cleavage planes of the mica and/or chlorite grains.

10. (a) Calcite-rich and nonfoliated—marble
    (b) Loosely coherent rock composed of broken fragments that formed along a fault zone—fault breccia
    (c) Represents a grade of metamorphism between slate and schist—phyllite
    (d) Very fine-grained and foliated; excellent rock cleavage—slate
    (e) Foliated and composed predominantly of platy minerals—schist
    (f) Composed of alternating bands of light and dark silicate minerals—gneiss
    (g) Hard, nonfoliated rock resulting from contact metamorphism—hornfels

11. Contact metamorphism is restricted to the thermal halo (aureole) surrounding a pluton, batholith, or other intrusive magma body. The effects of metamorphism are limited to a specific volume of wall rock around the magma body, and the metamorphic episode is over once the magma body is cooled and crystallized. In regional metamorphism, very large volumes of sedimentary, volcanic, and mid- to upper-crustal rocks

© 2008 Pearson Education, Inc., Upper Saddle River, NJ. All rights reserved. This material is protected under all copyright laws as they currently exist. No portion of this material may be reproduced, in any form or by any means, without permission in writing from the publisher.

are compressed at convergent plate margins, deeply buried, heated by Earth's geothermal heat, and invaded by hot, metamorphic fluids. The metamorphic episode is long lasting and ceases only when the compressive deformational event ends and the rocks are tectonically uplifted and cooled. Thus regional metamorphism generates by far the larger volume of metamorphic rock.

12. Hydrothermal metamorphism is a type of alteration that occurs when hot, ion-rich fluids circulate through fissures and cracks in rocks. It is closely associated with igneous activity because of the heat necessary to circulate the hydrothermal fluids. Because of the igneous component required for heat, hydrothermal metamorphism most commonly occurs along the axes of the mid-oceanic ridge systems. Along these areas, upwelling magma from the mantle generates new seafloor, and seawater, heated from the magma, circulates through and chemically reacts with the newly formed basaltic rocks.

13. Burial metamorphism refers to the low-grade metamorphism that occurs in association with very thick accumulations of sedimentary strata. Confining pressure, from the thick sedimentary layers, and geothermal heat cause recrystallization of constituent minerals to change the texture and/or mineralogy of the parent sedimentary rocks. The low temperatures and pressures associated with burial metamorphism seldom cause significant deformation that is more typically found in regional metamorphism.

14. Index minerals are characteristic minerals that have been observed to occur in certain metamorphic environments, which are indicative of metamorphic grade. Because index minerals have been observed in numerous metamorphic terrains around the world, geologists use them to determine the grade of metamorphism in a certain area. As the area of study expands, geologists then can use index minerals to define the various zones of regional metamorphism in a larger region.

15. Slate, derived from shale or mudstone, is a very fine-grained, metamorphic rock with well-developed rock cleavage, and the mineral grains are not visible to the naked eye. Slate forms at the lowest metamorphic grade of the three. An increase in heat and pressure causes a recrystallization of the minerals in the slate to larger, almost visible grains. The larger grains now reflect light and the resulting rock, called a phyllite, is characterized by a bright sheen on cleavage surfaces. Continued increases in heat and pressure (higher metamorphic grade) promote further recrystallization of micas and chlorite and a foliated texture of coarse-grained (easily visible) minerals develops. This highly foliated rock with visible platy mineral grains is known as schist. At the highest grades of metamorphism, the grains segregate into alternating bands of light- and dark-colored minerals. Further recrystallization may occur and the resulting banded rock is called gneiss.

16. Both gneisses and migmatites form under higher grades of metamorphism. Gneisses, as discussed in question 15 above, are foliated metamorphic rocks formed by segregation of minerals into light- and dark-colored bands. Migmatites form by partial melting under pressure-temperature conditions in the melting range for granitic compositions. Migmatites are streaky, layered rocks composed of alternating dark-colored, residual minerals of the original parent rock and light-colored streaks and veins that crystallized from the melted granitic fraction. Therefore, gneisses and migmatites are related in that they both occur at higher grades of metamorphic conditions. Migmatites represent the higher grade of the two and they are transitional into igneous rocks because they involve partial melting.

© 2008 Pearson Education, Inc., Upper Saddle River, NJ. All rights reserved. This material is protected under all copyright laws as they currently exist. No portion of this material may be reproduced, in any form or by any means, without permission in writing from the publisher.

Metamorphic Rocks

Lecture outline, art-only, and animation PowerPoint presentations for each chapter of *Essentials of Geology* are available on the IRC DVD (ISBN 0-13-604914-1).

NOTES:

© 2008 Pearson Education, Inc., Upper Saddle River, NJ. All rights reserved. This material is protected under all copyright laws as they currently exist. No portion of this material may be reproduced, in any form or by any means, without permission in writing from the publisher.

Mass Wasting: The Work of Gravity

Mass Wasting: The Work of Gravity begins with a discussion of the role of mass wasting in landform development. After presenting the controls and triggers of mass wasting, the classification of mass wasting processes on the basis of the type of material involved, the kind of motion displayed, and the velocity of the movement is examined. The chapter closes with a brief description of each type of mass wasting.

Learning Objectives

After reading, studying, and discussing the chapter, students should be able to:

- Discuss the relationship between mass wasting and landform development.
- List and briefly explain those factors that control and trigger mass movements.
- Compare and contrast the various categories of mass movements.
- List examples and briefly discuss mass movements based on the type of motion involved.
- Discuss the different rates of movement involved in mass wasting.
- List specific geographic examples of mass wasting, including falls, slides, and flows.
- Discuss the characteristics of slower mass movements, including creep and solifluction.
- Discuss observable phenomena that indicate mass wasting has occurred in a given area.

Chapter Outline

I. Mass wasting and landform development
    A. Mass wasting refers to the downslope movement of rock, regolith, and soil under the direct influence of gravity
    B. Role of mass wasting
        1. Step that follows weathering
        2. Combined effects of mass wasting and running water produce stream valleys
    C. For mass wasting to occur, there must be slopes
        1. Most rapid events occur in areas of rugged, geologically young mountains
        2. As a landscape ages, less dramatic downslope movements occur

II. Controls and triggers of mass wasting
    A. Gravity is the controlling force
    B. Important triggering factors include
        1. Saturation of the material with water

        a. Destroys particle cohesion
        b. Water adds weight
        2. Oversteepening of slopes
        a. Stable slope angle (angle of repose) is different for various materials
        b. Oversteepened slopes are unstable
        3. Removal of anchoring vegetation
        4. Ground vibrations from earthquakes
        a. May cause expensive property damage
        b. Can cause liquefaction—water saturated surface materials behave as fluidlike masses that flow
    C. Landslide without triggers
        1. Slope materials weaken over time
        2. Random events that are unpredictable

III. Classification of mass-wasting processes
    A. Generally each process is classified by
        1. Type of material involved
        a. Debris

© 2008 Pearson Education, Inc., Upper Saddle River, NJ. All rights reserved. This material is protected under all copyright laws as they currently exist. No portion of this material may be reproduced, in any form or by any means, without permission in writing from the publisher.

b. Mud
c. Earth
d. Rock
2. Type of motion
   a. Fall (free-fall of pieces)
   b. Slide (material moves along a surface)
   c. Flow (material moves as a viscous fluid)
3. The velocity of the movement
   a. Fast
   b. Slow

IV. Forms of mass wasting
  A. Slump
    1. Movement of a mass of rock or unconsolidated material as a unit along a curved surface
    2. Occurs along oversteepened slopes
  B. Rockslide
    1. Blocks of bedrock slide down a slope
    2. Fast and destructive
    3. Debris flow (mudflow)
      a. Flow of soil and regolith with a large amount of water

b. Often confined to channels
c. Serious hazard in dry areas with heavy rains
d. Debris flows composed mostly of volcanic materials on the flanks of volcanoes are called lahars
C. Earthflow
   1. Form on hillsides in humid regions
   2. Water saturates the soil
   3. Commonly involve materials rich in clay and silt
D. Slow movements
   1. Creep
     a. Gradual movement of soil and regolith downhill
     b. Aided by the alternate expansion and contraction of the surface material
   2. Solifluction
     a. Promoted by a dense clay hardpan or impermeable bedrock layer
     b. Common in regions underlain by permafrost
     c. Can occur on gentle slopes

Answers to the Review Questions

1. Mass wasting is the downslope movement of soil and weathered rock debris. Streams can deepen valleys by downcutting (erosion), but widening or enlarging of the valley via erosion of the sides or slopes is accomplished largely through mass wasting. Mass wasting delivers the weathered rock material and soil to the streams, which carry it away to a site of deposition.

2. Gravity is the controlling force of mass wasting. The steeper the slope, the greater the gravitational force acting to move materials toward the bottom of the slope. Other factors include: water, oversteepened slopes, the activities of people, earthquakes acting as triggers, etc.

3. Water in the pores of material destroys the cohesion among particles and also adds considerable weight to a mass of material.

4. The angle of repose is the steepest angle that a pile of dry, unconsolidated particles of fine sand or larger size can sustain before sliding, rolling, and avalanching eliminate the oversteepening. For dry sand, the angle is about 34 degrees. Most accumulations of broken rock, such as talus, contain different sizes of fragments, some of which may be quite large. These materials often have slightly steeper repose angles than does dry sand (35–39 degrees).

5. Vegetation generally serves to enhance slope stability because the network of root systems binds the soil and regolith together. Therefore, removal of vegetation by fire or logging increases the probability of mass wasting by eliminating the anchoring effect of plants.

© 2008 Pearson Education, Inc., Upper Saddle River, NJ. All rights reserved. This material is protected under all copyright laws as they currently exist. No portion of this material may be reproduced, in any form or by any means, without permission in writing from the publisher.

6. Although a given area may exhibit conditions that favor mass wasting, sometimes a triggering event is necessary to initiate mass movements. Earthquakes and the aftershocks that follow them often serve as trigger mechanisms for mass-wasting events. Earthquakes dislodge large volumes of rock and unconsolidated material that move downslope as slides and flows. Also, the shaking of unconsolidated materials by an earthquake reduces the cohesiveness between particles, which may result in slope failure.

7. Fall refers to the unimpeded, downslope movement of more or less individual rock fragments and particles. Usually, the first stage of a fall is through the air as fragments fall off the face or top of a cliff. After the fragments hit the ground surface, they bounce and roll for some additional distance downslope. Slide refers to a surface mass of rock or soil that moves downhill more or less intact, along a slip surface or fracture plane. Flow describes the movement of materials as a chaotic mixture by deforming or flowing internally; thus masses of wet soil and debris move mainly through shearing and flow movements inside the mass. Saturated mud and debris move mainly by viscous flow, although a minor component of basal slip is involved.

8. Rock avalanches are triggered when masses of rock break loose from high on a slope or cliff. The first stage of the avalanche involves free fall. As the fast-moving mass nears the ground, air is trapped and compressed beneath it, causing the mass to move (run out) over the compressed air layer with virtually no friction. Thus rock avalanches can move long distances at very high speeds; and, of course, they are very dangerous.

9. Rockslides involve rapid slippage of fracture-bounded blocks along inclined, weak layers and fractures in bedrock. Slump denotes the slow, downhill movement of a block of soil or relatively weak rock along a curved, spoon-shaped slip surface. As it moves downhill, the block often undergoes rotation, leaving its surface tilted back toward the upslope.

10. This famous slide along the south side of the Gros Ventre River occurred in June 1925. Tilted, sedimentary strata lie roughly parallel to the south slope of the valley; and the surface layer, relatively hard, resistant sandstone, rests on a much softer, shale stratum. The river had gradually downcut into the shale layer, depriving the inclined, sandstone slab of any lateral (buttressing) support on the downhill side. Water from melting snows and rain seeped into the soil and bedrock, saturating the ground above the shale and weakening the top of the supporting shale layer. These conditions allowed a large, fractured slab of sandstone to break loose and rapidly slide downhill. The slide formed an instant natural dam and was moving fast enough to climb a short distance up the opposite side of the valley. Two years later the dam burst, causing a tremendous flood on the lower Gros Ventre and upper Snake rivers.

11. Debris flows are essentially "soupy" to more viscous, well-mixed mud and water masses that behave and flow like liquids. They develop during periods of very intense rainfall or snowmelt in areas with little or no vegetation cover, and move faster than earthflows.

Earthflows have higher contents of solids (mud, sand, boulders, etc.) and less water than mudflows, are more viscous than mudflows, and move less rapidly. They are mass movement events in which sheets or slabs of saturated to nearly saturated soil and weathered debris slough off a hillside or roadcut and move downhill to the base of the slope. The leading part (toe) of a slump block often turns into an earthflow when the slump material is wet.

© 2008 Pearson Education, Inc., Upper Saddle River, NJ. All rights reserved. This material is protected under all copyright laws as they currently exist. No portion of this material may be reproduced, in any form or by any means, without permission in writing from the publisher.

12. Mudflows developed when hot ash was erupted onto snow on the upper slopes of both volcanoes. The soupy mud moved rapidly (20 mi/hr or so) down the stream valleys and suddenly "appeared" in stream and river valleys at the base of the volcanoes. Mudflows from both volcanoes caused extensive property damage, and those from Nevado del Ruiz caused the loss of many lives.

13. The alternate expansion and contraction of surface material caused by freezing and thawing or wetting and drying is one of the factors that contribute to the creep of earth materials. Other factors include saturation of the ground with water (resulting in a loss of internal cohesion) and disturbance of the soil (by plant roots, burrowing animals, or falling raindrops).

14. Solifluction is the downhill flowage of the water-saturated surface soil layer above permanently frozen ground (permafrost). In the summer, the soil thaws to some depth below the surface, but the water is trapped in the thawed soil because the permafrost zone is impermeable. Thus solifluction occurs only in the summer when the surface soil layer is thawed. In the winter, the surface soil layer is frozen solid.

Lecture outline, art-only, and animation PowerPoint presentations for each chapter of *Essentials of Geology* are available on the IRC DVD (ISBN 0-13-604914-1).

NOTES:

© 2008 Pearson Education, Inc., Upper Saddle River, NJ. All rights reserved. This material is protected under all copyright laws as they currently exist. No portion of this material may be reproduced, in any form or by any means, without permission in writing from the publisher.

Running Water

Running Water opens with an introduction to the hydrologic cycle and the exchange of water between the oceans, atmosphere, and land. The factors that control streamflow and their influence on a stream's ability to erode and transport materials are presented along with discussions of base level, graded streams, and stream erosion. Erosional and depositional features of streams are followed by a brief look at both narrow and wide stream valleys. The chapter concludes an examination of drainage patterns, floods, and flood control.

Learning Objectives

After reading, studying, and discussing the chapter, students should be able to:

- Discuss and explain the hydrologic cycle on Earth.
- Briefly discuss the concept of streamflow, including discharge and gradient.
- Explain the changes that occur from the head to the mouth of a stream.
- Compare and contrast the various mechanisms by which streams transport sediment.
- Distinguish between the competence and capacity of a stream.
- List and briefly describe the various types of stream deposits.
- Briefly explain the concept of base level and graded streams.
- Compare and contrast the characteristics of narrow and wide stream valleys.
- List and briefly describe the various types of drainage patterns.
- Briefly discuss flooding and flood control.

Chapter Outline

I. Hydrologic cycle
   A. Illustrates the circulation of Earth's water supply
   B. Processes involved in the cycle
      1. Precipitation
      2. Evaporation
      3. Infiltration
      4. Runoff
      5. Transpiration
   C. Cycle is balanced
II. Running water
   A. Begins as sheet flow
      1. Infiltration capacity controlled by
         a. Intensity and duration of the rainfall
         b. Prior wetted condition of the soil
         c. Soil texture
         d. Slope of the land
         e. Nature of the vegetative cover
   B. Streamflow
      1. Two types of flow determined primarily by velocity
         a. Laminar flow
         b. Turbulent flow
      2. Factors that determine velocity
         a. Gradient, or slope
         b. Channel characteristic
            1. Shape
            2. Size
            3. Roughness
         c. Discharge
   C. Changes from upstream to downstream
      1. Profile
         a. Cross-sectional view of a stream
         b. From head (headwaters or source) to mouth

© 2008 Pearson Education, Inc., Upper Saddle River, NJ. All rights reserved. This material is protected under all copyright laws as they currently exist. No portion of this material may be reproduced, in any form or by any means, without permission in writing from the publisher.

1. Profile is a smooth curve
2. Gradient decreases downstream
2. Factors that increase downstream
   a. Velocity
   b. Discharge
   c. Channel size
3. Factors that decrease downstream
   a. Gradient, or slope
   b. Channel roughness
D. Base level and graded streams
   1. Lowest point a stream can erode to
   2. Two general types
      a. Ultimate
      b. Local or temporary
   3. Changing causes readjustment of stream activities
      a. Raising base level causes deposition
      b. Lowering base level causes erosion
E. Stream erosion
   1. Lifting loosely consolidated particles by
      a. Abrasion
F. Transport of sediment by streams
   1. Transported material is called the stream's load
      a. Types of load
         1. Dissolved load
         2. Suspended load
         3. Bed load
      b. Capacity—the maximum load a stream can transport
   2. Competence
      a. Indicates the maximum particle size a stream can transport
      b. Determined by the stream's velocity
G. Deposition of sediment by a stream
   1. Caused by a decrease in velocity
      a. Competence is reduced
      b. Sediment begins to drop out
   2. Stream sediments
      a. Well sorted
      b. Called alluvium
   3. Channel deposits
      a. Bars
      b. Braided streams
      c. Deltas
   4. Floodplain deposits
      a. Natural levees

1. Form parallel to the stream channel
2. Built by successive floods over many years
   b. Back swamps
   c. Yazoo tributaries
5. Alluvial fans
   a. Develop where a high-gradient stream leaves a narrow valley
   b. Slopes outward in a broad arc
6. Deltas
   a. Form when a stream enters an ocean or lake
   b. Consist of three types of beds
      1. Foreset beds
      2. Topset beds
      3. Bottomset beds
   c. May develop distributaries
H. Stream valleys
   1. The most common landforms on Earth's surface
   2. Two general types of stream valleys
      a. Narrow valleys
         1. V-shaped
         2. Downcutting toward base level
         3. Features often include
            a. Rapids, and/or
            b. Waterfalls
      b. Wide valleys
         1. Stream is near base level
         2. Downward erosion is less dominant
         3. Stream energy is directed from side to side, forming a floodplain
         4. Features often include
            a. Floodplains
               1. Erosional floodplains
               2. Depositional floodplains
            b. Meanders
               1. Cut bank
               2. Cutoff
               3. Oxbow lakes
               4. Meander scar
I. Incised meanders and stream terraces
   1. Incised meanders
      a. Meanders in steep, narrow valleys
      b. Caused by
         1. Drop in base level or
         2. Uplift of land
   2. Terraces

© 2008 Pearson Education, Inc., Upper Saddle River, NJ. All rights reserved. This material is protected under all copyright laws as they currently exist. No portion of this material may be reproduced, in any form or by any means, without permission in writing from the publisher.

a. Remnants of a former floodplain
b. River has adjusted to a relative drop in base level by downcutting
J. Drainage patterns
  1. Pattern of the interconnected network of streams
  2. Common drainage patterns
    a. Dendritic
    b. Radial
    c. Rectangular
    d. Trellis
K. Floods and flood control
  1. Floods are the most common and most destructive geologic hazard
  2. Causes and types of floods

a. Result from natural-occurring and human-induced factors
b. Types of floods
  1. Regional floods
  2. Flash floods
  3. Ice-jam floods
  4. Dam-failure
3. Flood control
  a. Engineering efforts
    1. Artificial levees
    2. Flood-control dams
    3. Channelization
  b. Nonstructural approach through sound floodplain management

Answers to the Review Questions

1. [AU: Sentence fragment; please rewrite.]Evaporation, primarily from the ocean, transport via the atmosphere, and eventually precipitation back to the surface. If the water falls on the continents, much will find its way back to the atmosphere by evaporation and transpiration. However, some water will soak in (infiltration) and runoff.

2. Most precipitation originates by evaporation from the oceans. Over time, water evaporated from the oceans is replenished by inflow of freshwater from rivers and streams. Continental ice sheets and glaciers have a strong effect on sea level changes. Expanding glacial ice volumes result in lowered sea level, and shrinking ice sheets and glaciers effect rising sea level.

3. The three main parts or zones in a river system are a zone of erosion, a zone sediment transport, and a zone of deposition.

4. The gradient is the drop in elevation of the stream divided by the length of the flow path. Thus the gradient is 2000 m/250 km or 8 m/km.

5. The new gradient would be 2000 m/500 km or 4 m/km. If a fairly straight channel should develop meanders, the flow path would lengthen without any change in the elevation drop; thus the gradient is lowered. In this example, the length of the stream doubled ,so the gradient decreased by 50%.

6. The average velocity of a stream is given by the equation $V = Q/A$ where V = velocity, Q = discharge, and A = area of water cross section. Therefore, as discharge increases, the velocity increases as well.

7. Part of the load is dissolved in the water. Much of this solution load is contributed by underground water. Sediment is also carried in suspension (suspended load) and rolled or skipped along the bottom (bed load).

© 2008 Pearson Education, Inc., Upper Saddle River, NJ. All rights reserved. This material is protected under all copyright laws as they currently exist. No portion of this material may be reproduced, in any form or by any means, without permission in writing from the publisher.

Running Water

8. The suspended load will settle to the bottom of the jar while the solution load will remain dissolved in the water. The jar of water will probably not contain any of the stream's bed load, which is found only along the bottom of the stream channel.

9. Capacity refers to the maximum load a stream can carry and is directly related to the discharge. Competency, on the other hand, refers to the largest sized particles a stream is capable of transporting and is dependent upon stream velocity.

10. Bedrock channels are more likely to be found near the head of a stream.

11. Braided channels result from excessive bed load. Glacial outwash streams are good examples. Rivers and streams that lose discharge downstream also typically become braided because they can no longer efficiently move bed loads acquired upstream where discharges and competence are higher. In addition, bed load influx from a highly competent, steeper tributary, an abrupt decrease in gradient, and an abrupt widening of the channel cross section can result in excessive bed loads and braiding.

12. Base level is the lowest elevation to which a stream can downcut or lower its channel. The elevation of a major river at a junction with a tributary is the base level elevation (a temporary base level geologically) for the tributary. Sea level is the ultimate base level for rivers that discharge into the oceans; thus sea level is the base level for the Mississippi River. Base level for the Missouri River is the junction where it enters the Mississippi River.

13. Meanders initially develop on the floodplain of a stream that was relatively near base level. Then, a change in base level caused the stream to begin downcutting. This could be triggered by a drop in base level or an uplift in the land upon which the stream was flowing.

14. Natural levees are accumulations of sediment that parallel a channel on both banks that are built by successive floods over many years. When a stream overflows its banks, its velocity immediately diminishes, leaving coarse sediment deposited in strips bordering the channel and a lesser amount of fine sediment deposited over the valley floor. This uneven distribution of material produces the gentle slope of the natural levee.

Tributaries to a main stream with extensive, natural levees may flow for some distance parallel to the main stream before joining. These are called yazoo tributaries after the Yazoo River, a tributary to the lower Mississippi River in Mississippi.

15. Both alluvial fans and deltas represent depositional features that form in areas where gradients and velocities decrease abruptly. In an ideal sense, both show delta (Δ), map-view shapes, and smaller channels (braided, anastomosing channels on alluvial fans and distributaries on deltas) that diverge outward from the apex of the delta or fan.

16. (a) Streams diverging from a central high area such as a dome—radial
    (b) Branching, "treelike" pattern—dendritic
    (c) A pattern that develops when bedrock is crisscrossed by joints and faults— rectangular

© 2008 Pearson Education, Inc., Upper Saddle River, NJ. All rights reserved. This material is protected under all copyright laws as they currently exist. No portion of this material may be reproduced, in any form or by any means, without permission in writing from the publisher.

17. Flash floods are short events (generally several hours) that are confined to small areas. Flash floods are characterized by high discharges, rapid rises in water levels, and high velocities. They typically occur in narrow canyons or urban areas where runoff is rapid following intense rainfall episodes such as thunderstorms. Regional floods are longer-term events that cover larger areas (hundreds or thousands of square miles) and last for days or weeks. They result from seasonal fluctuations such as rapid snowmelt or large, slow-moving storm systems such as hurricanes. Flash floods would generally be deadlier because they occur with little or no warning and also because they involve rapid rises in water with high velocities. Regional floods take much longer to develop so there is more lead time for warnings and velocity and water levels increase much more slowly.

18. (1) Artificial levees are earthen mounds built on the banks of a river to increase the volume of water a river can hold. One drawback is that many artificial levees are not built to withstand periods of extreme flooding.

    (2) Flood-control dams are built to store floodwater and then let it out slowly. Some drawbacks are their cost and the fact that large dams can cause ecological damage to river environments.

    (3) Channelization involves altering a stream channel in order to speed the flow of water and prevent it from reaching flood height. However, preventing a river from returning to its previous course is often difficult.

Lecture outline, art-only, and animation PowerPoint presentations for each chapter of *Essentials of Geology* are available on the IRC DVD (ISBN 0-13-604914-1).

NOTES:

© 2008 Pearson Education, Inc., Upper Saddle River, NJ. All rights reserved. This material is protected under all copyright laws as they currently exist. No portion of this material may be reproduced, in any form or by any means, without permission in writing from the publisher.

Groundwater

Groundwater opens with a discussion of the importance of underground water as the largest reservoir of freshwater that is readily available to humans. Following an examination of the distribution and movement of groundwater, springs and wells are discussed. The chapter closes with investigations of the environmental problems of groundwater, geothermal energy, and the geologic work of groundwater.

Learning Objectives

After reading, studying, and discussing the chapter, students should be able to:

- Briefly discuss the importance of groundwater.
- Explain the distribution of underground water, including the concept of the water table.
- Understand the interaction between groundwater and surface streams.
- List and briefly discuss those factors influencing the storage and movement of groundwater.
- Compare and contrast springs, hot springs, and geysers.
- List and discuss in some detail the major problems associated with groundwater withdrawal.
- Explain briefly the geologic work accomplished by groundwater.
- Discuss the main features associated with karst development.

Chapter Outline

I.   Importance of groundwater
   A.   Groundwater is water found in the pores of soil and sediment, plus narrow joints and fractures in bedrock
   B.   Largest reservoir of freshwater that is readily available to humans
   C.   Geological roles
      1.   As an erosional agent, dissolving groundwater produces
         a.   Sinkholes
         b.   Caverns
      2.   An equalizer of streamflow

II.   Distribution of underground water
   A.   Belt of soil moisture—water held by molecular attraction on soil particles in the near-surface zone
   B.   Zone of saturation
      1.   Formation

         a.   Water not held as soil moisture percolates downward
         b.   Water reaches a zone where all the open spaces in sediment and rock are completely filled with water
         c.   Water within the pores is called groundwater
      2.   Water table—the upper limit of the zone of saturation
   C.   Zone of aeration
      1.   Area above the water table
      2.   Water cannot be pumped by wells

III.   The water table
   A.   Upper limit of the zone of saturation
   B.   Variations in the water table
      1.   Depth is highly variable
         a.   Varies seasonally and

© 2008 Pearson Education, Inc., Upper Saddle River, NJ. All rights reserved. This material is protected under all copyright laws as they currently exist. No portion of this material may be reproduced, in any form or by any means, without permission in writing from the publisher.

b. From year to year
2. Shape is usually a subdued replica of the surface topography
3. Factors that contribute to the irregular surface of the water table
   a. Water tends to "pile up" beneath high areas
   b. Variations in rainfall
   c. Variations in permeability from place to place
C. Interaction between groundwater and streams
   1. A basic link in the hydrologic cycle
   2. Three interactions
      a. Gaining streams—gain water from the inflow of groundwater through the streambed
      b. Losing streams—lose water to the groundwater system by outflow through the streambed
      c. A combination of the first two— stream gains in some sections and loses in others

IV. How groundwater moves
A. Exceedingly slow—typical rate of movement is a few centimeters per day
B. Energy for the movement is provided by the force of gravity
C. Water percolates into a stream from all possible directions

V. Factors influencing the storage and movement of groundwater
A. Porosity
   1. Percentage of the total volume of rock or sediment that consists of pore spaces
   2 Determines how much groundwater can be stored
   3. Variations can be great
B. Permeability, aquitards, and aquifers
   1. Permeability—the ability of a material to transmit a fluid
   2. Aquitard—an impermeable layer that hinders or prevents water movement (e.g., clay)
   3. Aquifer—permeable rock strata or sediment that transmits groundwater freely (e.g., sands and gravels)

VI. Features associated with groundwater
A. Springs
   1. Water table intersects Earth's surface
   2. Natural outflow of groundwater
   3. Can be caused by an aquitard creating a localized zone of saturation and a perched water table
B. Wells
   1. To ensure a continuous supply of water, a well must penetrate below the water table
   2. Pumping can cause
      a. Drawdown (lowering) of the water table and a
      b. Cone of depression in the water table
C. Artesian wells
   1. Applied to any situation in which groundwater under pressure rises above the level of the aquifer
   2. Types of artesian wells
      a. Nonflowing—pressure surface is below ground level
      b. Flowing—pressure surface is above the ground
      c. Not all artesian systems are wells, artesian springs also exist

VII. Problems associated with groundwater withdrawal
A. Treating groundwater as a nonrenewable resource
   1. In many places the water available to recharge the aquifer falls significantly short of the amount being withdrawn
   2. e.g., the high plains
B. Land subsidence
   1. Ground sinks when water is pumped from wells faster than natural recharge processes can replace it
   2. e.g., San Joaquin Valley of California
C. Groundwater contamination
   1. One common source is sewage
   2. Extremely permeable aquifers, such as coarse gravel, have such large openings that groundwater may travel long distances without being cleaned
   3. Sewage often becomes purified as it passes through a few dozen meters of

© 2008 Pearson Education, Inc., Upper Saddle River, NJ. All rights reserved. This material is protected under all copyright laws as they currently exist. No portion of this material may be reproduced, in any form or by any means, without permission in writing from the publisher.

an aquifer composed of sand or permeable sandstone

4. Other sources and types of contamination include substances such as
    a. Highway salt
    b. Fertilizers
    c. Pesticides
    d. Chemical and industrial materials leaking from
        1. Storage tanks
        2. Landfills
        3. Holding ponds

VIII. Hot springs and geysers
  A. Hot springs
      1. Water is 6–9°C warmer than the mean annual air temperature of the locality
      2. The water for most is heated by cooling of igneous rock
  B. Geysers
      1. Intermittent hot springs
      2. Water erupts with great force
      3. Occur where extensive underground chambers exist within hot igneous rock
      4. Groundwater heats, expands, changes to steam, and erupts
      5. Chemical sedimentary rock accumulates at the surface
          a. Siliceous sinter (from dissolved silica)
          b. Travertine (dissolved calcium carbonate)

IX. Geothermal energy
  A. Tapping natural underground reservoirs of steam and hot water
  B. Favorable geologic factors include
      1. A potent source of heat
      2. Large and porous reservoirs with channels connected to the heat source
      3. A cap of low permeability rocks
  C. Geothermal energy is not inexhaustible

X. Geologic work of groundwater
  A. Groundwater dissolves rock
      1. Groundwater is often mildly acidic
          a. Contains weak carbonic acid

b. Forms when rainwater dissolves carbon dioxide from the air and from decaying plants

2. Carbonic acid reacts with calcite in limestone to form calcium bicarbonate, a soluble material

B. Caverns
  1 Most are created by acidic groundwater dissolving soluble rock at or just below the surface in the zone of saturation
  2. Features found within caverns
      a. Form in the zone of aeration
      b. Composed of dripstone (travertine)
          1. Calcite deposited as dripping water evaporates
          2. Features, collectively called speleothems, include
              a. Stalactites hanging from the ceiling, and
              b. Stalagmites, which form on the floor of a cavern and reach upward

C. Karst topography
  1. Landscapes that to a large extent have been shaped by the dissolving power of groundwater
  2. Common features
      a. Irregular terrain
      b. Sinkholes, or sinks
          1. Surface depressions
          2. Formed by
              a. Slowly dissolving bedrock as the groundwater moves downward
              b. Sudden cavern collapse
      c. Striking lack of surface drainage (streams)
  3. Tower karst
      a. Southern China
      b. Region of steep sided hills
      c. Forms in tropical and subtropical regions with thick beds of highly jointed limestone
      d. Large volumes of limestone have been dissolved leaving only residual towers

© 2008 Pearson Education, Inc., Upper Saddle River, NJ. All rights reserved. This material is protected under all copyright laws as they currently exist. No portion of this material may be reproduced, in any form or by any means, without permission in writing from the publisher.

Answers to the Review Questions

1. Groundwater comprises about 14% of all freshwater. This quantity significantly exceeds water contained in rivers, lakes, unsaturated soils, and the atmosphere. Inasmuch as water stored in glaciers and ice caps accounts for 85% of all freshwater, groundwater comprises about 94% of all liquid freshwater.

2. Groundwater inflow sustains flow in perennial streams and accounts for most, if not all stream discharge during extended time intervals between precipitation events. Thus groundwater contributes to the geological work of streams.

3. Water percolates downward from Earth's surface into a zone where all of the open spaces in sediment and rock are filled with water. This zone is called the zone of saturation, and the water located here is called groundwater. The water table marks the upper boundary of groundwater.

4. Gaining streams are those streams that gain water from the inflow of groundwater through the streambed. This situation occurs when the elevation of the water table is higher than the level of the surface of the stream. A losing stream is the opposite situation where a stream loses water to the groundwater by outflow of water through the streambed. This results from the elevation of the water table being lower than the level of the stream surface.

5. Both describe important hydraulic characteristics of soil and rock. Porosity is defined as the volume percentage of open space (voids, pores, cracks, etc.) in a given volume of soil or rock. Highly porous materials can hold abundant water when saturated; low-porosity materials can hold only small amounts of water. Permeability refers to how easily water will flow from opening to opening through a porous material. To be permeable, a porous material must have openings and cracks (pore spaces) that connect with one another and are large enough for water to flow freely between pores.

6. Both terms describe bedrock or unconsolidated deposits in terms of their hydraulic properties. An aquitard is composed of impermeable material (water will not flow through it); thus an aquitard (an impermeable stratum or layer) can stop water percolating downward from the surface or prevent water from moving upward or downward from a saturated zone (an aquifer or aquifers). An aquifer is a general term to describe any saturated, water-bearing, subsurface, geologic stratum or deposit of porous, permeable bedrock or unconsolidated material.

7. If the pore spaces and interpore connections are very small, the material will have a low permeability despite having a high porosity. A water-saturated mud layer would be a good example. It has substantial water content (porosity), but the pores and connections are very small; thus water moves with great difficulty, and the mud has a very low permeability.

8. This situation results in a perched water table. Water seeping downward from the surface is stopped at the top of the aquitard and accumulates, forming a gently sloping, mound-shaped, local, saturated zone in an aquifer above the aquitard. This saturated zone has its own water table "perched" above the elevation of the regional water table.

© 2008 Pearson Education, Inc., Upper Saddle River, NJ. All rights reserved. This material is protected under all copyright laws as they currently exist. No portion of this material may be reproduced, in any form or by any means, without permission in writing from the publisher.

Groundwater

9. The term *artesian* is applied to any situation in which groundwater rises in a well above the level where it was initially encountered. The two conditions that must be present in order for artesian wells to exist are (1) an inclined aquifer with one end exposed at the surface to receive water and (2) impermeable layers both above and below the aquifer to prevent the water from escaping.

10. The area is fairly dry and there is little natural recharge to the aquifer. Thus continued pumping depletes the groundwater and causes the water table to drop. In some areas, the water table in the Ogallala aquifer has declined over 200 feet since large-scale pumping for agricultural irrigation was started.

11. The aquifer here is composed of unconsolidated sands and silts that shrink or compact when dewatered (when they change from a water-saturated to an unsaturated condition). Compaction is accomplished by permanent closing of some of the original pore space in the aquifer; thus the land surface subsides.

12. The sand aquifer would be most effective. The water would move more slowly, and the pollutants would be more likely to contact grain surfaces where they could be adsorbed or chemically degraded.

13. Toxic, flammable, explosive, and corrosive substances are classified as hazardous. These would include pesticides, gasoline, jet fuel, and chemicals such as sulfuric acid and benzene.

14. Most geothermal waters are heated by geologically young, hot, igneous bodies at depth; thus they are concentrated in areas of active or recent volcanism in the western states. Warm springs also occur in nonvolcanic areas, such as those in the Appalachian Mountains. In these situations, the groundwater circulates deep below the surface and is heated by the warmer rocks at depth; being less dense than cold water, it then rises back to the surface as a warm spring.

15. No. When hot fluids are pumped from heated reservoirs, water cannot be replaced and then heated sufficiently to recharge the reservoir.

16. Two common speleothems (dripstone features) are stalactites and stalagmites. Both are composed of calcium carbonate precipitated from water dripping from the roofs of caverns. Stalactites grow (hang) down from the ceiling; they are slender and pointed like icicles. Stalagmites grow up from the floor; they are stout, with blunt tips and rippled surfaces.

17. Karst topography. The term was coined in reference to the distinctive landforms developed on limestone bedrock in Slovenia, a small country that was once a province in the northeastern part of the former Yugoslavia.

18. Sinkholes develop only in areas underlain by soluble bedrock such as limestone, anhydrite, and gypsum. When a cavern suddenly collapses, a circular to elliptical, closed depression forms as the rocks and soil above the cavern subside. Also, sinkholes may slowly subside and enlarge as intersecting vertical fractures are gradually widened and enlarged into a pipelike channel by solution and removal of the soluble bedrock.

© 2008 Pearson Education, Inc., Upper Saddle River, NJ. All rights reserved. This material is protected under all copyright laws as they currently exist. No portion of this material may be reproduced, in any form or by any means, without permission in writing from the publisher.

Lecture outline, art-only, and animation PowerPoint presentations for each chapter of *Essentials of Geology* are available on the IRC DVD (ISBN 0-13-604914-1).

NOTES:

© 2008 Pearson Education, Inc., Upper Saddle River, NJ. All rights reserved. This material is protected under all copyright laws as they currently exist. No portion of this material may be reproduced, in any form or by any means, without permission in writing from the publisher.

Chapter 11

Glaciers and Glaciation

Glaciers and Glaciation begins with a discussion of glaciers as part of the hydrologic cycle. Following an examination of glacial movement, glacial erosion and deposition, as well as the features that result from each, are investigated in detail. The chapter concludes with an overview of glaciers of the past, some indirect effects of Ice Age glaciers, and the causes of glaciation.

Learning Objectives

After reading, studying, and discussing the chapter, students should be able to:

- Compare and contrast the various types of glaciers.
- Briefly discuss the formation and movement of glaciers.
- Discuss the processes involved in glacial erosion.
- Compare and contrast those landforms produced by glacial erosion.
- Discuss the processes associated with glacial deposition.
- Compare and contrast those landforms produced by glacial deposition.
- Briefly explain the glacial theory and the development of ice ages.
- List and briefly explain some of the proposed causes of glaciation.

Chapter Outline

I. Glaciers: a part of two basic cycles
  A. Glaciers are parts of the
    1. Hydrologic cycle, and the
    2. Rock cycle
  B. Definition: A thick mass of ice that originates on land from the accumulation, compaction, and recrystallization of snow
  C. Types of glaciers
    1. Valley (alpine) glaciers
      a. Exist in mountainous areas
      b. Flows down valley from an accumulation center at its head
    2. Ice sheets
      a. Exist on a larger scale than valley glaciers
      b. e.g., over Greenland and the Antarctic ice sheet
      c. Often called continental ice sheets
      d. Ice flows out in all directions from one or more snow-accumulation centers
    3. Other types of glaciers
      a. Ice caps
      b. Outlet glaciers

II. Movement of glacial ice
  A. Generally referred to as flow
    1. Two basic types
      a. Plastic flow
        1. Within the ice
        2. Under pressure, ice behaves as a plastic material
      b. Basal slip
        1. Entire ice mass slipping along the ground
        2. Most glaciers are thought to move by this process
    2. Zone of fracture
      1. Uppermost 50 meters

© 2008 Pearson Education, Inc., Upper Saddle River, NJ. All rights reserved. This material is protected under all copyright laws as they currently exist. No portion of this material may be reproduced, in any form or by any means, without permission in writing from the publisher.

2. Tension causes crevasses to form in brittle ice
B. Rates of glacial movement
 1. Average velocities vary considerably from one glacier to another
 2. Rates of up to several meters per day
 3. Some glaciers exhibit extremely rapid movements called surges
C. Budget of a glacier
 1. Zone of accumulation—the area where a glacier forms
  a. Outer limits are defined by the snowline
  b. Elevation of the snowline varies greatly
 2. Zone of wastage—the area where there is a net loss to the glacier due to
  a. Melting
  b. Calving—the breaking off of large pieces of ice (icebergs where the glacier has reached the sea)
 3. Balance, or lack of balance, between accumulation at the upper end of the glacier and loss at the lower end is referred to as the glacial budget
  a. If accumulation exceeds loss (called ablation), the glacial front advances
  b. If ablation increases and/or accumulation decreases, the ice front will retreat

III. Glacial erosion
 A. Glaciers are capable of great erosion and, as a medium of sediment transport, have no equal
 B. Glaciers erode the land primarily in two ways
  1. Plucking—lifting of rock blocks
  2. Abrasion
   a. Rocks within the ice acting like sandpaper to smooth and polish the surface below
   b. Abrasion produces
    1. Rock flour (pulverized rock)
    2. Glacial striations (grooves in the bedrock)
 C. Landforms created by glacial erosion
  1. Erosional features of glaciated valleys
   a. Glacial trough

b. Truncated spurs
c. Hanging valleys
d. Pater noster lakes
e. Cirques
f. Tarns
g. Fiords
h. Arêtes
i. Horns
 2. Roches mountonnées—most frequently where ice sheets have modified the terrain

IV. Glacial deposits
 A. Glacial drift
  1. All sediments of glacial origin
  2. Types of glacial drift
   a. Till—material that is deposited directly by the ice
   b. Stratified drift—sediments laid down by glacial meltwater
  3. Glacial erratics—boulders of rock different from the bedrock that are found in till or lying free on the surface
 B. Landforms made of glacial deposits
  1. Moraines
   a. Layers or ridges of till
   b. Types produced by alpine glaciers
    1. Lateral moraine
    2. Medial moraine
   c. Other types of moraines associated with both alpine glaciers and ice sheets
    1. End moraine
     a. Terminal moraine
     b. Recessional moraine
    2. Ground moraine
  2. Landforms made of stratified drift
   a. Outwash plains (with ice sheets) and
   b. Valley trains (when in a valley)
    1. Broad ramplike surface composed of stratified drift deposited by meltwater leaving a glacier found adjacent to the downstream edge of most end moraines
    2. Often pockmarked with basins or depressions called kettles
  3. Ice-contact deposits
   a. Drumlins

© 2008 Pearson Education, Inc., Upper Saddle River, NJ. All rights reserved. This material is protected under all copyright laws as they currently exist. No portion of this material may be reproduced, in any form or by any means, without permission in writing from the publisher.

1. Smooth, elongated, parallel hills
2. Steep side faces the direction from which the ice advances
3. Occur in clusters called drumlin fields
4. Formation not fully understood
   b. Deposited by meltwater flowing over, within, and at the base of motionless ice
      1. Eskers—sinuous ridges of sand and gravel
      2. Kames—originate when glacial meltwater washes sediment into openings and depressions in stagnant ice

V. Glaciers of the Ice Age
   A. Ice Age
      1. Several glacial advances, each separated by extended warmer periods
      2. Ice covered 30% of Earth's land area
      3. Began between two million and three million years ago
      4. Most of the major glacial stages occurred during a division of geologic time called the Pleistocene epoch
   B. Indirect effects of Ice Age glaciers
      1. Forced migration of animals and plants
      2. Changes in stream courses

3. Rebounding upward of the crust in former centers of ice accumulation
4. Worldwide change in sea level
5. Climatic changes

VI. Causes of glaciation
   A. Any successful theory must account for
      1. What causes the onset of glacial conditions, as well as
      2. What caused the alteration of glacial and interglacial stages that have been documented for the Pleistocene epoch
   B. Some possible causes
      1. Plate tectonics
         a. Continents were arranged differently in the past
         b. Changes in oceanic circulation
      2. Variations in Earth's orbit
         a. Milankovitch hypothesis
            1. Shape (eccentricity) of Earth's orbit varies
            2. Angle of Earth's axis (obliquity) changes
            3. Earth's axis wobbles (precession)
         b. Changes in climate over the past several hundred thousand years are closely associated with variations in the geometry of Earth's orbit

Answers to the Review Questions

1. Today, glaciers cover about 10% of the land area. Valley glaciers are found in high, mountainous regions at all latitudes. Ice sheets and ice caps are found only at high latitudes in such areas as Iceland, Greenland, and Antarctica; the Antarctic ice sheet is by far the largest. During the height of the Pleistocene glaciations, about 30% of the land area was ice covered. Due to lowered sea level, the Antarctic ice sheet was slightly larger than at the present time; most of the other ice-covered lands were beneath the continental ice sheets of North America and Europe.

2. The water in ice sheets and glaciers can be viewed as removed from the oceans and temporarily stored on land. Glacial ice, like groundwater, does eventually return to the sea, but the recycling time is hundreds to thousands of years compared to months or a few years for surface water runoff from rainfall events and melting snow. By a large margin, glacial ice represents the largest freshwater reservoir in the hydrologic cycle.

© 2008 Pearson Education, Inc., Upper Saddle River, NJ. All rights reserved. This material is protected under all copyright laws as they currently exist. No portion of this material may be reproduced, in any form or by any means, without permission in writing from the publisher.

As powerful agents of erosion, transport, and deposition, glaciers contribute to the accumulation of sediments directly (till, for example) and indirectly (sand and gravel from meltwater streams and loess from windblown glacial rock flour). Given the proper conditions for preservation and burial, these sediments can eventually lithify to rock as shown by occurrences of tillites, clastic rocks of glaciofluvial origin, and loessite in the rock record. Thus glaciers play an important role in the rock cycle as well as in the hydrologic cycle.

3. (a) The term *continental* is often used to describe this type of glacier.—This refers to continental glaciers or continental ice sheets such as the ones that cover most of Greenland and Antarctica today.

   (b) This type of glacier is also called an *alpine glacier.* —This would be a valley glacier, a long ice stream that flows downslope along a valley in a mountainous region.

   (c) This is a glacier formed when one or more valley glaciers spread out at the base of a steep mountain front.—A piedmont glacier.

   (d) Greenland is the only example in the Northern Hemisphere.—An ice sheet or continental ice sheet

   (e) This is a stream of ice leading from the margin of an ice sheet through the mountains to the sea. — The statement describes an outlet glacier.

4. Glacial flow involves two mechanisms. One is basal sliding, in which the entire glacier moves forward by sliding or slipping along the bedrock at the base of the glacier; the other flow mechanism involves internal deformation and plastic flow. Ice in the interior parts of the glacier slowly deforms and recrystallizes, producing a net downslope movement of all the ice above the zone of deformation. Ice higher in the zone of deformation moves faster than the ice beneath it, and surface ice in the center of the glacier moves faster than ice near the margins. Glaciers move very slowly on average; velocities may be less than a meter per year. Periods of unusually rapid glacial movements are called surges. As the temperature at the base of a glacier reaches the melting point, quantities of liquid water accumulate at the ice-bedrock contact. Frictional resistance is greatly reduced, and the ice tends to "float" on the meltwater. Thus basal slip is accelerated. Temperatures below freezing at depth in the glacier result in low basal slip and internal flowage velocities.

5. Crevasses are transverse open cracks or fissures in a glacier that extend from the surface to depths of about 50 meters. The cracks are widest at the surface and taper downward. The bottom tip of the crevasse marks the base of the brittle ice zone and the top of the plastic flow zone. The brittle surface ice layer, while being carried passively downslope by flowage in the plastic zone, responds to stresses by cracking and fracturing.

6. Excluding surges and other unsteady flow movements, the glacier will advance (its snout will move downslope) when the snow and ice accumulated during many consecutive years exceed that lost by melting and other forms of ablation. The glacier will retreat (the snout melts back to higher elevations) when the reverse is true; ablation exceeds accumulation. The snout will be stationary if accumulation and ablation are exactly balanced year after year.

© 2008 Pearson Education, Inc., Upper Saddle River, NJ. All rights reserved. This material is protected under all copyright laws as they currently exist. No portion of this material may be reproduced, in any form or by any means, without permission in writing from the publisher.

Glaciers and Glaciation

7. Glaciers are powerful agents of erosion. In alpine regions, the melting and refreezing of water at the base of the glacier can dislodge large blocks of rock (plucking) that become entrained in the ice at the bottom and sides of the glacier. Mass wasting also contributes significantly to the sediment load of valley glaciers. Plucking and abrasion along the base and sides of continental glaciers entrains rock, soil, and regolith, all of which are transported as sediment by the moving ice.

8. Nonglacial valleys were cut by streams and widened by mass wasting; they have V-shaped cross-sections; sinuous, longitudinal profiles; and lots of sharp ridges that extend downslope to the valley floor and stream. Glacial valleys were strongly scoured by the moving ice. They have U-shaped cross-sections with wide, relatively flat floors; very steep walls; and straight, longitudinal profiles. Truncated spurs are blunt facets eroded from ridges that extended to the valley floor before the valley was glaciated.

9. Large, open, bowl-shaped erosional basins (cirques) are present at the heads of the larger valleys. The highest mountains are horn peaks, and sharp, knife-edged ridges (arêtes) form common boundaries between neighboring cirques. Valleys are fairly straight, with U-shaped, cross-valley profiles and numerous truncated ridge spurs; hanging valleys and waterfalls may be evident where tributary canyons were left dangling high above the floor of the main valley.

10. Glacial drift denotes any sedimentary material deposited from melting ice or meltwater streams. Till is the unsorted, unstratified drift deposited directly as the ice melts. Stratified drift (also called outwash) denotes sand and gravel beds deposited from glacial meltwater streams. Many glaciated landscapes exhibit low, irregularly shaped hills, mounds, and ridges of till standing above lower, marshy areas. Outwash plains are typically flat, and like moraines, they may be pitted by kettles (depressions formed by collapse of drift into voids formed by melting of buried ice blocks).

   Glaciers can excavate deep valleys and lake basins, obliterate pre-glacial drainage systems, deposit moraines and outwash plains, carve mountain regions into alpine peaks and valleys, and leave behind the flat, silt covered floors of once immense lakes. Glaciation profoundly alters the morphology and appearance of landscapes.

11. The four types of moraines are end, lateral, medial, and ground. All are composed of till, and with the exception of ground moraine, they all form prominent, irregularly shaped mounds and ridges. End or terminal moraines form around the snouts of glaciers. A recessional moraine is any end moraine left by a retreating glacier, and a terminal moraine is a special end moraine that marks the position of the glacier's farthest advance.

12. Other depositional features include drumlins, which are streamlined, asymmetrical hills composed of till; eskers, ridges of sand and gravel deposited by streams flowing beneath the ice near the glacier's terminus; kames, steep-sided hills having a composition similar to eskers; and outwash plains, broad, ramplike surfaces composed of stratified drift deposited by meltwater as it leaves the glacier.

13. Since the steep side of a drumlin faces the direction from which the ice advanced, the ice advanced from the left.

© 2008 Pearson Education, Inc., Upper Saddle River, NJ. All rights reserved. This material is protected under all copyright laws as they currently exist. No portion of this material may be reproduced, in any form or by any means, without permission in writing from the publisher.

14. Kettles are circular-to-elliptical closed depressions in areas underlain by till or outwash. They form at the snout regions of glaciers where blocks of stagnant ice get buried or partly buried by till or outwash. When the ice melts, the till or outwash collapses into the void formerly occupied by the ice, leaving a depression in the land surface. Kettles are commonly occupied by lakes or marshes.

15. Pleistocene glaciers covered approximately 30% of Earth's land area. This figure represents three times more area than is presently covered by glacial ice.

16. High-latitude land areas are much more extensive in the Northern Hemisphere. Thus, during the Pleistocene glacial advances, ice sheets covered larger land areas in the Northern Hemisphere and, despite the extensive Antarctic ice sheet, contained twice the volume of ice as glaciers in the Southern Hemisphere. The Antarctic ice sheet expanded slightly due to lowered sea levels, but its thickness could not have increased much over present-day values because precipitation decreases rapidly with increased elevation and plastic flow rates increase as the ice sheet thickens.

17. Ice Age glaciers had several other effects on the landscape in addition to the obvious erosional and depositional features caused by glaciation. The advancing and retreating ice sheets forced the migration of many plants and animals, sometimes resulting in the extinction of organisms unable to tolerate the rapidly changing conditions. In areas of maximum ice accumulation, such as Scandinavia and the Canadian Shield, the land has been slowly rising over the past several thousand years in response to the downwarping of Earth's crust due to the weight of the ice. Perhaps one of the most dramatic effects of the Ice Age was the fall and rise of sea level associated with the advance and retreat of the glaciers. Finally, the formation and growth of ice sheets also triggered important climatic changes beyond the margins of the ice.

18. Glacial episodes in the geologic history of Earth coincide with times when large, continental areas were situated at high latitudes (consider Greenland and Antarctica today). The ice ages were made possible by the large landmasses at high latitudes (northern Europe, northern Russia and Siberia, Canada, and Alaska). However, plate movements during the Pleistocene are not large enough to have caused the glacial-interglacial climatic fluctuations. Thus they must have had some other cause. Possibilities include variations in the Sun's output and variations in received solar energy caused by slight variations in Earth's orbit.

Lecture outline, art-only, and animation PowerPoint presentations for each chapter of *Essentials of Geology* are available on the IRC DVD (ISBN 0-13-604914-1).

NOTES:

© 2008 Pearson Education, Inc., Upper Saddle River, NJ. All rights reserved. This material is protected under all copyright laws as they currently exist. No portion of this material may be reproduced, in any form or by any means, without permission in writing from the publisher.

Deserts and Wind

Deserts and Wind begins with a discussion of the common misconceptions about dry lands. Following an examination of the distribution and causes of dry regions, geologic processes in arid climates, the evolution of the dry Basin and Range region of the United States, and the work of wind are investigated. The chapter closes with an analysis of wind deposits.

Learning Objectives

After reading, studying, and discussing the chapter, students should be able to:

- Explain the distribution and origin of dry regions on Earth.
- Briefly discuss the major geologic processes operating in arid climates.
- Discuss the evolution and features of the Basin and Range Province.
- Briefly explain the mechanisms of transporting sediment by wind.
- Discuss the processes involved in wind erosion.
- Compare and contrast the features produced by wind erosion.
- Compare and contrast the various types of sand dunes.
- Discuss the origin and geologic occurrence of loess.

Chapter Outline

I. Distribution and causes of dry lands
  A. Dry regions cover 30% of Earth's land surface
  B. Two climatic types are commonly recognized
    1. Desert, or arid, and
    2. Steppe, or semiarid
  C. Drylands are concentrated in two regions
    1. Subtropics
      a. Low-latitude deserts
      b. In the vicinities of the Tropics of Cancer and Capricorn
      c. Areas of high pressure and sinking air that is compressed and warmed
    2. Middle-latitudes
      a. Located in the deep interiors of continents
      b. High mountains in the path of the prevailing winds produce a rainshadow desert

II. Geologic processes in arid climates
  A. Weathering
    1. Not as effective as in humid regions
    2. Mechanical weathering produces unaltered rock and mineral fragments
    3. Some chemical weathering in deserts does produce
      a. Clay
      b. Thin soils
      c. Oxidized minerals
  B. Role of water in arid climates
    1. Practically all streambeds are dry most of the time
    2. Desert streams are said to be ephemeral
      a. Carry water only during periods of rainfall
      b. Different names are used for desert streams in various regions

© 2008 Pearson Education, Inc., Upper Saddle River, NJ. All rights reserved. This material is protected under all copyright laws as they currently exist. No portion of this material may be reproduced, in any form or by any means, without permission in writing from the publisher.

1. e.g., Wash and arroyo (dry western United States)
2. e.g., Wadi (Arabia and North Africa)
3. e.g., Donga (South America)
4. e.g., Nullah (India)

3. Desert rainfall
   a. Rain often occurs as heavy shower
   b. Because desert vegetative cover is sparse, runoff is largely unhindered and flash floods are common
   c. Poorly integrated drainage system and streams lack an extensive system of tributaries
4. Most of the erosional work in a desert is done by running water

III. Basin and Range: evolution of a desert landscape
   A. Characterized by interior drainage
   B. Landscape evolution in the Basin and Range region
      1. Uplift of mountains—block faulting
      2. Interior drainage into basins produces
         a. Alluvial fans
         b. Bajadas
         c. Playas, and
         d. Playa lakes
      3. Ongoing erosion of the mountain mass
         a. Produces sediment that fills the basin
         b. Diminishes local relief
         c. Produces isolated erosional remnants called inselbergs

IV. Wind in the desert
   A. Transportation of sediment by wind
      1. Differs from that of running water in two ways
         a. Wind is less capable of picking up and transporting coarse materials
         b. Wind is not confined to channels and can spread sediment over large areas
      2. Mechanisms of transport
         a. Bedload
            1. Saltation—skipping and bouncing along the surface

2. About 20–25% of the sand transported in a sandstorm is moved this way
      b. Suspended load
   B. Wind erosion
      1. Wind is a relatively insignificant erosional agent, with most erosion in a desert performed by intermittent running water
      2. Mechanisms of wind erosion
         a. Deflation
            1. Lifting of loose material
            2. Deflation produces
               a. Blowouts—shallow depressions
               b. Desert pavement—a surface of coarse pebbles and cobbles
         b. Abrasion
            1. Produces ventifacts—interestingly shaped stones
            2. Limited in its vertical extent
   C. Wind deposits
      1. Significant depositional landforms are created by wind in some regions
      2. Two types of wind deposits
         a. Dunes
            1. Mounds or ridges of sand
            2. Often asymmetrically shaped
               a. Windward slope is gently inclined
               b. Leeward slope is called the slip face
                  1. Steep—about 34 degrees, the angle of repose for loose sand
                  2. Cross beds—sloping layers of sand that form on the slip face
            3. Slow migration in the direction of air movement
            4. Types of sand dunes
               a. Barchan dunes
               b. Transverse dunes
               c. Longitudinal dunes
               d. Parabolic dunes
               e. Star dunes
         b. Loess
            1. Blankets of windblown silt
            2. Two primary sources
               a. Deserts

© 2008 Pearson Education, Inc., Upper Saddle River, NJ. All rights reserved. This material is protected under all copyright laws as they currently exist. No portion of this material may be reproduced, in any form or by any means, without permission in writing from the publisher.

b. Glacial outwash deposits
3. Extensive deposits occur in
   a. Western and northern China
      1. Sediments blown from the desert basins
      2. Accumulations of 30 meters are common

b. Central United States
   1. Correlates with the rich soils of the Midwest
   2. An indirect product of glaciation

Answers to the Review Questions

1. Steppes are vast, slightly dry to semiarid plains and grasslands that are transitional between humid lands and much drier, true deserts. Steppes and deserts generally lie between 15 and 35 degrees north and south latitude; the Sahara Desert (Africa) and its bordering plains and semiarid grasslands are a good example. The desert and steppe regions of North America and central Asia extend to higher latitudes (40 to 45 degrees). Desert lands and steppes make up about 30% of Earth's land area.

2. Subtropical deserts coincide with zones of high air pressure called subtropical highs. These pressure systems are characterized by subsiding and warming air, conditions that are just the opposite of what are needed to produce clouds and precipitation. Middle-latitude deserts exist principally because of their positions in the deep interiors of large landmasses far removed from the ocean, which is the ultimate source of moisture for cloud formation and precipitation.

3. The Northern Hemisphere has, by far, larger areas of mountain-rimmed valleys and basins located in the interiors of the continents. Many of the middle-latitude deserts are in the western United States, Mexico, and central Asia. Thus deserts and dry lands at middle latitudes (35 to 45 degrees) are much more prevalent than in the Southern Hemisphere.

4. Mean annual precipitation alone is not a valid predictor of an area's moisture balance. A significant fraction of the precipitation runs off or evaporates; a smaller fraction infiltrates, adding to the soil moisture and contributing to groundwater recharge and perennial stream flow. Water lost through evaporation and runoff is effectively eliminated from the soil moisture budget.

5. Weathering rates are accelerated by persistently high levels of moisture, because most of the reactions in chemical weathering involve water, both as a reactant and as a medium for ion transport. Dry conditions, as in a desert, result in very slow rates of chemical weathering and in slow, overall weathering rates.

6. Rivers flowing across humid lands generally show increased discharges downstream as they are joined by perennial tributaries. However, rivers that flow from humid lands into desert regions commonly show decreased discharges downstream, losing water to infiltration and evapotranspiration while intermittent tributaries seldom add discharge. The Nile has a large enough upstream discharge to reach the sea, despite flowing across more than a thousand miles of desert lands in Egypt and northern Sudan.

7. Although wind erosion is more prominent than in humid environments and rainfall events are rare, running water is still generally the dominant agent of erosion in semiarid areas and in most desert areas. In dry lands with unconsolidated surface materials and little or no vegetation, runoff from rare but often intense storms can effect extensive erosion.

© 2008 Pearson Education, Inc., Upper Saddle River, NJ. All rights reserved. This material is protected under all copyright laws as they currently exist. No portion of this material may be reproduced, in any form or by any means, without permission in writing from the publisher.

8. In the early stage of erosion, slopes are very steep, mountain uplands are extensive and relatively undissected, and canyon gradients are very steep. Alluvial fans are small and localized at the mouths of individual canyons, and playas dot the relatively flat valley floors. As erosion proceeds, the uplands are dissected and the canyon systems extend to the crests of the mountains. The canyon gradients are less steep, and alluvial fans merge into an alluvial apron (bajada) that slopes gradually toward the valley floor. A bedrock erosional surface (pediment) is cut upslope into the mountains. By the late stages of erosion, the mountains are reduced in elevation and cover less area. Low, isolated bedrock ranges or knobs (inselbergs) rise above a vast expanse of gently sloping pediments and alluvium-floored valleys. Canyon systems in the mountains are short and gradients are low, individual alluvial fans are indistinct, and the valley floors grade imperceptibly upslope into bedrock pediments.

   These various evolutionary stages can be seen in the Basin and Range Province of the western and southwestern United States.

9. Sea level has no effect on the depth to which the wind can erode and excavate surface materials. The base level for wind erosion is marked by the water table or by layers of resistant material or bedrock. Many desert areas are in closed basins. In these and many other dry areas, river and stream channels may not necessarily be integrated and do not reach the sea. Thus base level for streams in many desert areas is independent of sea level.

10. In windstorms, sand rolls along the surface or moves by saltation, that is, the sand grains bounce into the air and are blown a short distance downwind before falling back to the surface. In very strong winds, fine-sized sand can remain suspended and travel for fairly long distances before falling back to the surface. Even in the most intense windstorms, the blowing sand grains seldom rise more than a meter or so above the land surface.

    Air temperature has an important effect on windblown sediment transport. Air density is inversely proportional to temperature; thus for a given speed, cold winds can move more and larger sediment grains than hot winds. Thus "hot desert" sands, such as those in Kuwait and Saudi Arabia, tend to be fine grained. Recall that during preparations for the Gulf War, concerns were expressed about how well mechanical equipment would perform in a "fine-grained sand" environment.

11. In humid areas, vegetation and soil moisture protect the surface particles from being picked up and transported by the wind. Thus blowing sand and dust are relatively uncommon and require unusual weather and environmental conditions. The opposite conditions exist in dry lands. Vegetation is sparse or absent, soil moisture is scarce, and surface particles can easily be picked up and entrained by the wind. Sparse vegetation provides few obstructions to slow down gusts and reduce ground-level turbulence. Thus sparsely vegetated lands are highly vulnerable to deflation.

12. Blowouts (depressions excavated by wind erosion) will not be deepened below the water table or below a resistant stratum or bedrock surface. Vegetation also inhibits deflation, but sea level (base level for most streams) is not important.

13. One common hypothesis for the formation of desert pavement attributes their origin to removal of sand and silt by blowing wind. Over time, the concentration of larger particles at the surface increases as the finer particles are blown away.

    An alternate hypothesis suggests that desert pavement develops on a surface that initially consists of coarse particles. Over time, the larger particles trap fine windblown grains that settle and sift downward through the spaces between the larger stones. The process is aided by infiltrating rainwater.

14. Dunes migrate sand grain by sand grain; yet, the overall shape and profile of the particular dune type is maintained. Dunes have a longer, more gentle slope facing into the prevailing wind and a shorter, steeper slope (the slip face) inclined in the downwind direction. Sand grains move up the gentle slope by rolling and saltation, then roll down the steeper, slip face or slide en mass when the angle of repose is exceeded. Thus a dune migrates in the downwind direction, always maintaining its characteristic form and profile.

15. (a) These are parabolic dunes. Other tipped dunes (barchan and barchanoid) have tips that point downwind.
    (b) Transverse dunes
    (c) Parabolic dunes
    (d) Solitary dunes whose tips point downwind.—Barchans (crescent-shaped)
    (e) Longitudinal dunes
    (f) This is a star dune, formed where prevailing wind directions vary with the seasons.
    (g) This is a good description of barchanoid dunes. They can be visualized as combinations of transverse and barchan dunes.

16. Loess is a poorly stratified, unlithified or slightly cemented deposit of windblown silt. The silt particles originate in one of two ways: (1) as rock flour (silt-sized, fairly fresh, rock particles produced by glacial erosion) carried down rivers and streams in the summer, deposited and left vulnerable to deflation during the other seasons, or (2) as weathered rock and soil particles picked up by the wind in desert areas and deposited in more humid areas bordering the desert.

    The desert silt loess is common in central and western China, the silt having been blown eastward from the central Asian and Mongolian desert basins. Although not directly glacial in origin, much of the silt could have been delivered to the basins by streams draining from glaciated mountain ranges during the Pleistocene. The rock flour type is common along the eastern and southeastern sides of the Mississippi River and its major tributaries. These streams were supplied with ample quantities of rock flour during the Pleistocene glacial stages.

Lecture outline, art-only, and animation PowerPoint presentations for each chapter of *Essentials of Geology* are available on the IRC DVD (ISBN 0-13-604914-1).

NOTES:

© 2008 Pearson Education, Inc., Upper Saddle River, NJ. All rights reserved. This material is protected under all copyright laws as they currently exist. No portion of this material may be reproduced, in any form or by any means, without permission in writing from the publisher.

Chapter 13

Shorelines

Shorelines begins with a discussion of the dynamics of the coastal zone followed by an examination of the formation and movement of waves. Following a discussion of wave erosion and refraction, shoreline features and erosion problems are explained in detail. The general characteristics of emergent and submergent coasts are also described. The chapter concludes with a brief explanation of tides.

Learning Objectives

After reading, studying, and discussing the chapter, students should be able to:

- Discuss the various parts of the coastal zone.
- Explain the formation and characteristics of waves.
- List and briefly define the various types of waves.
- Briefly discuss the mechanism of wave erosion.
- Explain wave refraction and how it relates to longshore transport.
- Compare and contrast shoreline features, including their origin and occurrence.
- List and briefly discuss those factors that affect shoreline erosion.
- Compare and contrast the characteristics of the Atlantic and Pacific Coasts of the United States.
- Briefly discuss the formation of emergent and submergent coastlines.
- Understand the origin and characteristics of tides.

Chapter Outline

I. The shoreline: a dynamic interface
   A. The shoreline is a dynamic interface (common boundary) among air, land, and sea
   B. Constantly being modified by waves
   C. Today, the coastal zone is experiencing intense human activity

II. The coastal zone
   A. Shoreline
      1. Line that marks the contact between land and sea
   B. Shore
      1. Area that extends between the lowest tide level and the highest elevation on land that is affected by storm waves
      2. Divided into the

   a. Foreshore—area exposed at low tide and submerged at high tide
   b. Backshore—area landward of the high-tide shoreline
   C. Beach is an accumulation of sediment found along the landward margin of the ocean
      1. Beaches consist of
         a. Berm—relatively flat platforms composed of sand
         b. Beach face—wet sloping surface that extends from the berm to the shoreline

III. Waves
   A. Wind-generated waves provide most of the energy that shapes and modifies shorelines
   B. Characteristics of waves

© 2008 Pearson Education, Inc., Upper Saddle River, NJ. All rights reserved. This material is protected under all copyright laws as they currently exist. No portion of this material may be reproduced, in any form or by any means, without permission in writing from the publisher.

Shorelines

1. Waves derive their energy and motion from the wind
2. Parts of a wave
   a. Crest—top of the wave
   b. Trough—low area between waves
3. Measurements of a wave
   a. Wave height—the distance between a trough and a crest
   b. Wavelength—the horizontal distance between crests
   c. Wave period—the time interval between the passage of two successive crests
4. Height, length, and period of a wave depend on
   a. Wind speed
   b. Length of time wind has blown
   c. Fetch—the distance that the wind has traveled across open water
C. Types of waves
   1. Wave of oscillation
      a. Wave energy moves forward, not the water itself
      b. Occur in the open sea in deep water
   2. Wave of translation
      a. Begins to form in shallower water when the water-depth is about one-half the wavelength and wave begins to "feel bottom"
      b. As the speed and length of the wave diminish, the wave grows higher
      c. The steep wave front collapses and the wave breaks along the shore
      d. Turbulent water advances up the shore and forms surf

IV. Wave erosion
   A. Breaking waves exert a great force
   B. Wave erosion is caused by
      1. Wave impact and pressure
      2. Abrasion by rock fragments

V. Wave refraction and longshore transport
   A. Wave refraction
      1. Bending of a wave
      2. Causes waves to arrive nearly parallel to the shore
      3. Consequences of wave refraction

a. Wave energy is concentrated against the sides and ends of headlands
b. Wave energy is spread out in bays and wave attack is weakened
c. Over time, wave erosion straightens an irregular shoreline
B. Moving sand along the beach
   1. Waves that reach the shoreline at an angle cause the sediment to move along a beach in a zigzag pattern called beach drift
   2. Oblique waves also produce longshore currents
      a. Currents in the surf zone
      b. Flow parallel to the coast
      c. Easily moves fine suspended sand and rolls larger sand and gravel along the bottom

VI. Shoreline features
   A. Features vary depending on
      1. The rocks of the shore
      2. Currents
      3. Wave intensity
      4. Whether the coast is
         a. Stable
         b. Sinking
         c. Rising
   B. Features caused by wave erosion
      1. Wave-cut cliffs
      2. Wave-cut platform
      3. Features associated with headlands
         a. Sea arch
         b. Sea stack
   C. Features related to beach drift and longshore currents
      1. Spits
         a. Elongated ridges of sand extending from the land into the mouth of an adjacent bay
         b. Often the end of a spit hooks landward in response to wave generated currents
      2. Baymouth bar—a sand bar that completely crosses a bay
      3. Tombolo—a ridge of sand that connects an island to the mainland or another island
   D. Barrier islands

© 2008 Pearson Education, Inc., Upper Saddle River, NJ. All rights reserved. This material is protected under all copyright laws as they currently exist. No portion of this material may be reproduced, in any form or by any means, without permission in writing from the publisher.

1. Mainly along the Atlantic and Gulf coasts
2. Low ridges of sand that parallel the coast 3 to 30 kilometers offshore
3. Probably form in several ways

   E. If the shoreline remains stable, the result of shoreline erosion and deposition is to eventually produce a straighter coast

VII. Shoreline erosion problems
   A. Influenced by the local factors
     1. Proximity to sediment-laden rivers
     2. Degree of tectonic activity
     3. Topography and composition of the land
     4. Prevailing wind and weather patterns
     5. Configuration of the coastline and near shore areas
   B. Three basic responses to erosion problems
     1. Building structures
       a. Types of structures
         1. Groin
           a. Built to maintain or widen beaches
           b. Constructed at a right angle to the beach to trap sand
         2. Breakwater
           a. Barrier built offshore and parallel to the coast
           b. Protects boats from the force of large breaking waves
         3. Seawall
           a. Barrier parallel to shore and close to the beach to protect property
           b. Stops waves from reaching the beach areas behind the wall
       b. Often the building of structures is not an effective means of protection
     2. Beach nourishment
       a. The addition of large quantities of sand to the beach system
       b. Only an economically viable long-range solution in a few areas
     3. Abandonment and relocation of buildings away from the beach

   C. Contrasting the Atlantic and Pacific coasts
     1. Shoreline erosion problems are different along the opposite coasts
     2. Atlantic and Gulf coasts
       a. Broad, gently sloping coastal plains
       b. Tectonically quiet regions
       c. Development occurs mainly on the barrier islands (also called barrier beaches or coastal barriers)
         1. Barrier islands face the open ocean and
         2. Receive the full force of storms
     3. Pacific Coast
       a. Relatively narrow beaches backed by steep cliffs and mountain ranges
       b. A major problem is a significant narrowing of many beaches
         1. Sediment for beaches has been interrupted by dams and reservoirs
         2. Narrow beaches allow for the erosion of the sea cliffs
       c. Shoreline erosion varies considerably from one year to the next largely because of the sporadic occurrence of storms

VIII. Emergent and submergent coasts
   A. Emergent coasts
     1. Develop because of
       a. Uplift of an area, or
       b. A drop in sea level
     2. Features of an emergent coast
       a. Wave-cut cliffs
       b. Wave-cut platforms
   B. Submergent coasts
     1. Caused by
       a. Land adjacent to the sea subsides, or
       b. Sea level rises
     2. Features of a submergent coast
       a. Highly irregular shoreline
       b. Estuaries—drowned river mouths

IX. Tides
   A. Daily changes in the elevation of the ocean surface
   B. Causes of tides

© 2008 Pearson Education, Inc., Upper Saddle River, NJ. All rights reserved. This material is protected under all copyright laws as they currently exist. No portion of this material may be reproduced, in any form or by any means, without permission in writing from the publisher.

1. Tidal bulges are caused by the gravitational forces of the
   a. Moon, and to a lesser extent the
   b. Sun
C. Spring and neap tides
   1. Spring tides
      a. Occur during new and full moons
      b. Gravitational forces of the Moon and Sun are added together
      c. Especially high and low tides
      d. Large daily tidal range
   2. Neap tides
      a. Occur during the first and third quarters of the moon
      b. Gravitational forces of the Moon and Sun are offset
      c. Daily tidal range is least

D. Other factors that influence tides
   1. Shape of the coastline
   2. Configuration of the ocean basin
E. Tidal currents
   1. Horizontal flow of water accompanying the rise and fall of the tide
   2. Types of tidal currents
      a. Flood current—advances into the coastal zone as the tide rises
      b. Ebb current—seaward-moving water as the tide falls
   3. Areas affected by the alternating tidal currents are called tidal flats
   4. Occasionally form tidal deltas

Answers to the Review Questions

1. The shoreline is the line that marks the contact between land and sea, whereas the shore is an area that extends between the lowest tide level and the highest elevation on land that is affected by storm waves. The coast extends inland from the shore as far as ocean-related features can be found, and the seaward edge of the coast is the coastline.

2. A beach is an accumulation of sediment found along the landward margin of the ocean or a lake. The berm is the relatively flat platform composed of sand adjacent to dunes or cliffs, and the beach face is the wet sloping surface that extends from the berm to the shoreline. Sources of beach sediment include erosion of adjacent cliffs or nearby coastal mountains and sediment delivered to the coast by rivers.

3. Waves are generated by wind blowing across the surface of the water. The main factors that determine wave characteristics are the wind speed, the length of time that the wind blows, and the expanse of water (fetch) affected. The longer period waves arriving at a beach were generated in distant storms at sea. Shorter period, "choppy" waves move at slower speeds and are dissipated at sea through wave interference.

4. Water particles follow prograde, circular paths as a deep-water wave passes overhead. The circular paths gradually decrease in diameter downward, shrinking to a point at a depth equal to one-half the wavelength. Water below this depth does not move in response to the passing wave.

5. Drag with the bottom slows an incoming wave; wave height increases and wavelength (distance between adjacent crests) decreases. As the water depth decreases, bottom drag increases; thus the top part of the wave moves forward faster than the base, causing the wave to collapse as a breaker or plunger. Water flowing back to the sea from previously breaking waves increases drag on incoming waves.

6. Crashing waves force compressed air and/or pressurized water into cracks and other openings, expanding them and breaking the material apart. Abrasion results from particles impacting one another, the bottom, and bedrock or human-made structures.

© 2008 Pearson Education, Inc., Upper Saddle River, NJ. All rights reserved. This material is protected under all copyright laws as they currently exist. No portion of this material may be reproduced, in any form or by any means, without permission in writing from the publisher.

7. In deeper water offshore, incoming waves move at constant speed, but they slow down in shallower waters. As an incoming wave approaches the shoreline at an oblique angle, the part of the wave in shallower water will have a lower speed than the part in deeper water. These different speeds for different parts of the same wave cause the wave to refract (bend). In general, wave refraction rotates obliquely incoming waves toward parallelism with the coastline. Over time, headland erosion and deposition in protected bays and coves tend to even out irregularities, thus straightening the coastline.

8. Large quantities of sand move along beaches and just offshore due to the action of longshore currents and longshore drift. Thus over time, a flow or stream of sand is continuously moving along the beach and parallel to the beach in the shallow, nearshore waters.

9. Wave-cut cliff: a seaward-facing cliff along a steep shoreline formed by wave erosion at its base and mass wasting

   Wave-cut platform: a bench in bedrock at sea level cut by wave erosion

   Marine terrace: a wave-cut platform that has been uplifted above sea level

   Sea stack: the result of wave refraction on a headland. When caves on opposite sides of a headland unite, a sea arch is formed. When the arch eventually collapses, it leaves an isolated remnant called a sea stack.

   Spit: an elongated ridge of sand formed by beach drift and longshore currents that projects from the land into the mouth of an adjacent bay

   Baymouth bar: a sand bar that completely crosses a bay, sealing it off from the open ocean

   Tombolo: a sand ridge connecting an island to the mainland or to another island

10. Barrier islands may evolve from old sand dunes, sand ridges, or topographic escarpments formed on the continental shelves at times when sea level was lower. As sea level rises, these act as sand traps and build to sea level or just above. With continued sea level rise, the newly built barrier island migrates landward as sand is slowly moved from the seaward to the landward side by wind and overwashing storm waves. Thus, previously formed sand deposits such as spits, offshore bars, baymouth bars, or coastal dunes could act as nuclei around which a barrier island system could later develop when sea level rises.

11. Groins are porous structures built into the surf zone in order to slow longshore currents and promote sand deposition on the upcurrent side. However, having been deprived of its sediment load, the current speeds up again after passing the groin; thus beach erosion intensifies on the downcurrent side. Therefore, in Figure 13.19, the longshore currents appear to be moving toward the top of the photograph as indicated by the narrower beaches on the leeward side of the groins.

12. Groins are porous structures built into the surf zone to slow longshore currents and promote sand deposition on the upcurrent side. However, having been deprived of its sediment load, the current speeds up again after passing the groin; thus beach erosion intensifies on the downcurrent side.

© 2008 Pearson Education, Inc., Upper Saddle River, NJ. All rights reserved. This material is protected under all copyright laws as they currently exist. No portion of this material may be reproduced, in any form or by any means, without permission in writing from the publisher.

Seawalls reflect wave energy and breaking waves directly out to sea, thus increasing erosion immediately in front of the seawall. For this reason, seawalls are often undercut and destroyed, and the intensified erosion steepens and narrows the beach.

Breakwaters are structures designed to protect boats from the force of large breaking waves. However, the quiet water zone behind the breakwater often allows sand to accumulate, thus filling up the boat anchorage.

13. One alternative to hard stabilization is beach nourishment. This process simply involves the addition of large quantities of sand to the beach system. Beach nourishment is not a permanent solution because it is often quite expensive, much of the transported sand will be eroded just like the original beach, and sometimes there are environmental effects associated with using different materials. A second alternative is relocation—moving storm-damaged or at-risk buildings and allowing nature to reclaim the beach.

14. Warmer conditions will cause faster melting of polar ice sheets, adding liquid water to the oceans. However, more significant is the fact that warmer air temperatures cause a gradual warming of the oceans. This results in a thermal expansion of the water, increased ocean volume, and a rise in sea level. The combined effect of melting ice and thermal expansion of the oceans has increased sea level at least 20 centimeters over the past century, and some models indicate that it may rise 50 centimeters or more during the next century.

15. Along the West Coast, much of the sand on beaches originates as clastic sediment in streams and rivers that discharge into the sea. Damming these streams traps the sand behind the dam and reduces the input of new sand to the beach system. With reduced input, not enough of the sand lost to offshore areas is being replaced; thus the beach is starved and narrowed by erosion. Narrowed beaches allow storm waves to directly impact a sea cliff with minimal loss of energy, which accelerates the retreat of the cliff.

16. The damage caused by hurricanes is due primarily to three factors; storm surge, wind damage, and inland freshwater flooding. The most devastating factor associated with a hurricane is the storm surge. A storm surge is the dome or bubble of water that moves onshore at or near the point where the center of the hurricane makes landfall. Storm surges cause extensive flooding and erosion that results in massive loss of property in the coastal zone. Also, storm surges are responsible for most of the hurricane-related deaths that occur. Wind damage is also a significant factor during a hurricane, and it is perhaps the most obvious or visible effect of a hurricane. Wind damage is generally much more widespread than that from the storm surge, and it often accounts for much of the monetary losses incurred from a hurricane. Inland freshwater flooding results from the torrential rains (often in excess of 10 inches) that accompany many hurricanes. The effects of such flooding may affect areas located long distances from the coast.

17. Emergent coastlines develop as sea level is dropping or when the land is rising faster than sea level. Since sea level has been steadily rising for at least the past 30,000 years, present-day emergent coastlines only develop where coastal lands are being tectonically uplifted. A good example of this would be the coast of California. Such areas typically have higher elevations, higher relief, and steeper, narrower river and steam valleys than tectonically stable continental margins with wide coastal plains and continental shelves.

© 2008 Pearson Education, Inc., Upper Saddle River, NJ. All rights reserved. This material is protected under all copyright laws as they currently exist. No portion of this material may be reproduced, in any form or by any means, without permission in writing from the publisher.

Emergent coastlines feature landforms of marine depositional and erosional origin that have been elevated above sea level. Old, wave-cut cliffs and platforms (now steep slopes and terraces) are common. The terraces typically have thin covers of very young marine sediments and depositional or erosional features such as sand bars, coral limestone, and old sea stacks.

18. Estuaries are present along both coastlines, but the ones along submergent coastlines are much larger in size. Estuaries represent the flooded, lower portions of stream and river valleys. Since sea level has been rising steadily, large estuaries and estuarine systems have developed along tectonically stable continental margins with wide continental shelves and coastal plains; the Atlantic and Gulf coasts of the United States are good examples. Along wide coastal plains, each incremental rise in sea level inundates much larger areas than along tectonically rising coasts where elevations and relief are higher and stream valleys are more likely to be steep-sided and narrow.

19. Fundamentally, ocean tides are formed by gravitational and rotational forces exerted in the Sun-Moon-Earth system. These forces deform the ocean surface from a sphere to an ellipse, producing two bulges with their apices lying along the lines of action of the resultant forces. The gravitationally dominated bulge points toward the Moon-Sun system and a rotationally dominated bulge of equal size points in the opposite direction. As the Earth rotates, these two bulges act as whole-ocean waves, sloshing back and forth to produce the tides.

The Sun has a less important effect on the tides than the Moon. Although far more massive than the Moon, the Sun is so much farther away that its gravitational force is only about half that exerted by the Moon.

20. Earth's axis is inclined (not perpendicular) to the equatorial plane of the Sun (the plane of the ecliptic). In general, a plane through the crests of the tidal bulges is inclined to Earth's equatorial plane. Rotation through the tidal bulges thus results in unequal amplitudes for the two daily high tides at a specific coastal location. Only at times when the resultant of the tide-causing forces is parallel to Earth's equatorial plane would the daily high tides have equal amplitudes. This would occur twice each month about midway between the dates of the spring and neap tides.

21. These terms describe currents associated with rising and falling tides (sea level). A flood current describes a tidal current moving into an estuary on a rising sea level (incoming tide), and an ebb current describes a tidal current moving from an estuary into the open sea as the tide (sea level) is falling.

Lecture outline, art-only, and animation PowerPoint presentations for each chapter of *Essentials of Geology* are available on the IRC DVD (ISBN 0-13-604914-1).

NOTES:

© 2008 Pearson Education, Inc., Upper Saddle River, NJ. All rights reserved. This material is protected under all copyright laws as they currently exist. No portion of this material may be reproduced, in any form or by any means, without permission in writing from the publisher.

Earthquakes and Earth's Interior begins with a brief description of the effects of the major earthquakes that have taken place in California within the last decade. Following an explanation of how earthquakes occur, the types of seismic waves, their propagation, and how they appear on a typical seismic trace are presented. This is followed by a discussion of earthquake epicenters—how they are located and their worldwide distribution. Earthquake intensity and magnitude are also explained. The destruction caused by seismic vibrations and their associated perils introduces a discussion of earthquake prediction. The chapter closes with an explanation of how earthquakes are used to discover Earth's interior structure and a brief description of Earth's interior composition.

Learning Objectives

After reading, studying, and discussing the chapter, students should be able to:

- Explain the origin of earthquakes, including their relationship to faults.
- Briefly discuss elastic rebound and the accumulation of strain in rocks.
- Discuss seismology, including the characteristics and recording of earthquake waves.
- Understand the occurrence of earthquakes in relation to tectonic plate boundaries.
- Discuss the measurement of earthquake intensity and magnitude.
- Discuss the various types of destruction associated with earthquakes.
- Explain earthquake prediction in terms of both short-range and long-range forecasting.
- List and briefly explain the layers of the Earth defined by composition and physical properties.
- Briefly discuss Earth's major boundaries, including the Moho and the crust-mantle boundary.
- Discuss the composition of Earth's layers.

Chapter Outline

I. What is an earthquake?
A. An earthquake is the vibration of Earth produced by the rapid release of energy
   1. Energy released radiates in all directions from its source, the focus
   2. Energy is in the form of waves
   3. Sensitive instruments around the world record the event
B. Earthquakes and faults
   1. Movements that produce earthquakes are usually associated with large fractures in Earth's crust called faults

2. Most of motion along faults can be explained by the plate tectonics theory
C. Elastic rebound
   1. Mechanism for earthquakes was first explained by H.F. Reid
      a. Rocks on both sides of an existing fault are deformed by tectonic forces
      b. Rocks bend and store elastic energy
      c. Frictional resistance holding the rocks together is overcome

© 2008 Pearson Education, Inc., Upper Saddle River, NJ. All rights reserved. This material is protected under all copyright laws as they currently exist. No portion of this material may be reproduced, in any form or by any means, without permission in writing from the publisher.

d. Slippage at the weakest point (the focus) occurs
e. Vibrations (earthquakes) occur as the deformed rock "springs back" to its original shape (elastic rebound)

2. Earthquakes most often occur along existing faults whenever the frictional forces on the fault surfaces are overcome

D. Foreshocks and aftershocks
1. Adjustments that follow a major earthquake often generate smaller earthquakes called aftershocks
2. Small earthquakes, called foreshocks, often precede a major earthquake by days or, in some cases, by as much as several years

II. San Andreas fault: an active earthquake zone
A. San Andreas is the most studied fault system in the world
B. Displacement occurs along discrete segments 100 to 200 kilometers long
1. Some portions exhibit slow, gradual displacement known as fault creep
2. Other segments regularly slip, producing small earthquakes
3. Still other segments store elastic energy for hundreds of years before rupturing in great earthquakes
   a. Process described as stick-slip motion
   b. Great earthquakes should occur about every 50 to 200 years along these sections

III. Seismology
A. The study of earthquake waves, seismology, dates back almost 2000 years to the Chinese
B. Seismographs, instruments that record seismic waves
1. Records the movement of Earth in relation to a stationary mass on a rotating drum or magnetic tape
2. More than one type of seismograph is needed to record both vertical and horizontal ground motion

3. Records obtained are called seismographs
C. Types of seismic waves
1. Surface waves
   a. Travel along outer part of Earth
   b. Complex motion
   c. Cause greatest destruction
   d. Waves exhibit greatest amplitude and slowest velocity
   e. Waves have the greatest periods (time interval between crests)
   f. Often referred to as long waves, or L waves
2. Body waves
   a. Travel through Earth's interior
   b. Two types based on mode of travel
      1. Primary (P) waves
         a. Push-pull (compress and expand) motion, changing the volume of the intervening material
         b. Travel through
            1. Solids
            2. Liquids
            3. Gases
         c. Generally, in any solid material, P waves travel about 1.7 times faster than S waves
      2. Secondary (S) waves
         a. "Shake" motion at right angles to their direction of travel
         b. Temporarily change the shape of the material that transmits them
         c. Travel only through solids
         d. Slower velocity than P waves
         e. Slightly greater amplitude than P waves

IV. Locating the source of earthquakes
A. Terms
1. Focus—the place within Earth where earthquake waves originate
2. Epicenter—location on the surface directly above the focus
B. Epicenter is located using the difference in velocities of P and S waves

© 2008 Pearson Education, Inc., Upper Saddle River, NJ. All rights reserved. This material is protected under all copyright laws as they currently exist. No portion of this material may be reproduced, in any form or by any means, without permission in writing from the publisher.

1. Three station recordings are needed to locate an epicenter
2. Each station determines the time interval between the arrival of the first P wave and the first S wave at their location
3. A travel-time graph is used to determine each station's distance to the epicenter
4. A circle with a radius equal to the distance to the epicenter is drawn around each station
5. The point where all three circles intersect is the earthquake epicenter

C. Earthquake belts
   1. About 95% of the energy released by earthquakes originates in a few relatively narrow zones that wind around the globe
   2. Major earthquake zones include the
      a. Circum-Pacific belt
      b. Oceanic ridge system

V. Measuring the size of earthquakes
   A. Two measurements that describe the size of an earthquake are
      1. Intensity—a measure of the degree of earthquake shaking at a given locale based on the amount of damage
      2. Magnitude—estimates the amount of energy released at the source of the earthquake
   B. Intensity scales
      1. Modified Mercalli Intensity Scale was developed using California buildings as its standard
      2. The drawback of intensity scales is that destruction may not be a true measure of the earthquakes actual severity
   C. Magnitude scales
      1. Richter magnitude
         a. Concept introduced by Charles Richter in 1935
         b. Richter scale
            1. Based on the amplitude of the largest seismic wave recorded
            2. Accounts for the decrease in wave amplitude with increased distance

3. Largest magnitude recorded on a Wood-Anderson seismograph was 8.9
4. Magnitudes less than 2.0 are not felt by humans
5. Each unit of Richter magnitude increase corresponds to
   a. A tenfold increase in wave amplitude
   b. About a 32-fold energy increase

2. Other magnitude scales
   a. Several "Richter-like" magnitude scales have been developed
   b. Moment magnitude
      1. Developed because none of the "Richter-like" magnitude scales adequately estimates the size of very large earthquakes
      2. Derived from the amount of displacement that occurs along a fault
      3. Calculated using
         a. Average amount of displacement along the fault
         b. Area of the rupture surface
         c. Shear strength of the faulted block
      4. Has gained wide acceptance among seismologists and engineers

VI. Earthquake destruction
   A. Amount of structural damage attributable to earthquake vibrations depends on
      1. Intensity and
      2. Duration of the vibrations
      3. Nature of the material upon which the structure rests
      4. Design of the structure
   B. Destruction from seismic vibrations
      1. Ground shaking
         a. Soft sediments generally amplify vibrations more than solid bedrock
         b. Regions within 20 to 50 kilometers of the epicenter will experience about the same intensity of ground shaking
      2. Liquefaction of the ground

© 2008 Pearson Education, Inc., Upper Saddle River, NJ. All rights reserved. This material is protected under all copyright laws as they currently exist. No portion of this material may be reproduced, in any form or by any means, without permission in writing from the publisher.

a. Unconsolidated materials saturated with water turn into a mobile fluid

b. Underground objects may float toward the surface

C. Tsunamis, or seismic sea waves

1. Destructive waves that are often inappropriately called "tidal waves"

2. Result from

a. Vertical displacement along a fault located on the ocean floor or

b. From a large undersea landslide triggered by an earthquake

3. In the open ocean, height is usually less than 1 meter

4. In shallower coastal waters, the water piles up to heights that occasionally exceed 30 meters

5. Can be very destructive

D. Landslides and ground subsidence

E. Fire

VII. Can earthquakes be predicted?

A. Short-range prediction

1. Goal is to provide a warning of the location and magnitude of a large earthquake within a narrow time frame

2. Research has concentrated on monitoring possible precursors— phenomena that precede a forthcoming earthquake such as measuring

a. Uplift

b. Subsidence

c. Strain in the rocks

3. Currently, no reliable method exists for making short-range earthquake predictions

A. Long-range forecasts

1. Give the probability of a certain magnitude earthquake occurring on a time scale of 30 to 100 years, or more

2. Based on the premise that earthquakes are repetitive or cyclical

a. Using historical records or

b. Paleoseismology

3. Are important because they provide information used to

a. Develop the Uniform Building Code and

b. Assist in land-use planning

VIII. Seismic waves and Earth's structure

A. The rather abrupt changes in seismic-wave velocities that occur at particular depths helped seismologists conclude that Earth must be composed of distinct shells

B. Layers defined by composition

1. Because of density sorting during an early period of partial melting, Earth's interior is not homogeneous

2. Three principal compositional layers

a. Crust—the comparatively thin outer skin that ranges from 3 kilometers (2 miles) at the oceanic ridges to 70 kilometers (40 miles in some mountain belts)

b. Mantle—a solid rocky (silica-rich) shell that extends to a depth of about 2900 kilometers (1800 miles)

c. Core—an iron-rich sphere having a radius of 3486 kilometers (2161 miles)

C. Layers defined by physical properties

1. With increasing depth, Earth's interior is characterized by gradual increases in

a. Temperature—at a depth of 100 kilometers temperature is between 1200°C and 1400°C, whereas the temperature at Earth's center may exceed 6700°C

b. Pressure—with depth, increased pressure tends to increase rock strength

c. Density

2. Depending on the temperature and depth, a particular Earth material may behave

a. Like a brittle solid

b. Deform in a putty-like manner, or

c. Melt and become liquid

3. Main layers of Earth's interior based on physical properties and hence mechanical strength

a. Lithosphere (sphere of rock)

1. Earth's outermost layer

2. Consists of the crust and uppermost mantle

© 2008 Pearson Education, Inc., Upper Saddle River, NJ. All rights reserved. This material is protected under all copyright laws as they currently exist. No portion of this material may be reproduced, in any form or by any means, without permission in writing from the publisher.

3. Relatively cool, rigid shell
4. Averages about 100 kilometers in thickness, but may be 250 kilometers or more thick beneath the older portions of the continents
   b. Asthenosphere (weak sphere)
    1. Beneath the lithosphere, in the upper mantle to a depth of about 600 kilometers
    2. Small amount of melting in the upper portion mechanically detaches the lithosphere from the layer below, allowing the lithosphere to move independently of the asthenosphere
   c. Mesosphere or lower mantle
    1. Between the depths of 660 kilometers and 2900 kilometers
    2. Rigid layer
    3. Rocks are very hot and capable of very gradual flow
   d. Outer core
    1. Composed mostly of an iron-nickel alloy
    2. Liquid layer
    3. 2270 kilometers (1410 miles) thick
    4. Convective flow within generates Earth's magnetic field
   e. Inner core
    1. Sphere with a radius of 3486 kilometers (2161 miles)
    2. Material is stronger than the outer core
    3. Behaves like a solid

IX. Discovering Earth's major layers
  A. The Moho (Mohorovicic discontinuity)
    1. Discovered in 1909 by Andriaja Mohorovicic
    2. Separates crustal materials from underlying mantle

3. Identified by a change in the velocity of P waves
  B. The core-mantle boundary
    1. Discovered in 1914 by Beno Gutenberg
    2. Based on the observation that P waves die out at 105 degrees from the earthquake and reappear at about 140 degrees, but about 2 minutes later than expected—this 35-degree-wide belt is named the P wave shadow zone
    3. Characterized by bending (refracting) of the P waves
    4. The fact that S waves do not travel through the core provides evidence for the existence of a liquid layer beneath the rocky mantle
  C. Discovery of the inner core
    1. Predicted by Inge Lehmann in 1936
    2. Region of seismic reflection and refraction within the core

X. Discovering Earth's composition
  A. Crust
    1. Thinnest of Earth's divisions
    2. Varies in thickness
     a. Exceeds 70 km in some mountainous regions
     b. Thinner than 3 kilometers in some oceanic areas
    3. Two parts
     a. Continental crust
      1. Lighter
      2. Granitic rocks
     b. Oceanic crust
      1. Denser
      2. Composed mainly of the igneous rock basalt
  B. Mantle
    1. Solid, rocky layer
    2. Composed of rocks like peridotite
  C. Core
    1. Thought to be mainly dense iron and nickel
    2. Two parts
     a. Outer core—molten
     b. Inner core—solid

© 2008 Pearson Education, Inc., Upper Saddle River, NJ. All rights reserved. This material is protected under all copyright laws as they currently exist. No portion of this material may be reproduced, in any form or by any means, without permission in writing from the publisher.

Answers to the Review Questions

1. An earthquake is ground shaking caused by a sudden cracking and rupturing of highly strained rock and quick, lateral and/or vertical movements of the blocks on either side of the rupture surface. Failure occurs when the cumulative strains finally exceed the internal, cohesive bonds that hold the rock together. Failure (rupture and block movements) is catastrophic, usually taking only a few tens of seconds to a minute, and a high percentage of the strain energy is converted to ground vibrations. Following the earthquake, strain begins gradually building again toward a future quake.

2. A fault is the plane or zone of fracture separating two blocks that are abruptly displaced during an earthquake. The focus is the point at depth, usually in a fault zone, where the displacement and sudden release of elastic energy initiate. It marks the initial rupture site associated with the earthquake. The epicenter is the point on the surface directly above the focus.

3. H.F. Reid, a professor at Johns Hopkins University, based his elastic rebound idea on studies of the 1906 San Francisco earthquake.

4. Reid concluded that the quake was due to excess elastic strain energy being suddenly (catastrophically) released as the highly overstrained rocks snapped back (rebounded) to a state of much lower strain. Cool lithospheric rocks have elastic limits large enough to support earthquake-causing elastic strains. Hence, most earthquakes originate in the lithosphere. Because they are much warmer, asthenospheric rocks begin deforming by flowage (plastic deformation) at much lower stress magnitudes. Therefore, any stored elastic strain energies in the asthenosphere are too small in magnitude to produce a strong earthquake.

5. Creep movements should reduce the likelihood of an earthquake by reducing the level of strain accumulated in the fault-zone rocks. A fault without creep may reflect two fundamentally different conditions. First, the stresses may be too small to move the blocks, and there is no accumulation of elastic strain. In this case the fault is clearly inactive. In the other case, the fault is active but locked; the blocks cannot respond to tectonic stresses by moving, so elastic strain accumulates. A locked fault has a high probability for hosting a damaging future quake. and such areas, known as seismic gaps, are of special interest in earthquake forecasting.

6. A seismograph produces scaled and timed records of ground motion, ground velocity, and ground acceleration that result from earthquake (seismic) waves moving through the instrument site. The sensing part of the instrument is usually placed underground in a rigid, concrete vault. The rigid structure vibrates in concert with the passing seismic waves, and ground motions (displacement, velocity, and acceleration) are sensed by optical or electromagnetic sensors set in motion by the seismic vibrations. These variations are converted to electrical signals, amplified, and recorded as a function of time, giving an accurate record of the seismic wave patterns.

7. Approximately 1500 kilometers.

8. P waves (primary or compressional waves) travel though matter as particle vibrations along lines parallel to the ray path or to the path traced by a point traveling with the wave front. P waves move through solids, liquids, and gases, the "vibrations" being in the form of "push-pull" waves. S waves (secondary or shear waves) move by particle vibrations at right angles to the ray path, and they are transmitted only by solids, not by liquids or gases. Also, P waves always travel faster than S waves in a given material.

Compressional waves (P waves) are transmitted through solids and fluids because the transmitting material need not have any shear strength. S waves are shear waves and can propagate only in materials with a finite shear strength. Thus S waves are transmitted only by solids, not by liquids and gases.

© 2008 Pearson Education, Inc., Upper Saddle River, NJ. All rights reserved. This material is protected under all copyright laws as they currently exist. No portion of this material may be reproduced, in any form or by any means, without permission in writing from the publisher.

9. Surface waves have much higher amplitudes than body waves (P and S waves) and account for nearly all of the dangerous ground displacements and accelerations associated with earthquakes. The horizontally vibrating surface waves generally present more danger to buildings and other structures than surface waves with vertical motion. Closer to the epicenter of a shallow-focus quake, the various waves more or less arrive at the same time, giving a cumulative effect to the first strong ground motions.

10. Circum-Pacific belt. The earthquakes here are associated with active subduction zones around the rim of the Pacific Ocean where the oceanic crust is sinking into the mantle beneath island arcs or continental margins.

11. Two factors account for the greater loss of life from the Armenian earthquake. First, the damaged cities in Armenia were densely populated and very near the epicenter. Second, most people lived in large, multifamily, concrete slab apartment buildings that collapsed or were heavily damaged. A 5.8-magnitude aftershock finished off many of the damaged or weakened buildings. Although the Northridge, California, earthquake was larger in terms of moment magnitude, poor construction practices in Armenia resulted in a much higher number of deaths.

12. Thirty (30).

13. Moment magnitude has gained popularity among seismologists because (1) it is the only magnitude scale that correctly estimates the size of very large earthquakes; (2) it is determined by the size of the rupture surface and the amount of displacement, thus it is a better reflection of the total energy released during a quake; and (3) it can be verified by both field studies (measurement of fault displacements) and by seismographic methods.

14. Many factors can be noted, particularly the amplitude of the ground displacement or acceleration, the length of time that shaking occurs, and the character of the ground shaking. In general, vertical ground motion is not as dangerous as lateral or horizontal shaking, and short-period (high-frequency) vibrations are less dangerous than longer-period vibrations. Stability of the foundation material, building design, and construction quality are also important factors.

15. Fires, such as those that followed the 1906 San Francisco quake, and secondary effects such as landslides, dam failures, and tsunamis, can be more dangerous than the ground shaking. Damaged utilities, water and sewer systems, and waste disposal systems leave an earthquake-ravaged area without reliable communications and electricity and vulnerable to serious public health problems. In addition, hazardous materials, toxic chemicals, and radioactive substances may be released from broken pipelines, damaged storage facilities, and from truck and train accidents.

16. The Richter earthquake-magnitude scale is based on standardized measurements of ground vibration amplitudes and the total energy released during the earthquake. It is a logarithmic numerical scale, and a theoretical consideration of rock strength suggests that 9 is about the highest magnitude possible. The Richter scale is quantitative because magnitudes are based on measured wave amplitudes and a physically valid relationship between amplitude and wave energy. In recent years, a newer magnitude scale based on the integrated seismic moment has been utilized. For low to moderate magnitude quakes originating along short fault segments, the two magnitude values are similar. For large earthquakes associated with extensive rupture zones (Richter magnitude above 8), the moment method gives higher values for the total energy released. These larger magnitudes are considered realistic since the Richter scale determination basically assumes that the seismic energy emanates from a single point rather than from the rupture surface.

© 2008 Pearson Education, Inc., Upper Saddle River, NJ. All rights reserved. This material is protected under all copyright laws as they currently exist. No portion of this material may be reproduced, in any form or by any means, without permission in writing from the publisher.

The Mercalli earthquake-intensity scale is based on visual observations. It gives an estimate of the ground-shaking intensity in terms of human perceptions, eyewitness accounts, and damage to buildings or other property. As such, it is a subjective scale, and the ratings are strongly dependent on local site characteristics such as foundation stability and building design. The scale (from I to XII) utilizes Roman numerals.

17. A tsunami, or seismic sea wave, is associated with an earthquake because it is generated by movement of the ocean floor (faulting). These waves transfer vast quantities of energy, often great distances. When the energy is released as the wave breaks in shallow water, it can cause tremendous destruction.

18. In addition to magnitude, earthquake casualties and damage depend on many other natural and cultural factors. Aftershocks can slow or stop rescue efforts and cause additional damage and casualties. Amplified ground shaking and liquefaction intensify damage to structures built on quick clay and soft, unconsolidated, and/or water-saturated foundation materials. Landslides, rockslides, and rolling boulders can account for far more deaths and injuries than are attributable directly to the ground shaking. Local building practices, construction materials, time of year, the climatic season, and time of day are also important factors to be considered.

19. The asthenosphere, located between 70 and 700 kilometers deep, consists of approximately 10% melted rock. This zone lies wholly within the mantle. The lithosphere lies above the asthenosphere and includes the crust and part of the upper mantle (that part above the asthenosphere). The asthenosphere behaves plastically while the lithosphere is rigid.

20. Crust—The continental crust is much like average andesite or shale in chemical composition. The upper crust is enriched in granitic rocks rich in silicon and potassium and low in magnesium and iron. Quartz, orthoclase, and sodium-rich plagioclase are common minerals. The lower crust is more mafic; silicate minerals such as olivine, hornblende, and pyroxene are abundant. The oceanic crust is composed largely of basaltic lavas and intrusive gabbro made of iron-magnesium silicates such as olivine, pyroxene, and calcium-rich plagioclase.

Mantle—The mantle is believed to be mainly ultramafic, silicate rock, with magnesium silicates (olivine and pyroxene) being dominant. At great depth, denser minerals with similar compositions exist under higher temperature and pressure conditions.

Core—The outer core is a liquid, mainly iron alloyed with nickel and lower atomic number elements such as sulfur, silicon, and perhaps potassium. Recent theoretical studies have suggested that oxygen might be one of the lighter elements as well. Iron generally fits the melting point and density requirements for the core material, and it also conducts electricity, which is a requirement for generation of Earth's magnetic field. The inner core is thought to be a solidified, crystalline, iron-rich alloy with a composition similar to that of the liquid outer core.

Lecture outline, art-only, and animation PowerPoint presentations for each chapter of *Essentials of Geology* are available on the IRC DVD (ISBN 0-13-604914-1).

© 2008 Pearson Education, Inc., Upper Saddle River, NJ. All rights reserved. This material is protected under all copyright laws as they currently exist. No portion of this material may be reproduced, in any form or by any means, without permission in writing from the publisher.

NOTES:

© 2008 Pearson Education, Inc., Upper Saddle River, NJ. All rights reserved. This material is protected under all copyright laws as they currently exist. No portion of this material may be reproduced, in any form or by any means, without permission in writing from the publisher.

Plate Tectonics: A Scientific Theory Unfolds

Plate Tectonics: A Scientific Theory Unfolds opens by examining the lines of evidence that Alfred Wegener used in the early 1900s to support his continental drift hypothesis. This evidence included the fit of the continents, fossils, rock types, structural similarities between continents, and paleoclimates. Also presented are the main objections to Wegener's ideas.

Following a brief overview, the theory of plate tectonics is examined in detail. The movement of lithospheric plates and different types of plate boundaries are examined extensively. Ages and distribution of ocean-basin sediments, hot spots, and paleomagnetism are used to provide additional support for plate tectonics. The chapter closes with comments about the driving mechanism of plate tectonics.

Learning Objectives

After reading, studying, and discussing the chapter, students should be able to:

- Briefly discuss the evidence used by Alfred Wegener to support his theory of continental drift.
- Briefly explain the theory of plate tectonics.
- Compare and contrast the distribution and geologic characteristics of tectonic plate boundaries, including divergent, convergent, and transform boundaries.
- Discuss the evidence used to test the plate tectonics model, including ocean drilling and hot spots.
- Describe how the continents were arranged in the past.
- Discuss mantle convection and the various mechanisms proposed to explain plate motion.

Chapter Outline

I. Continental drift: an idea before its time
  A. Alfred Wegener
    1. First proposed hypothesis, 1915
    2. Published *The Origin of Continents and Oceans*
  B. Wegener's continental drift hypothesis
    1. Supercontinent called Pangaea began breaking apart about 200 million years ago
    2. Continents "drifted" to present positions
    3. Continents "broke" through the ocean crust
    4. Evidence used by Wegener
      a. Fit of South America and Africa
      b. Fossil matches across the seas
      c. Rock type and structure matches
      d. Ancient climates

  5. Main objection to Wegener's proposal was its inability to provide a mechanism

II. Plate tectonics: the new paradigm
  A. More encompassing than continental drift
  B. Associated with Earth's rigid outer shell
    1. Called the lithosphere
    2. Consists of several plates
      a. Plates are moving slowly
      b. Largest plate is the Pacific plate
      c. Plates are mostly beneath the ocean
  C. Asthenosphere
    1. Exists beneath the lithosphere
    2. Hotter and weaker than lithosphere
    3. Allows for movement of lithosphere

© 2008 Pearson Education, Inc., Upper Saddle River, NJ. All rights reserved. This material is protected under all copyright laws as they currently exist. No portion of this material may be reproduced, in any form or by any means, without permission in writing from the publisher.

D. Plate boundaries
  1. All major interactions among plates occur along their boundaries
  2. Types of plate boundaries
    a. Divergent plate boundaries (constructive margins)
      1. Two plates move apart
      2. Mantle material upwells to create new seafloor
      3. Ocean ridges and seafloor spreading
        a. Oceanic ridges develop along well-developed boundaries
          1. Represent 20% of Earth's surface
          2. Rift valleys may develop along the axis
        b. Along ridges, seafloor spreading creates new seafloor
          1. Topographic differences are controlled by spreading rates
          2. A spreading rate of 5–9 centimeters per year is the norm
      4. Continental rifts form at spreading centers within a continent
    b. Convergent plate boundaries (destructive margins)
      1. Plates collide, an ocean trench forms, and lithosphere is subducted into the mantle
      2. Types of convergence
        a. Oceanic-continental convergence
          1. Denser oceanic slab sinks into the asthenosphere
          2. Pockets of magma develop and rise
          3. Continental volcanic arcs form
            a. Andes
            b. Cascades
            c. Sierra Nevada system
        b. Oceanic-oceanic convergence
          1. Two oceanic slabs converge and one descends beneath the other
          2. Often forms volcanoes on the ocean floor
          3. Volcanic island arcs form as volcanoes emerge from the sea
            a. Aleutian Islands
            b. Mariana Islands
            c. Tonga Islands
         c. Continental-continental convergence
          1. When subducting plates contain continental material, two continents collide
          2. Can produce new mountain ranges such as the Himalayas
    c. Transform fault boundaries
      1. Plates slide past one another
        a. No new crust is created
        b. No crust is destroyed
      2. Transform faults
        a. Most join two segments of a mid-ocean ridge
        b. At the time of formation, they roughly parallel the direction of plate movement
        c. Aid the movement of oceanic crustal material

E. Evidence for the plate tectonics model
  1. Paleomagnetism
    a. Probably the most persuasive evidence
    b. Ancient magnetism preserved in rocks
    c. Paleomagnetic records show
      1. Polar wandering (evidence that continents moved)
      2. Earth's magnetic field reversals
        a. Recorded in rocks as they form at oceanic ridges
        b. Record of reversals across ocean ridges confirms seafloor spreading
  2. Earthquake patterns
    a. Associated with plate boundaries
    b. Deep-focus earthquakes along trenches provide a method for tracking the plate's descent
  3. Ocean drilling
    a. Deep Sea Drilling Project (ship: *Glomar Challenger*)

© 2008 Pearson Education, Inc., Upper Saddle River, NJ. All rights reserved. This material is protected under all copyright laws as they currently exist. No portion of this material may be reproduced, in any form or by any means, without permission in writing from the publisher.

b. Age of deepest sediments
    1. Youngest are near the ridges
    2. Older are at a distance from the ridge
c. Ocean basins are geologically young
  4. Hot spots
    a. Rising plumes of mantle material
    b. Volcanoes can form over them
      1. Example: Hawaiian Island chain
      2. Chains of volcanoes mark plate movement
  F. Measuring plate motion
    1. By using hot spot "tracks" like those of the Hawaiian Island-Emperor Seamount chain
    2. Using space-age technology to directly measure the relative motion of plates
      a. Very Long Baseline Interferometry (VLBI)

b. Global Positioning System (GPS)
G. Driving mechanism of plate tectonics
  1. No one model explains all facets of plate tectonics
  2. Earth's heat is the driving force
  3. Several models have been proposed
    a. Slab-pull and slab-push model
      1. Descending oceanic crust pulls the plate
      2. Elevated ridge system pushes the plate
    b. Plate-mantle convection
      1. Mantle plumes extend from mantle-core boundary and cause convection within the mantle
      2. Models
        a. Layering at 660 kilometers
        b. Whole-mantle convection
        c. Deep-layer model

Answers to the Review Questions

1. Alfred Wegener is credited with developing the continental drift hypothesis.

2. The puzzle-like fit of the continents, especially Africa and South America.

3. Pangaea, the supercontinent named by Alfred Wegener, is thought to have begun to break apart about 200 million years ago, with the fragments eventually forming the present continents.

4. Wegener and his associates found that the fit of the continents, fossil evidence, paleoclimatic evidence, and similarities in rock type and structural features all seemed to link the now-separated continental landmasses.

5. If *Mesosaurus* was able to swim well enough to cross the vast ocean currently separating Africa and South America, its remains should also be found on other continents. Since this is not the case, we conclude that South America and Africa were joined during the time period that these animals existed.

6. Early in this century, migration of land animals was thought to have occurred via land bridges. According to this view, these land bridges were recently submerged as sea level rose following the last glacial event.

7. First, it is difficult to explain, by assuming that a general cooling trend occurred, why late Paleozoic glaciation was essentially confined to the Southern Hemisphere. This and other paleoclimatic data can best be reconciled by assuming that the continents were located at different latitudes from where they are today. Second, glacial striations in some locations indicate that the ice movement was from areas presently occupied by water. We know, however, that thick accumulations of ice can form only on land.

8. The first approximations of plate boundaries were made on the basis of earthquake and volcanic activity.

9. Divergent boundaries—where plates are moving apart

© 2008 Pearson Education, Inc., Upper Saddle River, NJ. All rights reserved. This material is protected under all copyright laws as they currently exist. No portion of this material may be reproduced, in any form or by any means, without permission in writing from the publisher.

Plate Tectonics: A Scientific Theory Unfolds

Convergent boundaries—where plates are moving together
Transform fault boundaries—where plates slide past one another along faults

10. Seafloor spreading refers to the creation of new seafloor at the oceanic ridges along with its conveyor belt movement away from the ridge crests. Seafloor spreading occurs today along the oceanic ridges.

11. Subduction zones occur in the deep-ocean trenches where slabs of oceanic crust are descending into the mantle. Subduction zones are associated with convergent plate boundaries.

12. Lithosphere is being consumed at convergent boundaries where a slab of oceanic crust is plunging into the asthenosphere. The production and the destruction of the lithosphere must occur at about the same rate, because Earth is neither growing nor shrinking in size.

13. The Himalayan Mountains formed as a result of a collision between the Indian landmass and the Asian continent.

14. Transform fault boundaries, like the San Andreas fault, represent areas where plates slip past one another. Lithosphere is neither produced (as along divergent boundaries) nor destroyed (as along convergent boundaries) along transform faults.

15. If the movement along the San Andreas fault continues in its present manner, the part of California west of the fault will indeed slide out to sea, eventually becoming an island off the west coast of the United States and Canada. This, however, will take millions of years.

16. Paleomagnetism is the natural magnetism in rock bodies that was acquired from Earth's magnetic field at the time the rock formed.

17. Evidence from studies of paleomagnetism indicates that Earth's magnetic poles have migrated during the past 500 million years. This apparent migration can also be explained if the magnetic poles remained stationary while the landmasses moved. Thus, continental drift does in fact account for the apparent wandering of Earth's magnetic poles.

18. The age of the oldest sediments recovered by deep-ocean drilling is about 160 million years. Some continental crust has been dated at 3.9 billion years.

19. Hot spots are relatively stationary plumes of molten rock rising from Earth's mantle. According to the plate tectonics theory, as a plate moves over a hot spot, magma often penetrates the surface, thereby generating a volcanic structure. In the case of the Hawaiian Islands, as the Pacific plate moved over a hot spot, the associated igneous activity produced a chain of five major volcanoes. The oldest of the Hawaiian Islands is Kauai. The youngest, and only active volcanic island in the chain, is the island of Hawaii.

20. Three mechanisms that have proposed to explain plate motion include slab pull, ridge push, and slab suction. Slab pull refers to the sinking of older, denser slabs of oceanic lithosphere into the asthenosphere

© 2008 Pearson Education, Inc., Upper Saddle River, NJ. All rights reserved. This material is protected under all copyright laws as they currently exist. No portion of this material may be reproduced, in any form or by any means, without permission in writing from the publisher.

and "pulling" the trailing plate along. Ridge push is a gravity-driven mechanism that results from the elevated position of the oceanic ridge, which causes slabs of lithosphere to move down the flanks of the ridge. Slab suction arises from the drag of a subducting slab on the adjacent mantle. An induced mantle circulation pulls the subducting and overriding plates toward the trench or "sucks" in nearby plates.

21. Himalayas: These have formed along a convergent continent-continent collisional boundary between the Indian subcontinent and Eurasia.

    Aleutian Islands: These islands are the oceanward part of a volcanic island arc situated on the northwestern margin of the North American plate; the volcanoes lie above the subducting Pacific plate.

    Red Sea: The Red Sea occupies a major rift zone and very young seafloor spreading center that has opened between Africa and the Arabian block.

    Andes Mountains: The Andes are a volcanic and plutonic arc resting on the western margin of the South American plate; they lie above subducting, oceanic lithosphere of the Nazca and Antarctic plates.

    San Andreas fault: This is a transform fault that forms the boundary between the North American and Pacific plates. The crustal sliver composed of westernmost California and the Baja California peninsula on the eastern edge of the Pacific plate is moving northwestward with respect to North America.

    Iceland: Iceland and nearby smaller islands constitute a major zone of basaltic volcanism that probably overlies a mantle hot spot located directly beneath the Mid-Atlantic Ridge, the divergent boundary between the Eurasian and North American plates.

    Japan: The Japanese Islands lie on the eastern margin of the Eurasian plate, above subducting parts of the Pacific and Philippine oceanic plates.

    Mount Saint Helens: This is a very young stratovolcano in the state of Washington; it is part of the Cascade Range, a continental-margin, volcanic arc extending from the Canadian border to northern California.

Lecture outline, art-only, and animation PowerPoint presentations for each chapter of *Essentials of Geology* are available on the IRC DVD (ISBN 0-13-604914-1).

NOTES:

© 2008 Pearson Education, Inc., Upper Saddle River, NJ. All rights reserved. This material is protected under all copyright laws as they currently exist. No portion of this material may be reproduced, in any form or by any means, without permission in writing from the publisher.

Origin and Evolution of the Ocean Floor

Origin and Evolution of the Ocean Floor begins with a brief overview of the ocean floor and methods used for mapping the seafloor. Following an examination of the features associated with passive and active continental margins, the chapter continues with investigations of trenches, abyssal plains, and other features of deep-ocean floor. The origin and structure of oceanic crust is discussed, followed by continental rifting and the destruction of oceanic lithosphere. The chapter concludes with a discussion of the opening and closing of ocean basins in the supercontinent cycle.

Learning Objectives

After reading, studying, and discussing the chapter, students should be able to:

- Briefly explain the technology utilized in mapping the ocean floor.
- Discuss the geologic characteristics and features associated with passive and active continental margins.
- Briefly discuss features of the deep-ocean basins, including deep-ocean trenches, abyssal plains, and seamounts.
- Understand the origin of oceanic lithosphere, including the role of oceanic ridges and the mechanism of seafloor spreading.
- Discuss the structure and geologic characteristics of oceanic crust.
- Briefly discuss continental rifting and evolution of ocean basins.
- Discuss subduction and the destruction of oceanic lithosphere.

Chapter Outline

I. Mapping the ocean floor
   A. Depth was originally measured by lowering weighted lines overboard
   B. Echo sounder (also referred to as sonar)
      1. Invented in the 1920s
      2. Primary instrument for measuring depth
      3. Reflects sound from ocean floor
   C. Multibeam sonar
      1. Employs and array of sound sources and listening devices
      2. Obtains a profile of a narrow strip of seafloor
   D. Seismic reflection profiles
      1. Low-frequency sounds are produced by explosions

      2. Reflected sound waves reveal contacts and fault zones on the seafloor
   E. Viewing the ocean floor from space
      1. Satellites use radar altimeters to measure subtle differences of the ocean surface
      2. Small variations reflect the gravitational pull of features on the seafloor
   F. Three major topographic units of the ocean floor
      1. Continental margins
      2. Deep-ocean basins
      3. Mid-ocean ridges

© 2008 Pearson Education, Inc., Upper Saddle River, NJ. All rights reserved. This material is protected under all copyright laws as they currently exist. No portion of this material may be reproduced, in any form or by any means, without permission in writing from the publisher.

II. Continental margins
  A. Passive continental margins
    1. Found along most coastal areas that surround the Atlantic ocean
    2. Not associated with plate boundaries
       a. Experience little volcanism and
       b. Few earthquakes
    3. Features comprising a passive continental margin
       a. Continental shelf
          1. Flooded extension of the continent
          2. Varies greatly in width
          3. Gently sloping
          4. Contain important mineral deposits
             a. Petroleum
             b. Natural gas
             c. Sand and gravel
          5. Some areas are mantled by extensive glacial deposits
          6. Most consist of thick accumulations of shallow-water sediments
       b. Continental slope
          1. Marks the seaward edge of the continental shelf
          2. Relatively steep structure
          3. Boundary between continental crust and oceanic crust
       c. Continental rise
          1. Found in regions where trenches are absent
          2. Continental slope merges into a more gradual incline—the continental rise
          3. Thick accumulation of sediment
          4. At the base of the continental slope, turbidity currents that follow submarine canyons deposit sediment that forms deep-sea fans
  B. Active continental margins
    1. Continental slope descends abruptly into a deep-ocean trench
    2. Located primarily around the Pacific Ocean
    3. Accumulations of deformed sediment and scraps of ocean crust form accretionary wedges
    4. Some subduction zones have little or no accumulation of sediments

III. Features of the deep-ocean basin
  A. Deep-ocean trench
    1. Long, relatively narrow features
    2. Deepest parts of ocean
    3. Most are located in the Pacific Ocean
    4. Sites where moving lithospheric plates plunge into the mantle
    5. Associated with volcanic activity
  B. Abyssal plains
    1. Likely the most level places on Earth
    2. Sites of thick accumulations of sediment
    3. Found in all oceans
  C. Seamounts, guyots, and oceanic plateaus
    1. Seamounts are isolated volcanic peaks on the seafloor
    2. Many seamounts form near oceanic ridges
    3. Seamounts sometimes emerge as an island
    4. May sink and form flat-topped seamounts called guyots
    5. Vast outpourings of basaltic lavas on the ocean floor create extensive volcanic structures called oceanic plateaus

IV. Anatomy of the oceanic ridge
  A. Broad, linear swells along divergent plate boundaries are called oceanic ridges
    1. Occupy elevated positions
    2. Extensive faulting and earthquakes
    3. High heat flow
    4. Numerous volcanic structures
  B. Oceanic ridge characteristics
    1. Longest topographic feature on Earth's surface
       a. Over 70,000 kilometers (43,000 miles) in length
       b. Twenty percent of Earth's surface
       c. Winds through all major oceans
    1. Term ridge is misleading—widths of 1000–4000 kilometers give the appearance of broad, elongated swells

© 2008 Pearson Education, Inc., Upper Saddle River, NJ. All rights reserved. This material is protected under all copyright laws as they currently exist. No portion of this material may be reproduced, in any form or by any means, without permission in writing from the publisher.

2. Axis of some ridge segments exhibit deep down-faulted structures called rift valleys
3. Portions of the mid-Atlantic ridge have been studied in considerable detail

V. Origin of oceanic lithosphere
   A. Seafloor spreading
      1. Concept formulated in the early 1960s by Harry Hess
      2. Seafloor spreading occurs along relatively narrow zones, called rift zones, located at the crests of ocean ridges
      3. As plates move apart, magma wells up into the newly created fractures and generates new slivers of oceanic lithosphere
      4. New lithosphere moves from the ridge crest in a conveyor belt fashion
      5. Zones of active rifting are 20–30 kilometers wide
   B. Why are oceanic ridges elevated?
      1. Primary reason is because newly created oceanic lithosphere is hot and occupies more volume than cooler rocks
      2. As the basaltic crust travels away from the ridge crest, it is cooled by seawater and because it is moving away from the source of heat
      3. As the lithosphere moves away, it thermally contracts and becomes more dense
      4. Thickness actually increases due to mechanical properties of the mantle
   C. Spreading rates and ridge topography
      1. Ridge systems exhibit topographic differences
      2. Topographic differences are controlled by spreading rates
         a. At slow spreading rates (1–5 centimeters per year), a prominent rift valley develops along the ridge crest that is usually
            1. 30–50 kilometers across
            2. 1500–3000 meters deep
            3. Rugged

         b. At intermediate spreading rates (5–9 centimeters per year), rift valleys that develop are
            1. Shallow
            2. Often less than 200 meters deep
            3. Topographically rather smooth
         c. At spreading rates greater than 9 centimeters per year, no median rift valley develops and these areas are
            1. Usually narrow (roughly 10 kilometers wide) topographic highs
            2. Extensively faulted
            3. Composed of numerous horsts and grabens

VI. Structure of the oceanic crust
   A. Four distinct layers
      1. Layer 1—sequence of unconsolidated sediments
      2. Layer 2—consisting of pillow lavas
      3. Layer 3—numerous interconnected dikes called sheet dikes
      4. Layer 4—gabbro, in a sequence of rocks called an ophiolite
   B. Formation of oceanic crust
      1. Basaltic magma originates from partially melted mantle peridotite
      2. Molten rock injected into fractures above the magma chambers creates the sheeted dike complex
      3. The submarine lava flows chill quickly and the congealed margin is forced forward by the accumulating lava to produce large tube-shaped protuberances known as pillow basalts
      4. Crystallization of the central magma chamber forms the coarse-grained gabbro
   C. Interactions between seawater and oceanic crust
      1. Seawater circulates downward through the highly fractured crust
      2. Basaltic rock is altered by hydrothermal metamorphism
      3. Hydrothermal fluids dissolves ions of various metals and precipitates

© 2008 Pearson Education, Inc., Upper Saddle River, NJ. All rights reserved. This material is protected under all copyright laws as they currently exist. No portion of this material may be reproduced, in any form or by any means, without permission in writing from the publisher.

them on the seafloor as particle-filled clouds called black smokers

VII. Continental rifting: The birth of a new ocean basin
   A. Evolution of an ocean basin
      1. A new ocean basin begins with the formation of a continental rift
         a. Splits landmasses into two or more smaller segments
         b. Examples include the East African Rift, Baikal rift, the Rhine Valley, Rio Grande Rift, and the Basin and Range
         c. Produced by extensional forces acting on the lithospheric plates
      2. The Red Sea is an example of a rift valley that has lengthened and deepened in a narrow linear sea
      3. If spreading continues, the Red Sea will grow wider and develop an oceanic ridge similar to the Atlantic Ocean
      4. Not all rift valleys develop into full-fledged spreading centers (e.g., a failed rift running through the central United States from Lake Superior to Kansas)
   B. Mechanisms for continental rifting
      1. Two mechanisms have been proposed
      2. Mantle plumes and hotspots
         a. Regions of hotter than normal mantle cause decompression melting that results in a volcanic region called a hotspot
         b. Hot mantle plumes may cause the overlying crust to dome and weaken
         c. Lifting and stretching of the crust results in a continental rift similar to the East African Rift
      3. Slab pull and slab suction
         a. Subduction of old oceanic lithosphere may pull a continent attached to a subducting slab and create a rift
         b. Another possible force might result from sinking of a cold slab, causing the trench to retreat or roll back due to flow in the asthenosphere—this is known as slab suction

VIII. Destruction of oceanic lithosphere
   A. Why oceanic lithosphere subducts
      1. Oceanic lithosphere subducts because its overall density is greater than the underlying mantle
      2. Subduction of older, colder lithosphere results in descending angles of nearly 90 degrees
      3. Younger, warmer oceanic lithosphere is more buoyant and angles of descent are small
         a. The lithospheric slab moves horizontally beneath a block of continental lithosphere
         b. This phenomenon is called buoyant subduction
      4. Subduction may be prevented or modified when oceanic crust is unusually thick because of seamounts
   B. Subducting plates: The demise of an ocean basin
      1. Plate movements have been reconstructed for the past 200 million years using magnetic stripes on the ocean floor
      2. Research indicates that parts, or even entire oceanic basins, have been destroyed along subducted zones
      3. The Farallon plate once occupied much of the eastern Pacific basin
         a. Beginning 180 million years ago, the Farallon plate was subducting beneath the Americas faster than it was being generated
         b. The plate got continually smaller and now only fragments of the original plate remain as the Juan de Fuca, Cocos, and Nazca plates

© 2008 Pearson Education, Inc., Upper Saddle River, NJ. All rights reserved. This material is protected under all copyright laws as they currently exist. No portion of this material may be reproduced, in any form or by any means, without permission in writing from the publisher.

Origin and Evolution of the Ocean Floor

Answers to the Review Questions

1. The echo sounder pulse travels a distance equal to twice the water depth. In 6 seconds, the pulse travels 9000 meters (1500 m/sec × 6 sec = 9000 m); thus the depth (1/2 of 9000 meters) is 4500 meters.

2. Satellites equipped with radar altimeters are able to determine features on the seafloor by measuring subtle differences in elevation on the ocean surface. The satellites bounce microwaves off of the ocean surface, which is affected by the gravitational pull of seafloor features. Therefore, mountains and ridges produce elevated areas on the ocean surface while canyons and trenches cause slight depressions.

3. The three major topographic units of the ocean floor are the continental margins, deep-ocean basins, and oceanic (mid-ocean) ridges.

4. The three major features listed in their order from the coastline seaward are the continental shelf, continental slope, and continental rise. The shelf is a relatively flat, flooded extension of the continent. Water depths increase very gradually seaward to the edge of the shelf. The continental slope extends seaward and downward from the shelf edge and merges downward into the continental rise. It has the steepest slopes of the three listed features. On trailing passive continental margins, the shelf is part of the continent. The slope marks the eroded scarp left from an original continental rift zone, and the rise marks a fan-shaped accumulation of clastic sediments carried down from the shelf and slope by turbidity currents.

5. An active continental margin exhibits a very narrow continental shelf and a relatively steep, narrow, continental slope that merges into a deep ocean trench along most of the coastline. Along a passive continental margin, the continental shelf is wide, and the shelf is terminated by a well-defined continental slope with a wide, gently sloping continental rise at its base. There are no deep ocean trenches, and the rise merges oceanward into an abyssal plain. In terms of plate tectonics, the east coast of North America is a good example of a passive continental margin and therefore is not very active tectonically. In contrast, the west coast of South America represents an active continental margin that is characterized by subduction, volcanism, and earthquakes: all evidence of a tectonically active region.

6. To a great extent, the Pacific Ocean is rimmed by deep ocean trenches or deep, near shore basins that trap sediment and prevent turbidity currents from moving farther offshore. The Atlantic Ocean is rimmed mainly by passive continental margins, and turbidity currents with their sediment load can move far out into the deeper parts of the ocean basin. The abyssal plain marks the smooth, upper surface of turbidity current sediments deposited on the original basaltic bedrock of the ocean floor. For the most part, the Atlantic Ocean floor is not being subducted, so there has been plenty of geologic time for turbidite sediments to accumulate.

7. Seamounts are isolated volcanic peaks that rise hundreds of meters above the ocean floor. Over time, the volcano may grow large enough to emerge as an island. During the time they exist as islands, some of the volcanoes are eroded to near sea level by running water and wave action. Over millions of years, the islands gradually sink below the surface of the water as a moving plate carries them away from their place of origin. The submerged, flat-topped seamounts are called guyots.

© 2008 Pearson Education, Inc., Upper Saddle River, NJ. All rights reserved. This material is protected under all copyright laws as they currently exist. No portion of this material may be reproduced, in any form or by any means, without permission in writing from the publisher.

8. Mid-ocean ridges are topographically elevated features that are located near the center of most ocean basins. The ridges are broken into segments that are offset by large transform faults. Also, along the axis of some of the segments are deep down-faulted structures called rift valleys. The rift valleys are characterized by active volcanoes, recent underwater lava flows, and black smokers, which are a type of hydrothermal vent that spews dark mineral-rich water.

9. Unlike continental mountains where compressional forces fold and metamorphose sedimentary rocks along convergent boundaries, oceanic ridges form where tensional forces fracture and pull the oceanic crust apart. As a result of the rifting, the oceanic ridges are composed of layers and piles of basaltic rocks that are faulted into elongated blocks.

10. Along the oceanic ridges, the lithospheric plates separate, and hot mantle rocks rise upward to replace the material that has shifted horizontally. The rising mantle rock experiences a decrease in confining pressure and partially melts to create the basaltic magmas. This process is called decompression melting.

11. Oceanic ridges are thought to form over rising plumes of hot mantle rock. Partial melting occurs as the plume approaches the top of the mantle. The basaltic magma rises and solidifies as lava flows and intrusive gabbro, which form new oceanic crust. Temperatures are higher at any given depth under the ridge than under parts of the seafloor distant from the ridge. Magmas and high-temperature rocks occupy more space than equivalent masses of cooler, solid rock; thus the seafloor is elevated along the mid-ocean ridge. Also, the rising-mantle convection currents may contribute to the "excess" elevation of the ridges.

12. Hydrothermal metamorphism of basalt on the seafloor is accomplished with heated seawater (from circulating through the hot crust) reacting with the existing minerals, such as olivine and plagioclase feldspar, to form more stable minerals such as chlorite and calcite. The seawater is heated during this process, and it becomes locally saturated with dissolved ions that are precipitated as metallic sulfide minerals on the seafloor.

13. A black smoker is a particle-filled cloud that results from the metallic-rich solutions along oceanic ridges that emanate from hot springs on the seafloor. The black smokers mix with the cold seawater and metallic sulfide minerals are precipitated.

14. The four layers of the ocean crust include: (1) a surface layer comprised of unconsolidated sediments; (2) a second layer composed mainly of basaltic lavas that contain abundant pillow-like structures; (3) a rocky layer below the lavas where numerous interconnected dikes have a nearly vertical orientation, which is called the sheeted dike complex; and (4) a lower unit made up mainly of gabbro.

15. The sheeted dike complex forms from magma that is injected into fractures of the oceanic crust. The lower unit represents crystallization of the central magma chamber as it cools slowly to form gabbro.

16. Several continental rifts exist on Earth, but the East African Rift is perhaps the best example of an active continental rift zone.

© 2008 Pearson Education, Inc., Upper Saddle River, NJ. All rights reserved. This material is protected under all copyright laws as they currently exist. No portion of this material may be reproduced, in any form or by any means, without permission in writing from the publisher.

17. When initially formed, oceanic crust is warm and buoyant, which explains the elevated position of oceanic ridges above the deep-ocean basins. Over time the oceanic slab cools and thickens as it moves away from the ridge. After about 15 million years, the oceanic lithosphere is now more dense than the underlying asthenosphere and subduction can occur.

18. The Farallon was a large oceanic plate that once occupied much of the eastern Pacific basin. Around 180 million years ago, the Americas were moving westward, and the Farallon plate was being subducted along the west coasts of North and South America. The Farallon plate was subducting beneath the Americas faster than it was being generated, so it got smaller and smaller. Today, the Juan de Fuca, Cocos, and Nazca plates are the remaining fragments of the once much larger Farallon plate.

Lecture outline, art-only, and animation PowerPoint presentations for each chapter of *Essentials of Geology* are available on the IRC DVD (ISBN 0-13-604914-1).

NOTES:

© 2008 Pearson Education, Inc., Upper Saddle River, NJ. All rights reserved. This material is protected under all copyright laws as they currently exist. No portion of this material may be reproduced, in any form or by any means, without permission in writing from the publisher.

Crustal Deformation and Mountain Building

Crustal Deformation and Mountain Building begins with a brief examination of the processes of crustal deformation, including the factors that affect rock deformation. The various types of folds (anticlines, synclines, domes, and basins) and faults (both dip-slip and strike-slip) are investigated. Mountain building at convergent boundaries is discussed in detail, including subduction, continental collisions, and accretion of terranes. The chapter concludes with a discussion of fault block mountains and the concept of isostasy.

Learning Objectives

After reading, studying, and discussing the chapter, students should be able to:

- Discuss rock deformation and list the factors that influence the strength of a rock.
- List the major types of folds and faults and describe how they form.
- Discuss mountain building associated with subducting plate boundaries, including a comparison of island arcs and Andean-type mountain building.
- Explain mountain building associated with continent-continent collisions.
- Briefly discuss the relationship of terranes to mountain building.
- Discuss vertical movements of Earth's crust, including isostatic adjustment and mantle convection.

Chapter Outline

I. Deformation
  A. Deformation is a general term that refers to all changes in the original form and/or size of a rock body
  B. Most crustal deformation occurs along plate margins
  C. Factors that influence the strength of a rock
    1. Temperature and confining pressure
    2. Rock type
    3. Time

II. Folds
  A. Rocks bent into a series of waves
  B. Most folds result from compressional forces that shorten and thicken the crust
  C. Types of folds
    1. Anticline—upfolded, or arched, rock layers
    2. Syncline—downfolded rock layers
    3. Anticlines and synclines can be
      a. Symmetrical—limbs are mirror images

      b. Asymmetrical—limbs are not mirror images
      c. Overturned—one limb is tilted beyond the vertical
    4. Where folds die out, they are said to be plunging
    5. Other types of folds
      a. Dome
        1. Circular or slightly elongated
        2. Upwarped displacement of rocks
        3. Oldest rocks in core
      b. Basin
        1. Circular or slightly elongated
        2. Downwarped displacement of rocks
        3. Youngest rocks in core

III. Faults
  A. Faults are fractures (breaks) in rocks along which appreciable displacement has taken place
  B. Types of faults
    1. Dip-slip fault

© 2008 Pearson Education, Inc., Upper Saddle River, NJ. All rights reserved. This material is protected under all copyright laws as they currently exist. No portion of this material may be reproduced, in any form or by any means, without permission in writing from the publisher.

a. Movement along the inclination (dip) of fault plane

b. Parts of a dip-slip fault
1. Hanging wall—the rock above the fault surface
2. Footwall—the rock below the fault surface

c. Types of dip-slip faults
1. Normal fault
a. Hanging wall block moves down
b. Associated with fault-block mountains
c. Prevalent at spreading centers
d. Caused by tensional forces
2. Reverse and thrust faults
a. Hanging wall block moves up
b. Caused by strong compressional stresses
c. Reverse fault—dips greater than 45 degrees
d. Thrust fault—dips less than 45 degrees

2. Strike-slip faults
a. Dominant displacement is horizontal and parallel to the trend, or strike
b. Transform fault
1. Large strike-slip fault that cuts through the lithosphere
2. Often associated with plate boundaries

3. Joints
a. Fractures along which no appreciable displacement has occurred
b. Most are formed when rocks in the outermost crust are deformed

IV.   Mountain building
A.   Mountain building has occurred during the recent geologic past
1.   American Cordillera—the western margin of the Americas from Cape Horn to Alaska, which includes the Andes and Rocky Mountains
2.   Alpine-Himalayan chain
3.   Mountainous terrains of the western Pacific
B.   Older Paleozoic- and Precambrian-age mountains
1.   Appalachians

2.   Urals in Russia
C.   Orogenesis—the processes that collectively produce a mountain belt
1.   Compressional forces producing folding and thrust faulting
2.   Metamorphism
3.   Igneous activity
D.   Several hypotheses have been proposed for the formations of Earth's mountain belts
1.   With the development of plate tectonics, it appears that most mountain building occurs at convergent plate boundaries

V.   Subduction and mountain building
A.   Island-arc mountain building
1.   Occurs where two ocean plates converge and one is subducted beneath the other
2.   Volcanic island arcs result from the steady subduction of oceanic lithosphere
a.   Continued development can result in the formation of mountainous topography consisting of igneous and metamorphic rocks
B.   Andean-type mountain building
1.   Mountain building along continental margins
2.   Involves the convergence of an oceanic plate and a plate whose leading edge contains continental crust
a.   Exemplified by the Andes Mountains
3.   Volcanic-arc building
a.   Subduction and partial melting of mantle rock generates primary magmas
b.   Magma is less dense than surrounding rock, so it begins to buoyantly rise
c.   Differentiation of magma produces andesitic volcanism
4.   Emplacement of plutons
a.   Thick continental crust impedes the ascent of magma
b.   A large percentage of the magma never reaches the surface and is emplaced as plutons

© 2008 Pearson Education, Inc., Upper Saddle River, NJ. All rights reserved. This material is protected under all copyright laws as they currently exist. No portion of this material may be reproduced, in any form or by any means, without permission in writing from the publisher.

    c. Uplift and erosion exposes these massive structures called batholiths (i.e., Sierra Nevada in California and Peruvian Andes)

    d. Batholiths are typically intermediate to felsic compositions

  5. Development of an accretionary wedge

    a. An accretionary wedge is a chaotic accumulation of deformed and thrust-faulted sediments and scraps of oceanic crust

C. Sierra Nevada and Coast Ranges

  1. One of the best examples of an active Andean-type orogenic belt

  2. Subduction of the Pacific Basin under the western edge of the North American plate

  3. Sierra Nevada batholith is a remnant of a portion of the continental volcanic arc

  4. Franciscan Formation of California's Coast Ranges constitutes the accretionary wedge

VI. Continental collisions

A. Terranes and mountain building

B. Another mechanism of orogenesis

C. The nature of terranes

  1. Small crustal fragments collide and merge with continental margins

  2. Accreted crustal blocks are called terranes (any crustal fragments whose geologic history is distinct from that of the adjoining terranes)

  3. Prior to accretion some of the fragments may have been microcontinents

  4. Others may have been island arcs, submerged crustal fragments, extinct volcanic islands, or submerged oceanic plateaus

D. Accretion and orogenesis

  1. As oceanic plates move, they carry embedded oceanic plateaus, island arcs, and microcontinents to Andean-type subduction zones

  2. Thick oceanic plates carrying oceanic plateaus or "lighter" igneous rocks of island arcs may be too buoyant to subduct

  3. Collision of the fragments with the continental margin deforms both blocks, adding to the zone of deformation and to the thickness of the continental margin

  4. Many of the terranes found in the North American Cordillera were once scattered throughout the eastern Pacific

E. Himalayan Mountains

  1. Youthful mountains—collision began about 45 million years ago

  2. India collided with Eurasian plate

  3. Spreading center that propelled India northward is still active

  4. Similar but older collision occurred when the European continent collided with the Asian continent to produce the Ural Mountains

F. Appalachian Mountains

  1. Formed long ago and substantially lowered by erosion

  2. Resulted from a collision among North America, Europe, and northern Africa

  3. Final orogeny occurred about 250 million to 300 million years ago

VII. Fault-block mountains

A. Continental rifting can produce uplift and the formation of mountains known as fault-block mountains

  1. Fault-block mountains are bounded by high-angle normal faults that flatten with depth

  2. Mountains in which faulting and gradual uplift have contributed to their development include the Sierra Nevada of California and the Grand Tetons of Wyoming

B. Basin and Range province

  1. One of the largest regions of fault-block mountains on Earth

  2. Tilting of these faulted structures has produced nearly parallel mountain ranges that average 80 kilometers in length

© 2008 Pearson Education, Inc., Upper Saddle River, NJ. All rights reserved. This material is protected under all copyright laws as they currently exist. No portion of this material may be reproduced, in any form or by any means, without permission in writing from the publisher.

3. Extension beginning 20 million years ago has stretched the crust to twice its original width
4. High heat flow and several episodes of volcanism provide evidence that mantle upwelling caused doming of the crust and subsequent extension

VIII. Buoyancy and the principle of isostasy
   A. Evidence for crustal uplift includes wave-cut platforms high above sea level

B. Reasons for crustal uplift
   1. Not so easy to determine
   2. Isostasy
      a. Concept of a floating crust in gravitational balance
      b. When weight is removed from the crust, crustal uplifting occurs
         1. Called isostatic adjustment
         2. Crustal buoyancy can account for considerable vertical movement

Answers to the Review Questions

1. Rock deformation describes how the shape and volume of a rock change in response to stress. Think of a small reference cube or sphere embedded in an undeformed rock. With the application of stress, the rock deforms (undergoes strain), and any changes in the volume and dimensions of the reference object are recorded by the strain.

2. Brittle deformation describes material failure by cracking and rupture. Faults and joints in rocks are good examples. Brittle deformation is favored by shallow depths, low rock temperatures, and massive rigid rocks. Ductile deformation describes material failure by internal flowage; recrystallization is usually involved, especially at elevated temperatures. Ductile deformation is enhanced by elevated temperatures and confining pressures.

3. Rocks fail by brittle and ductile deformation when applied stresses exceed their elastic limit (strength). Temperature, confining pressure, and mineral composition exert important influences on rock strength and rock deformation.

4. Anticlines are folds with two well-defined limbs dipping in opposite directions away from a long, linear, fold axis. Strata are raised or buckled upward along the axial part of the fold relative to their elevations farther out on the limbs; thus after erosion, older strata are exposed along the axial part of the fold. Synclines are folds with two well-defined limbs that dip inward toward a long, linear fold axis. Strata are lowered or buckled down in the axial region; thus after erosion, younger strata are exposed in the axial portions of synclines.

    Domes are more or less circular zones of upraised rocks in which the beds follow the geometry of a dome and dip away in all directions from a high point or apex. Unlike an anticline, the dome structure does not have an axis. Geometrically, a basin may be thought of as an inverted dome. The strata dip inward in all directions toward the central, most downbuckled point in the structure.

5. Both are types of folds; they typically form in layered, sedimentary strata. Monoclines have only one limb, and strata that are steeply inclined within the structure are subhorizontal and relatively undeformed laterally. Anticlines have two well-developed limbs that dip away from one another in opposite directions.

6. The Black Hills are a late Cretaceous to early Tertiary, elliptically shaped, domal uplift of crystalline rocks associated in an as yet unknown way with subduction of old Pacific Ocean floor (the Farallon plate) beneath western North America.

© 2008 Pearson Education, Inc., Upper Saddle River, NJ. All rights reserved. This material is protected under all copyright laws as they currently exist. No portion of this material may be reproduced, in any form or by any means, without permission in writing from the publisher.

7. Both are dip-slip movements in which one block moves up and the other down along the fault surface. Assume that dip-slip faults with vertical dips (the fault surface is vertical) are normal faults. For dip-slip faults with inclinations or dips other than vertical, the hanging wall-footwall designation is very useful. The hanging wall block is the block that is entirely above the fault surface, and the footwall block is entirely below. In normal fault movement, the hanging wall block slides down along the fault surface with respect to the footwall block. In reverse fault movement, the hanging wall block slides upward along the fault surface with respect to the footwall block.

8. Based on the relations shown in the photo (Fig. 17.8), the sense of displacement is normal. The hanging wall block (left) slipped down with respect to the footwall block (right). Even without the arrows on the photograph showing relative motion, the stratigraphic sequence can be matched across the fault to determine the sense of movement along the fault.

9. A horst is an uplifted fault block bounded by two normal faults. A graben is a down-dropped fault block bounded by two normal faults. A graben valley is the down-dropped surface of an active or recently active graben. The valley is bounded by uplifted fault blocks, which may or may not be horsts. Death Valley in southeastern California is a good example of a graben valley.

10. Fault-block mountains are associated with geologically young, high-angle normal faults that flatten or merge with a regional-scale low-angle fault at depth. Uplifted blocks form the mountain ranges and down-dropped blocks form the valleys. The topography replicates active or recently active fault movements. Long, linear fault-block ranges and valleys are horsts and grabens.

11. Both are brittle failure, dip-slip faults caused by lateral compression. The hanging wall block moves up and over the footwall block, and overall, horizontal distance perpendicular to the fault trace is shortened. The main distinction is based on the dip angle or inclination of the fault. Reverse faults are high-angle dip-slip faults and thrusts are low-angle dip-slip faults.

12. Transform fault.

13. Faults and joints are both fractures in rock. Along faults, the fracture-bounded blocks have been displaced (offset) from their unfractured positions; the blocks are not significantly displaced along joints.

14. Mountain building is most directly associated with convergent plate boundaries. Rising and sinking movements are gradual, in contrast with the catastrophic collapse that follows large-volume pyroclastic flow eruptions.

15. A volcanic island arc occurs where two oceanic plates converge and one is subducted beneath the other. The interaction of these two plates results in partial melting of the mantle wedge located above the subducting plate. The rising magma creates volcanoes on the seafloor that eventually grow into a chain of volcanic islands known as a volcanic arc. The Aleutian Islands, Japan, and the volcanic islands of the Philippines all represent modern examples of island arcs.

16. The rising topography, magmatism, and metamorphism associated with the development of a volcanic arc are only one phase in the development of a major mountain belt. Once established, a volcanic arc continues to travel on the oceanic plate where it formed. Eventually, the volcanic arc will be transported toward a convergent boundary where the oceanic plate is subducting beneath continental crust. The assemblage of rocks associated with the volcanic arc will collide with the continental plate, resulting in crustal shortening, folding, thrust faulting, and the development of a major mountain belt. Thus, major mountain belts such as the Himalayas or Appalachians contain complex, highly deformed rocks, many of which originated in a volcanic arc.

© 2008 Pearson Education, Inc., Upper Saddle River, NJ. All rights reserved. This material is protected under all copyright laws as they currently exist. No portion of this material may be reproduced, in any form or by any means, without permission in writing from the publisher.

17. As a subducting plate bends and begins its descent into the mantle, most sediments are scraped from basaltic oceanic crust and piled onto the leading edge of the upper plate, much as snow piles up in front of a moving snowplow. These sediments accumulate (accrete) as a wedge-shaped stack of reverse-fault slices with the tapered edge of the wedge pointing toward the subduction zone. This complexly deformed and faulted sediment pile is the accretionary wedge.

18. Continental margins are characterized by their tectonic activity. Passive margins, the east coasts of North and South America for example, exhibit subdued, "quiet" tectonic movements such as slow uplift and subsidence punctuated by occasional localized faulting. They have wide continental shelves and their continental slopes merge seaward into abyssal plains. Passive margins form originally by continental rifting and are modified by erosion and deposition as they move away from a mid-ocean ridge. For this reason, they are also known as "trailing" margins.

    Active continental margins occupy areas of plate convergence, subduction, and local transform faulting. Tectonism, intrusion, and volcanism are active and long-lived. The western margins of North and South America are good examples.

19. Both represent compressive, continental-margin orogens and magmatic arcs driven by subduction of oceanic lithosphere. The Sierra Nevada owe their present-day lofty elevations to late Cenozoic normal faulting, but most of the rocks making up the range are mid- to late-Mesozoic batholithic granites and granodiorites. These represent solidified mid-crustal chambers that once fed magma upward to a contemporaneous continental-margin volcanic arc. The arc was situated on the western margin of North America above a subducting part of the since-disappeared Pacific Ocean floor that lay east of the East Pacific Rise. Thus rocks of both ranges originated in similar convergent continental-margin settings, but the major episode of subduction associated with emplacement of the Sierran granites ended in early Cenozoic time. The subduction along the western margin of South America has been more or less continuous since early to middle Mesozoic time.

20. The Appalachian Mountains are considered a collision-type mountain range that formed in the late Paleozoic. Europe, northern Africa, and North America collided and were all part of the supercontinent Pangaea before it began to split apart less than 200 million years ago. Thus, the Appalachians formed from a collision-type mountain-building episode (along with several other complex episodes) despite the fact that the nearest continent today is more than 5000 kilometers away.

21. The Ural Mountains, a north–south range in west-central Russia, mark the closure site of an ancient marine basin that once existed between the European and Siberian parts of the Eurasian plate. As the two continents converged and joined, the sediments in the former marine basin were lithified, crumpled, and uplifted into a mountain range that includes fossiliferous marine sedimentary rocks.

22. *Terrane* refers to a distinct and recognizable series of rock formations that has been transported by plate tectonic processes. The word *terrain* is used in a physiographic or geomorphic sense to describe the form and nature of a landscape. For example, the terrain of southeastern Pennsylvania is characterized by gently rolling, forested hills interspersed with cultivated fields and open pastures in the valleys.

23. Three structures that fall under the general heading of "oceanic plateaus" include submerged continental fragments, extinct volcanic islands, such as the Hawaiian Islands, and submerged volcanic plateaus created by voluminous outpourings of lava associated with hot-spot activity. These "oceanic plateaus" are not the only structures to be carried by oceanic crustal plates. Other features, such as volcanic island arcs and microcontinents, are also transported on oceanic crust and may eventually be accreted onto a continent at an Andean-type tectonic margin.

© 2008 Pearson Education, Inc., Upper Saddle River, NJ. All rights reserved. This material is protected under all copyright laws as they currently exist. No portion of this material may be reproduced, in any form or by any means, without permission in writing from the publisher.

24. The final stage in the evolutionary history of the Appalachian orogen was energized by the continental collision between North Africa (then part of Gondwanaland) and North America in Pennsylvanian time. The northern Cordillera evolved over a long-lasting interval of plate convergence starting in early to mid-Mesozoic time. Along most of the North American Pacific margin, convergence was replaced by transform faulting beginning in mid-Cenozoic time. Terrane accretion, volcanism and plutonism, folding, thrust faulting, and horizontal shortening and crustal thickening characterized its evolution, but compressive deformation occurred without continental collision. This was the major difference in the tectonic evolution of the two orogens. However, prior to closure of the proto-Atlantic Ocean basin, the evolutionary history of the Appalachian orogen was very similar to that of the northern Cordillera, where the active continental margin faced a subducting oceanic plate carrying an island arc or two, numerous seamounts and other small terrane blocks, but no piggy-backed continental mass.

25. Fault-block mountains develop in areas where widespread uplift causes fragmentation of the brittle upper crust. Most active block-bounding faults have steep dips, but subhorizontal dips characterize associated, deformational zones at mid-crustal levels. Stresses are tensional; deformation involves horizontal stretching and crustal thinning. The impulse for uplift may come from below, but internal gravitational stresses drive the deformation.

    In contrast, most major mountain belts include two fundamental geologic components in their development: (1) volcanism and batholithic intrusion and (2) horizontal shortening accompanied by crustal thickening. The compressive stresses are generated laterally owing to plate convergence and subduction, and folding and thrust faulting are common structural characteristics.

26. Glacial rebound following the melting of Pleistocene ice sheets provides support for the idea that lithosphere attempts to achieve isostatic balance by crustal uplift. Areas in Canada and Scandinavia have risen measurably during historic time and are still rising slowly. Owing to the added weight (load) of the ice, the crust-mantle boundary was locally lowered as higher-density mantle material flowed away from the volume occupied by the depressed basal part of the crust. When the ice melted, mantle material flowed back into the region formerly occupied by the lower-density crustal material, causing the crust-mantle boundary and the land surface to rise to their preglacial equilibrium positions.

27. The fundamental idea involved is the Archimedes principle. Objects floating in a more dense fluid displace a volume of fluid equal in weight to the weight of the floating object. Thus when weight is added, the object will sink until a new equilibrium level is achieved. If weight is subtracted, the floating object will rise for the same reason. The same idea applies to mountains, blocks of unusually thick, low-density continental rock whose basal portion is floating in denser mantle rock. As a mountain range is eroded, it will slowly rise to adjust for the loss of weight. Isostasy is the concept, and the resulting uplift or subsidence is termed an *isostatic movement*.

28. Glacial rebound following the melting of Pleistocene ice sheets provides support for the idea that lithosphere attempts to achieve isostatic balance. Areas in Canada and Scandinavia have risen measurably during historic time and are still rising slowly. Owing to the added weight (load) of the ice, the crust-mantle boundary was locally lowered as higher-density mantle material flowed away from the volume occupied by the depressed basal part of the crust. When the ice melted, mantle material flowed back into the region formerly occupied by the lower-density crustal material, causing the crust-mantle boundary and the land surface to rise to their preglacial equilibrium positions.

© 2008 Pearson Education, Inc., Upper Saddle River, NJ. All rights reserved. This material is protected under all copyright laws as they currently exist. No portion of this material may be reproduced, in any form or by any means, without permission in writing from the publisher.

Crustal Deformation and Mountain Building

Lecture outline, art-only, and animation PowerPoint presentations for each chapter of *Essentials of Geology* are available on the IRC DVD (ISBN 0-13-604914-1).

NOTES:

© 2008 Pearson Education, Inc., Upper Saddle River, NJ. All rights reserved. This material is protected under all copyright laws as they currently exist. No portion of this material may be reproduced, in any form or by any means, without permission in writing from the publisher.

Geologic Time

Geologic Time opens with a discussion of the fundamental principles of relative dating, including the law of superposition, principle of original horizontality, principle of crosscutting relationships, and the uses of inclusions and unconformities. How rock units in different localities can be correlated is also investigated. The types of fossils and their significance to understanding geologic time precede a discussion of the conditions favoring preservation. Also examined is the use of fossils in correlating and dating rock units. Following an explanation of radioactivity, the fundamentals and importance of radiometric dating are presented. The chapter concludes with an examination of the geologic time scale.

Learning Objectives

After reading, studying, and discussing the chapter, students should be able to:

- Explain the difference between relative and absolute dating of earth materials.
- Discuss the Principle of Original Horizontality and how it relates to the Law of Superposition.
- Briefly explain other principles used in relative age dating.
- List and briefly explain the three types of unconformities.
- Discuss the correlation of rock layers using physical criteria and fossils.
- Briefly explain radioactivity and how it relates to absolute age dating.
- Discuss the procedure of radiometric dating and explain how it is used to obtain absolute ages.
- List the isotopes commonly used in the radiometric dating of Earth materials.
- Briefly explain the significance and divisions of the geologic timescale.

Chapter Outline

I. Two types of dates are used in determining geological ages
   A. Relative dates—placing rocks and events in their proper sequence of formation
   B. Numerical dates—that specify the actual number of years that have passed since an event occurred

II. Principles and rules of relative dating
   A. Law of superposition
     1. Nicolaus Steno—1669
     2. In an undeformed sequence of sedimentary rocks (or layered igneous rocks), the oldest rocks are on the bottom
   B. Principle of original horizontality
     1. Layers of sediment are generally deposited in a horizontal position

     2. Rock layers that are flat have not been disturbed
   C. Principle of crosscutting relationships—a younger feature cuts through an older feature
   D. Inclusions
     1. One rock unit is enclosed within another
     2. Rock containing the inclusions is younger
   E. Unconformities
     1. An unconformity is a break in the rock record, a long period during which deposition ceased, erosion removed previously formed rocks, and then deposition resumed
     2. Types of unconformities

© 2008 Pearson Education, Inc., Upper Saddle River, NJ. All rights reserved. This material is protected under all copyright laws as they currently exist. No portion of this material may be reproduced, in any form or by any means, without permission in writing from the publisher.

a. Angular unconformity—tilted rocks are overlain by flat-lying rocks

b. Disconformity—strata on either side are parallel

c. Nonconformity—older metamorphic or intrusive igneous rocks in contact with younger sedimentary strata

III. Fossils: evidence of past life
  A. Fossil—the remains or traces of prehistoric life
  B. Types of fossils
    1. The remains of relatively recent organisms—teeth, bones, etc.
    2. Entire animals, flesh included
    3. Given enough time, remains may be petrified (literally "turned into stone")
    4. Molds and casts
    5. Carbonization
    6. Others
      a. Tracks
      b. Burrows
      c. Coprolites (fossil dung)
      d. Gastroliths (polished stomach stones)
  C. Conditions favoring preservation
    1. Rapid burial
    2. Possession of hard parts
  D. Correlation of rock layers
    1. Matching rocks of similar age in different regions
    2. Often relies upon fossils
      a. William Smith (late 1700s–early 1800s) noted that sedimentary strata in widely separated areas could be identified and correlated by their distinctive fossil content
      b. Principle of fossil succession— fossil organisms succeed one another in a definite and determinable order, and therefore any time period can be recognized by its fossil content
    3. Index fossils
      a. Widespread geographically
      b. Limited to short span of geologic time

E. Fossils are also important environmental indicators

IV. Dating with radioactivity
  A. Reviewing basic atomic structure
    1. Structure of an atom
      a. Nucleus
        1. Protons—positively charged
        2. Neutrons
          a. Neutral charge
          b. Protons and electrons combined
      b. Orbiting the nucleus are electrons - negative electrical charges
    2. Atomic number
      a. An element's identifying number
      b. Number of protons in the atom's nucleus
    3. Mass number
      a. Number of protons plus (in addition to) the number of neutrons in an atom's nucleus
      b. Isotope
        1. Variant of the same parent atom
        2. Different number of neutrons
        3. Different mass number than the parent atom
  B. Radioactivity
    1. Spontaneous breaking apart (decay) of atomic nuclei
    2. Radioactive decay
      a. Types of radioactive decay
        1. Alpha emission
          a. Emission of 2 protons and 2 neutrons (an alpha particle)
          b. Mass number is reduced by 4 and the atomic number is lowered by 2
        2. Beta emission
          a. An electron (beta particle) is given off from the nucleus
          b. Mass number remains unchanged and the atomic number increases by 1
        3. Electron capture
          a. An electron is captured by the nucleus
          b. Electron combines with a proton to form a neutron

© 2008 Pearson Education, Inc., Upper Saddle River, NJ. All rights reserved. This material is protected under all copyright laws as they currently exist. No portion of this material may be reproduced, in any form or by any means, without permission in writing from the publisher.

c. Mass number remains unchanged and the atomic number decreases by 1

b. Parent—an unstable radioactive isotope

c. Daughter products—isotopes resulting from the decay of a parent

C. Radiometric dating

1. Principle of radioactive dating

a. The percentage of radioactive atoms that decay during one half-life is always the same: 50%

b. However, the actual number of atoms that decay continually decreases

c. Comparing the ratio of parent to daughter yields the age of the sample

2. Useful radioactive isotopes for providing radiometric ages

a. Rubidium-87

b. Thorium-232

c. Two isotopes of uranium

d. Potassium-40

3. Sources of error

a. A closed system is required

b. To avoid problems, one safeguard is to use only fresh, unweathered material

D. Dating with carbon-14

1. Half-life of only 5730 years

2. Used to date very recent events

3. Carbon-14 is produced in the upper atmosphere

a. Incorporated into carbon dioxide

b. Absorbed by living matter

4. Useful tool for anthropologists, archeologists, historians, and geologists who study very recent Earth history

E. Importance of radiometric dating

1. Radiometric dating is a complex procedure that requires precise measurement

2. Rocks from several localities have been dated at more than 3 billion years

3. Confirms the idea that geologic time is immense

V. Geologic timescale

A. Subdivides geologic history into units

B. Originally created using relative dates

C. Structure of the timescale

1. Eon

a. Greatest expanse of time

b. Names

1. Phanerozoic ("visible life")—the most recent eon, begins about 540 million years ago

2. Proterozoic

3. Archean

4. Hadean—the oldest eon

c. Collectively, the Hadean, Archean, and Proterozoic eons are often referred to as the Precambrian

2. Era

a. Subdivision of an eon

b. Eras of the Phanerozoic eon

1. Cenozoic ("recent life")

2. Mesozoic ("middle life")

3. Paleozoic ("ancient life")

3. Eras are subdivided into periods

4. Periods are subdivided into epochs

D. Precambrian time

1. Nearly 4 billion years prior to the Cambrian period

2. Not divided into smaller time units because the events of Precambrian history are not known in great enough detail

a. First abundant fossil evidence does not appear until the beginning of the Cambrian period

b. Precambrian rocks have been subjected to a great many changes

E. Difficulties in dating the geologic time scale

1. Not all rocks can be dated by radiometric methods

a. The grains composing detrital sedimentary rocks are not the same age as the rock in which they occur

b. The age of a particular mineral in a metamorphic rock may not necessarily represent the time when the rock formed

2. Datable materials (e.g., volcanic ash beds and igneous intrusions) are often used to bracket various episodes in Earth history and arrive at age

© 2008 Pearson Education, Inc., Upper Saddle River, NJ. All rights reserved. This material is protected under all copyright laws as they currently exist. No portion of this material may be reproduced, in any form or by any means, without permission in writing from the publisher.

Answers to the Review Questions

1. Absolute dating involves a numerical age measurement in actual time units, like thousands or millions of years. Relative dating involves placing sequences of rocks, geological features, and events in the correct order in which they occurred, without necessarily knowing their absolute ages.

2. The law of superposition is the idea or notion that beds in a sequence of horizontal, sedimentary strata become younger upward in the sequence. In other words, younger strata are deposited over older strata. A feature that truncates or cuts across another geologic feature is the younger of the two. This is known as the principle of crosscutting relationships. For example, a dike of basalt injected into a crack in sedimentary strata is younger than the strata.

3. The principle of original horizontality states that, in general, stratification in sedimentary beds was horizontal when the beds were deposited.

4. (a) Is fault A older or younger than the sandstone layer? Fault A cuts the sandstone layer so the fault is younger.
    (b) Is dike A older or younger than the sandstone layer? Dike A also crosscuts the sandstone layer so the dike is younger.
    (c) Was the conglomerate deposited before or after fault A? Fault A stops at the base of the conglomerate; thus the conglomerate layer truncates the fault and is younger than the fault.
    (d) Was the conglomerate deposited before or after fault B? The conglomerate is cut and displaced by fault B; thus fault B is younger.
    (e) Which fault is older, A or B? The faults do not cross, but the relationship between the faults and the conglomerate proves that fault A is older than fault B.
    (f) Is dike A older or younger than the batholith? Dike A does not cut the batholith so other relationships must be used. Dike B clearly cuts the batholith; the sill fed by dike B is crosscut by dike A, proving that dike A is younger than dike B and younger than the batholith.

5. A depositional contact or unconformity would be proven if detrital rock and mineral grains from the granite were found in the sandstone. Also the granite just below the contact might show reddish discoloration or other evidences of having been weathered before the sandstone was deposited. Bedding in the sandstone will be parallel or nearly parallel to the contact; there will be no evidence for contact metamorphism in the sandstone; and the sandstone will not be cut by the granitic dikes.

   If the contact is intrusive, the sandstone may be cut by granitic dikes and may show contact metamorphism. Rock and mineral grains in the sandstone will not show any direct correlation to the granite, and bedding in the sandstone will probably not be parallel to the contact.

6. These are all erosion surfaces buried beneath younger strata. The older strata below an angular unconformity were tilted before the younger strata were deposited; thus the older and younger strata exhibit a sharp, angular, erosional discordance. Strata above and below a disconformity exhibit parallel stratification or bedding orientations, indicating that the underlying, older strata were not tilted or deformed before the younger strata were deposited. Younger, sedimentary beds deposited on an eroded mass of older, igneous or metamorphic rock make up a nonconformity.

© 2008 Pearson Education, Inc., Upper Saddle River, NJ. All rights reserved. This material is protected under all copyright laws as they currently exist. No portion of this material may be reproduced, in any form or by any means, without permission in writing from the publisher.

7. Correlation is the process of establishing equivalency of rock units, ages, depositional environments, and events in geologic history (faults, tectonic events, unconformities, etc.) in different areas. Correlation can be local (between rocks intersected in neighboring drill holes) or worldwide (continent to continent).

8. Different types of fossilization include;
   (a) *actual remains*: usually hard parts from organisms of the recent geologic past
   (b) *petrified*: the original substance has been replaced by mineral matter or pore spaces have been filled with a mineral
   (c) *mold*: when a shell or other structure is buried in sediment and then dissolved by underground water
   (d) *cast*: the hollow space of a mold is subsequently filled with mineral matter
   (e) *tracks*: animal footprints made in soft sediment that was later lithified

9. Smith was an English naturalist who first convinced other geologic thinkers of his day that strata containing the same assemblages of fossils were correlative from place to place. Thus Smith can be thought of as the founder of the study of stratigraphy and as a leading advocate of using fossil assemblages to correlate equivalent-aged strata (the principle of faunal succession).

10. Fossil organisms have great diversity, and certain individual organisms and/or assemblages of organisms are characteristic of beds deposited during specific periods of geologic time. Thus fossils are useful for correlating the same bed or same sequence of beds among different localities and for determining the geologic ages of the beds.

11. Fossils are very useful environmental indicators.

12. Each time beta decay occurs, the atomic number raises by 1 and does not affect the mass number. Each alpha decay decreases the atomic number by 2 and the mass number by 4. Thus, for 6 alpha decays and 4 betas, the atomic number of the daughter would be $(90 - 6 \times 2 + 4) = 82$, which is the atomic number of lead. The mass number of the daughter would be $(232 - 6 \times 4) = 208$. The stable daughter is lead-208.

13. With careful sample collection and laboratory procedures, the radiometric methods consistently give accurate, reliable, absolute ages. No other method can be applied to all of geologic time. Fossils are accurate and reliable for Phanerozoic sedimentary rocks, but are not found in most igneous and metamorphic rocks and are very rare in Precambrian rocks. The Phanerozoic time scale has been accurately calibrated with radiometric ages, and Proterozoic and Archean chronologies are based entirely on radiometric dates.

14. A ratio of 1:1 would be produced in 10,000 years (one half-life). After two half-lives, 25% of the original parent would be left and 75% of the daughter would have formed. The ratio (25:75) is 1:3, so the sample is 20,000 years old (2 half-lives × 10,000 years in one half-life = 20,000 years).

© 2008 Pearson Education, Inc., Upper Saddle River, NJ. All rights reserved. This material is protected under all copyright laws as they currently exist. No portion of this material may be reproduced, in any form or by any means, without permission in writing from the publisher.

Geologic Time

15. Tree rings are the concentric rings visible at the end of a log or a tree stump. They represent the layer of wood that is added each year to the tree in a temperate region. The size and density of rings reflect the environmental conditions (primarily climate) that existed during the year in which the tree formed. Because rings are added each year, the age of the tree when it was cut down can be determined. This procedure could be used to help date recent geologic events if such events, like a landslide or flood, created a new land surface. Fallen trees or stumps could then be used to determine the minimum number of years since the geologic event occurred.

16. If the abundances of the parent or daughter isotopes in a mineral or rock sample have been changed by any process other than radioactive decay, the parent-to-daughter ratio will not be a true measure of the age of the sample.

17. The work must be done carefully, and the laboratory environment must be free of materials that might contaminate the sample and produce a change in the measured parent-to-daughter isotopic ratio. Other precautions include careful sample collection, good mineral separations, repeated analyses of the same samples to establish precision limits, and age determinations by other methods to check for consistency and accuracy. Finally, careful attention to geologic relationships will reduce the chances of misinterpreting the results.

18. To make calculations easier, let us round the age of Earth to 5 billion years.
    (a) What fraction of geologic time is represented by recorded history (assume 5000 years for the length of recorded history)? The percentage is 5×10^3 yrs divided by 5×10^9 yrs $\times 100\%$ which equals $1 \times 10^{-4}\%$ or 0.0001%.

    (b) The first abundant fossil evidence does not appear until the beginning of the Cambrian period (570 million years ago). What percentage of geologic time is represented by abundant fossil evidence? The percentage is 6×10^8 yrs divided by 5×10^9 yrs $\times 100\% = 1.2 \times 10\%$ or 12%.

19. The following are the various divisions listed from longest to shortest time intervals: eons, eras, periods, and epochs.

20. In general, sedimentary rocks do not contain minerals that are both suitable for dating and that crystallized when the bed was deposited. One exception would be feldspar or mica grains in volcanic ash deposited at the time of the eruption. Minerals such as glauconite crystallize as sedimentary grains but contain large quantities of non-radiogenic daughter elements, making an age determination imprecise.

© 2008 Pearson Education, Inc., Upper Saddle River, NJ. All rights reserved. This material is protected under all copyright laws as they currently exist. No portion of this material may be reproduced, in any form or by any means, without permission in writing from the publisher.

21. The contact between sedimentary beds I (younger and horizontal) and sedimentary beds A (older and tilted) is an angular unconformity. The contact between igneous rock D (older) and the sedimentary beds I is a nonconformity.

Youngest

(10)   alluvial fan E; dike, cinder cone, and lava flow, F

(9)   fault G

(8)   igneous rock, dike and sill, C

(7)   igneous intrusion K

(6)   sedimentary beds J

(5)   sedimentary beds I

(4)   intrusive igneous rock D (a batholith)

(3)   dike of igneous rock B

(2)   sedimentary strata A

(1)   metamorphic rock mass H

Oldest

Lecture outline, art-only, and animation PowerPoint presentations for each chapter of *Essentials of Geology* are available on the IRC DVD (ISBN 0-13-604914-1).

NOTES:

© 2008 Pearson Education, Inc., Upper Saddle River, NJ. All rights reserved. This material is protected under all copyright laws as they currently exist. No portion of this material may be reproduced, in any form or by any means, without permission in writing from the publisher.

<table>
<tr><td></td><td>Chapter</td></tr>
<tr><td></td><td>**19**</td></tr>
</table>

Earth's Evolution through Geologic Time

Earth's Evolution through Geologic Time opens with a presentation of the origin of Earth, including the physical and chemical differentiation during the early evolution of Earth. Also examined are the formation of Earth's primitive atmosphere and how it changed over time. The geologic history of the Precambrian is presented along with a brief discussion of crustal evolution and the assembling of continents. The supercontinent cycle is presented in some detail, and the chapter concludes with an examination of the significant geologic and biologic events that occurred during the Paleozoic, Mesozoic, and Cenozoic Eras.

Learning Objectives

After reading, studying, and discussing the chapter, students should be able to:

- Explain how the planets in the solar system originated.
- Briefly discuss the physical and chemical differentiation that took place during the early evolution of Earth.
- Discuss how Earth's atmosphere formed by a process called outgassing.
- Understand how Earth's atmosphere evolved over time.
- Briefly explain the geologic history of the Precambrian, including crustal evolution and the assembling of crustal fragments to form cratons.
- Explain the supercontinent cycle, including associated climatic and sea level changes.
- List the principal geologic events that took place during the Phanerozoic eon.
- Summarize the history of life during the Paleozoic, Mesozoic, and Cenozoic eras.

Chapter Outline

I. Early evolution of Earth
    A. Origin of planet Earth
        1. Most researchers believe that Earth and the other planets formed at essentially the same time from the same primordial material as the Sun
        2. Nebular hypothesis
            a. Solar system evolved from an enormous rotating cloud called the solar nebula
            b. Nebula was composed mostly of hydrogen and helium
            c. About 5 billion years ago the nebula began to contract
            d. Assumes a flat disk shape with the protosun (pre-Sun) at the center
            e. Inner planets begin to form from metallic and rocky clumps of

substances with high melting points
            f. Larger outer planets began forming from fragments with a high percentage of ices—water, carbon dioxide, ammonia, and methane
    B. Formation of Earth's layered structure
        1. As Earth formed, high-velocity impacts caused the temperature to increase, and iron and nickel began to melt and sink toward the center
        2.Buoyant masses of molten rock rose to the surface to produce a primitive crust
        3.Early chemical segregation established the three basic divisions of Earth's interior
            a. An iron-rich core

© 2008 Pearson Education, Inc., Upper Saddle River, NJ. All rights reserved. This material is protected under all copyright laws as they currently exist. No portion of this material may be reproduced, in any form or by any means, without permission in writing from the publisher.

b. A thin primitive crust, and
c. The mantle between the core and crust
4. A primitive atmosphere evolved as gaseous materials escaped from Earth's interior

II. Earth's atmosphere evolves
  A. Primitive atmosphere formed from volcanic gases
    1. A process called outgassing
    2. Water vapor, carbon dioxide, nitrogen, and several trace gases
    3. Very little free oxygen
  B. Water vapor condenses and forms primitive oceans as Earth cools
  C. Bacteria evolve
  D. Plants evolve and photosynthesis produces oxygen
  E. Oxygen content in the atmosphere increases
  F. By about 4 billion years after Earth formed, abundant ocean-dwelling organisms that require oxygen existed

III. Earth's history
  A. Precambrian era
    1. 4.5 billion to 540 million years ago
    2. 88% of Earth's history
    3. Only sketchy knowledge
    4. Most Precambrian rocks are devoid of fossils
    5. Precambrian rocks
      a. Most are buried from view
      b. Each continent has a "core area" of Precambrian rocks called a shield
      c. Extensive iron ore deposits
      d. Absent are fossil fuels
    6. Precambrian fossils
      a. Most common are stromatolites
        1. Material deposited by algae
        2. Common about 2 billion years ago
      b. Microfossils of bacteria and algae have been found in chert
        1. Southern Africa (3.1 billion years of age)
        2. Lake Superior area (1.7 billion years of age)
      c. Plant fossils date from the middle Precambrian

d. Animal fossils date from the late Precambrian
e. Diverse and multicelled organisms exist by the close of the Precambrian

  B. Paleozoic era
    1. 540 million years ago to about 248 million years ago
    2. First life forms with hard parts
    3. Abundant Paleozoic fossils
    4. Early Paleozoic history
      a. Southern continent of Gondwanaland exists
      b. North America
        1. A barren lowland
        2. Seas move inland and recede several times, and shallow marine basins evaporate leaving rock salt and gypsum deposits
        3. Taconic orogeny, a mountain building event, affects eastern North America
    5. Early Paleozoic life
      a. Restricted to seas
      b. Vertebrates had not yet evolved
      c. Life consisted of several invertebrate groups
        1. Trilobites
        2. Brachiopods
        3. Cephalopods
      d. First organisms with hard parts, such as shells—perhaps for protection
    6. Late Paleozoic history
      a. Supercontinent of Pangaea forms
      b. Several mountain belts formed during the movements of the continents
      c. World's climate becomes very seasonal, causing the dramatic extinction of many species
    7. Late Paleozoic life
      a. Organisms diversified dramatically
      b. Land plants
      c. Fishes evolve into two groups of bony fish
        1. Lung fish
        2. Lobe-finned fish, which become the amphibians

© 2008 Pearson Education, Inc., Upper Saddle River, NJ. All rights reserved. This material is protected under all copyright laws as they currently exist. No portion of this material may be reproduced, in any form or by any means, without permission in writing from the publisher.

d. Insects invade the land
e. Amphibians diversify rapidly
f. Extensive coal swamps develop
C. Mesozoic era
1. 248 million years ago to about 65 million years ago
2. Often called the "age of dinosaurs"
3. Mesozoic history
   a. Begins with much of the world's land above sea level
   b. Seas invade western North America
   c. Breakup of Pangaea begins forming the Atlantic ocean
   d. North American plate began to override the Pacific plate
   e. Mountains of western North America began forming
4. Mesozoic life
   a. Survivors of the great Paleozoic extinction
   b. Gymnosperms become the dominant trees
   c. Reptiles (first true terrestrial animals) readily adapt to the dry Mesozoic climate
   d. Reptiles have shell-covered eggs that can be laid on the land
   e. Dinosaurs dominate
   f. One group of reptiles led to the birds
   g. Many reptile groups, along with many other animal groups, become extinct at the close of the Mesozoic
      1. One hypothesis is that a large asteroid or comet struck Earth
      2. Another possibility is extensive volcanism
D. Cenozoic era
1. 65 million years ago to the present
2. Often called the "age of mammals"
3. Smaller fraction of geologic time than either the Paleozoic or the Mesozoic
4. North America
   a. Most of the continent was above sea level throughout the Cenozoic era
   b. Many events of mountain building, volcanism, and earthquakes in the west

c. Eastern North America
   1. Stable with abundant marine sedimentation
   2. Eroded Appalachians were raised by isostatic adjustments
d. Western North America
   1. Building of the Rocky Mountains was coming to an end
   2. Large region is uplifted
      a. Basin and Range province formed
      b. Re-elevates the Rockies
      c. Rivers erode and form gorges (e.g., Grand Canyon and Black Canyon
      d. Volcanic activity is common
         1. Fissure eruptions form the Columbia Plateau
         2. Volcanoes form from northern California to the Canadian border
      e. Coast Ranges form
      f. Sierra Nevada become fault-block mountains
5. Cenozoic life
   a. Mammals replace reptiles as the dominant land animals
   b. Angiosperms (flowering plants with covered seeds) dominate the plant world
      1. Strongly influenced the evolution of both birds and mammals
      2. Food source for both birds and mammals
   c. Two groups of mammals evolve after the reptilian extinctions at the close of the Mesozoic
      1. Marsupials
      2. Placentals
   d. Mammals diversify quite rapidly, and some groups become very large
      1. e.g., Hornless rhinoceros, which stood nearly 16 feet high
      2. Many large animals became extinct

© 2008 Pearson Education, Inc., Upper Saddle River, NJ. All rights reserved. This material is protected under all copyright laws as they currently exist. No portion of this material may be reproduced, in any form or by any means, without permission in writing from the publisher.

　　e.　　Humans evolve
Answers to the Review Questions

1. The metallic core of Earth is important to humans today because it supports our magnetic field, which prevents cosmic rays (solar winds) from reaching the surface.

2. Hydrogen and helium most likely made up much of the early universe.

3. Supernova.

4. The theory for the origin of the solar system, called the nebular hypothesis, states that approximately 5 billion years ago the bodies of the solar system condensed from an enormous cloud. As the cloud contracted and began to rotate, the protosun began forming. The protoplanets (planets in the making) formed from material that had condensed and accreted inside the cloud. The inner planets, Mercury, Venus, Earth, and Mars were unable to retain appreciable amounts of the lighter components of the primordial cloud; while the outer planets (Jupiter, Saturn, Uranus, and Neptune) accumulated large amounts of hydrogen and other light materials because of their much colder temperatures.

5. Outgassing refers to the process by which Earth's early atmosphere was formed by gases, trapped in the planet's interior, erupted from volcanoes over millions of years. Outgassing continues today from hundreds of active volcanoes worldwide.

6. Earth's early atmosphere comprised mainly water vapor and carbon dioxide.

7. The free oxygen in Earth's atmosphere today originated from green plants releasing oxygen during the process of photosynthesis.

8. Water in the first oceans came from the water vapor erupted from volcanoes via outgassing.

9. Carbon dioxide is highly soluble in water, and it is removed from our atmosphere by the precipitation of calcium carbonate to form the chemical sedimentary rock, limestone. Marine organisms, such as foraminifera, remove calcium carbonate from seawater to make their shells and other hard parts.

10. Precambrian history is more difficult to decipher because of the lack of fossils, which hinders correlation of rocks. Also, rocks of this great age are metamorphosed and deformed, extensively eroded, and obscured by younger overlying strata.

11. Cratons are thoughts to form from the collision and accretion of various types of terranes. Such collisional tectonics deforms and metamorphoses the sediments caught between the converging crustal fragments, which shortens and thickens the developing crust. Partial melting in the deepest regions of these collision zones generates silica-rich magmas that intrude the crustal rocks above.

12. Supercontinents are large landmasses that contain all, or nearly all, of the existing continents on Earth at any given time. The supercontinent cycle is the idea that rifting and dispersal of one supercontinent is followed by a long period during which the fragments are gradually reassembled into a new supercontinent having a different configuration.

13. The movement of continents can produce global climate change because they change the patterns of ocean currents and global wind patterns. As a result of such changes, the distribution of temperatures and precipitation worldwide changed as well.

© 2008 Pearson Education, Inc., Upper Saddle River, NJ. All rights reserved. This material is protected under all copyright laws as they currently exist. No portion of this material may be reproduced, in any form or by any means, without permission in writing from the publisher.

14. (a) Paleozoic; (b) Precambrian; (c) Cenozoic; (d) Precambrian; (e) Mesozoic; (f) Cenozoic; (g) Paleozoic; (h) Paleozoic; (i) Mesozoic; (j) Precambrian; (k) Mesozoic; (l) Paleozoic; (m) Paleozoic; (n) Cenozoic; (o) Paleozoic; (p) Mesozoic; (q) Precambrian; (r) Cenozoic

15. During the Cenozoic, the eastern continental margin of North America was tectonically stable and the site of abundant marine sedimentation. The western margin, on the other hand, was the leading edge of the North American plate. As a result, plate interactions during the Cenozoic gave rise to many events of mountain building, volcanism, and earthquakes in the West.

16. In order to move onto the land from the oceans plants had to develop a mechanism for obtaining water and also a structure that allowed them to stay upright, despite gravity and wind.

17. The lobe-finned fish are thought to have developed the ability to stay out of water for longer periods of time and eventually became the first amphibians.

18. Amphibians are not considered to be true land animals because they are born in the water and originally they have gills and tails. Over time these features disappear as the amphibians become air-breathing organisms with legs.

19. Unlike amphibians, reptiles have shell-covered eggs that can be laid on land. The appearance of shell-covered eggs in the Mesozoic eliminated a water-dwelling stage, and it was an important evolutionary step in the development of reptiles.

20. The extinction of the dinosaurs is thought to have been caused by a large meteorite impacting Earth. This hypothesis is supported by a thin layer of sediment that contains high levels of iridium, an element rare in Earth's crust but found in high proportions in stony meteorites.

Lecture outline, art-only, and animation PowerPoint presentations for each chapter of *Essentials of Geology* are available on the IRC DVD (ISBN 0-13-604914-1).

NOTES:

© 2008 Pearson Education, Inc., Upper Saddle River, NJ. All rights reserved. This material is protected under all copyright laws as they currently exist. No portion of this material may be reproduced, in any form or by any means, without permission in writing from the publisher.

Test Item File to Accompany

Essentials of Geology
Tenth Edition

What follows are sets of multiple choice, true-false, and completion questions, including answer keys, for each of the textbook chapters. The questions are intended to test the major concepts of each chapter.

The chapter questions are also available as MS Word documents and as a TestGen set on the Instructors Resource Center on DVD. Using TestGen, questions can be sorted and arranged, individual questions can be selected, deleted, or edited, and new questions can be added. After tests are prepared, they may be stores, retrieved, and/or printed. Answer keys, which correspond to the order of the test questions, are also prepared by Testgen and may be stored, retrieve, and/or printed.

Contents

Chapter 1   An Introduction to Geology

1) What are the basic differences between the disciplines of physical and historical geology?
- A) physical geology is the study of fossils and sequences of rock strata; historical geology is the study of how rocks and minerals were used in the past
- B) historical geology involves the study of rock strata, fossils, and geologic events, utilizing the geologic time scale as a reference; physical geology includes the study of how rocks form and of how erosion shapes the land surface
- C) physical geology involves the study of rock strata, fossils, and deposition in relation to plate movements in the geologic past; historical geology charts how and where the plates were moving in the past
- D) none of the above – physical geology and historical geology are essentially the same

Answer: B
Diff: 1

2) _____ was the highly influential, ancient Greek philosopher noted for his writings and teachings on natural philosophy and on the workings of Earth.
- A) Nero
- B) Odysseus
- C) Aristotle
- D) Pappagapolis

Answer: C
Diff: 1

3) Compared to the age of Earth accepted as correct today, how did 17th and 18th century proponents of catastrophism envision the Earth's age?
- A) They believed Earth to be much older than current estimates
- B) They believed it to be about the same as current estimates, give or take a few million years.
- C) They believed Earth to be much younger than current estimates
- D) None of the above — they didn't really address the age of Earth

Answer: C
Diff: 1

4) Which one of the following observations and inferences is consistent with the idea of uniformitarianism?
- A) sand rolling along a stream bottom shows that sediment is moving downstream
- B) erupting volcanoes overlie burning, subterranean, coal beds
- C) lava flows on the seafloor precipitated from seawater
- D) all of the above

Answer: A
Diff: 1

5) _____ was an important 18th century English geologist and proponent of uniformitarianism.
    A) Charles Lyell
    B) Isaac Newton
    C) James Hutton
    D) James Ussher
Answer: C
Diff: 1

6) The currently accepted age of Earth is _____ years.
    A) 4.6 thousand
    B) 6.4 trillion
    C) 4.6 billion
    D) 6.4 million
Answer: C
Diff: 1

7) Which of the following best describes the fundamental concept of superposition?
    A) strata with fossils are generally deposited on strata with no fossils
    B) older strata generally are deposited on younger strata without intervening, intermediate age strata
    C) older fossils in younger strata indicate a locally inverted geologic time scale
    D) any sedimentary deposit accumulates on older rock or sediment layers
Answer: D
Diff: 1

8) The _____ division of the geologic time scale is an era of the Phanerozoic eon.
    A) Paleocene
    B) Paleozoic
    C) Permian
    D) Proterozoic
Answer: B
Diff: 1

9) The _____ forms the relatively cool, brittle plates of plate tectonics.
    A) asthenosphere
    B) lithosphere
    C) astrosphere
    D) eosphere
Answer: B
Diff: 1

10) A _____ is a well-tested and widely accepted view that best explains certain scientific observations.
    A) hypothesis
    B) generalization
    C) law
    D) theory
Answer: D
Diff: 1

11) All of the following are possible steps of scientific investigation except for _____.
   A) the collection of scientific facts through observation and measurement
   B) assumption of conclusions without prior experimentation or observation
   C) the development of one or more working hypotheses or models to explain facts
   D) development of observations and experiments to test the hypotheses

   Answer: B
   Diff: 1

12) _____ rocks form by crystallization and consolidation of molten magma.
   A) Sedimentary
   B) Indigenous
   C) Primary
   D) Igneous

   Answer: D
   Diff: 1

13) _____ rocks always originate at the surface of the solid Earth.
   A) Secondary
   B) Igneous
   C) Metamorphic
   D) Sedimentary

   Answer: D
   Diff: 1

14) During the late nineteenth and early twentieth centuries, direct observations showed that a glacier in Switzerland flowed forward in the downhill direction while its snout (terminus) was retreating higher up the valley? Which of the following explains these observations in a rational, scientific way?
   A) cooler temperatures meant slower forward glacier flow resulting in snout retreat
   B) the glacial hypothesis was finally accepted as a scientific theory
   C) rocky debris in the valley downhill from the snout was deposited by Noah's flood
   D) the melting rate of ice in the glacier exceeded the rate at which new snow and ice were added to the glacier

   Answer: D
   Diff: 2

15) In correct order from the center outward, Earth includes which units?
   A) core, inner mantle, outer mantle, crust
   B) inner core, outer core, mantle, crust
   C) inner core, crust, mantle, hydrosphere
   D) core, crust, mantle, hydrosphere

   Answer: B
   Diff: 1

16) The _____ refers to the sum total of all life on Earth.
   A) hydrosphere
   B) atmosphere
   C) biosphere
   D) asthenosphere

   Answer: C
   Diff: 1

17) A _____ system is one in which energy moves freely in and out, but no matter enters or leaves the system.
   A) closed
   B) open
   C) feedback
   D) equilibrated

   Answer: A
   Diff: 1

18) _____ is often paraphrased as "the present is the key to the past."
   A) Biblical prophecy
   B) Uniformitarianism
   C) Aristotelian logic
   D) Catastrophism

   Answer: B
   Diff: 1

19) _____, a popular natural philosophy of the 17th and early 18th centuries, was based on a firm belief in a very short geologic history for Earth.
   A) Ecospherism
   B) Exoschism
   C) Uniformitarianism
   D) Catastrophism

   Answer: D
   Diff: 1

20) The _____ proposes that the bodies of our solar system formed at essentially the same time from a rotating cloud of gases and dust.
   A) Big Band theory
   B) Plate Tectonics theory
   C) Nebular hypothesis
   D) Heliocentric theory

   Answer: C
   Diff: 1

21) The _____ is not a part of the Earth's physical environment.
   A) solid Earth
   B) astrosphere
   C) hydrosphere
   D) atmosphere

   Answer: B
   Diff: 1

22) _____ is the process by which rocks breakdown in place to produce soils and sediments.
   A) Weathering
   B) Lithification
   C) Subduction
   D) Metamorphism

   Answer: A
   Diff: 1

23) Which one of the following statements is not correct?
    A) metamorphic rocks may melt to magma
    B) sedimentary rocks may weather to igneous rocks
    C) magmas crystallize to form igneous rocks
    D) igneous rocks can undergo metamorphism

Answer: A
Diff: 1

24) The composition of the core of Earth is thought to be _____.
    A) basalt
    B) granite
    C) peridotite
    D) solid iron-nickel alloy

Answer: D
Diff: 1

25) The asthenosphere is actually a part of the _____ of the Earth.
    A) outer core
    B) crust
    C) inner core
    D) mantle

Answer: D
Diff: 1

26) The _____ is thought to be a liquid, metallic region in the Earth's interior.
    A) inner core
    B) lithosphere
    C) mantle
    D) outer core

Answer: D
Diff: 1

27) The _____ is the thinnest layer of the Earth.
    A) crust
    B) outer core
    C) mantle
    D) inner core

Answer: A
Diff: 1

28) All of the following provide evidence or clues to the composition of Earth's interior except for

_____.
    A) diamond-bearing rocks
    B) slivers of crustal and mantle rocks now exposed at Earth's surface
    C) comets
    D) meteorites

Answer: C
Diff: 1

29) The relatively stable interior portion of a continent is known as a _____.
   A) craton
   B) shield
   C) platform
   D) belt
   Answer: A
   Diff: 1

30) Active mountain belts are most likely to be found _____.
   A) along the margins of continents
   B) in the interior regions of continents
   C) scattered throughout continents
   D) along only the eastern margins of continents
   Answer: A
   Diff: 1

31) The continental shelf is located _____.
   A) between the continental slope and continental rise
   B) between the continental rise and the abyssal plains
   C) seaward of the continental slope
   D) landward of the continental slope
   Answer: D
   Diff: 1

32) The most prominent feature on the ocean floor are the _____.
   A) deep–ocean trenches
   B) oceanic ridges
   C) seamounts
   D) lava plateaus
   Answer: B
   Diff: 1

33) In sedimentary rocks, lithification includes _____.
   A) compaction and cementation
   B) cementation and weathering
   C) compaction and transportation
   D) crystallization and cooling
   Answer: A
   Diff: 1

Word Analysis. Examine the words and/or phrases for each question below and determine the relationship among the majority of words/phrases. Choose the option which does not fit the pattern.

34) a. hypothesis   b. theory   c. fact   d. observation
   Answer: C
   Diff: 1

35) a. hydrosphere   b. biosphere   c. atmosphere   d. solid Earth
   Answer: B
   Diff: 1

36) a. protosun   b. Oort cloud   c. protoplanets   d. meteorites

Answer: B
Diff: 2

37) a. crust   b. mantle   c. lithosphere   d. core

Answer: C
Diff: 1

38) a. mountain belt   b. shield   c. craton   d. stable platform

Answer: A
Diff: 1

39) a. abyssal plain   b. seamount   c. oceanic ridge   d. continental slope

Answer: D
Diff: 1

40) a. pressure   b. foliation   c. hydrothermal fluids   d. melting

Answer: D
Diff: 1

41) Aristotle and other prominent Greek philosophers were the first ones to promote the doctrine of uniformitarianism.

Answer: FALSE
Diff: 1

42) Internally, the Earth consists of spherical shells with different compositions and densities.

Answer: TRUE
Diff: 1

43) The asthenosphere is a relatively cool and rigid shell that overlies the lithosphere.

Answer: FALSE
Diff: 1

44) The doctrine of uniformitarianism implies that the current forces and processes shaping the Earth have been operating for a very long time.

Answer: TRUE
Diff: 1

45) The law of superposition applies primarily to sedimentary rocks and lava flows.

Answer: TRUE
Diff: 1

46) The currently accepted age of Earth is approximately 4.5 million years.

Answer: FALSE
Diff: 1

47) A scientific theory is a tentative or untested explanation that is proposed to explain scientific observations.

Answer: FALSE
Diff: 1

48) Oceans cover slightly less than half of the Earth's surface.

Answer: FALSE
Diff: 1

49) In an open system both energy and matter flow into and out of the system.

Answer: TRUE
Diff: 1

50) According to the nebular hypothesis, all of the bodies in the universe evolved from a rotating cloud of gases and dust about 5 billion years ago.

Answer: FALSE
Diff: 1

51) The lithosphere, asthenosphere, and mesosphere are all layers of Earth defined by their composition.

Answer: FALSE
Diff: 1

52) Much of our modeling of Earth's interior comes from the study of seismic or earthquake waves.

Answer: TRUE
Diff: 2

53) Continental shields and stable platforms are part of the interior region known as a craton.

Answer: TRUE
Diff: 1

54) According to the rock cycle, any type of rock (igneous, sedimentary, or metamorphic) may be transformed into another type of rock, given enough time.

Answer: TRUE
Diff: 1

55) Igneous rocks are produced largely by the deposition and consolidation of surface materials like sand and mud.

Answer: FALSE
Diff: 1

56) List the two, broad, traditional subject areas of geologic study.

Answer: physical and historical geology
Diff: 1

57) The statement "the present is the key to the past," describes what basic geologic concept or doctrine?

Answer: uniformitarianism
Diff: 1

58) The _____ states that fossil organisms succeed one another in a definite and determinable order.

Answer: principle of fossil succession
Diff: 1

59) In natural systems, mechanisms that drive or enhance change are called _____.

Answer: positive feedback mechanisms
Diff: 1

60) The thin, outer layer of Earth, from 7 to 40 km in thickness, is called the _____.

Answer: crust
Diff: 1

61) The _____ is the relatively rigid zone above the asthenosphere that includes the crust and upper mantle.

Answer: lithosphere
Diff: 1

62) The _____ is the solid, rocky shell between the crust and outer core.

Answer: mantle
Diff: 1

63) The convective flow of liquid, metallic iron in the _____ is thought to generate Earth's magnetic field.

Answer: outer core
Diff: 1

64) Moving from the shoreline towards the deep-ocean basin, the continental margin may include the _____, _____, and the _____.

Answer: continental shelf, continental slope, continental rise
Diff: 1

65) What type of rock comprises most of the exposed surface of Earth (roughly 75%)?

Answer: sedimentary
Diff: 1

Critical thinking and discussion questions. Use complete sentences, correct spelling, and the information presented in Chapter 1 to answer the questions below.

66) Aside from near oceanic trenches, most earthquakes originate at depths of 100 kilometers or less. Considering the physical properties of Earth's interior, what type of mechanical behavior (in rocks) must be necessary for earthquakes to occur? Explain.
Diff: 2

67) Catastrophism obviously influenced seventeenth and eighteenth century thought by implying that Earth only needed to be a few thousand years old to explain landscapes and geologic features. However, catastrophic and often sudden changes are at least a part of the rock record that geologist's attempt to interpret. List three geologic catastrophes that would most likely affect landscapes or features on Earth and be recorded in rocks. How might these events be explained in the rock record using only uniformitarianism (or the implication of slow, gradual change)?
Diff: 3

68) Earth's physical environment is traditionally divided in the hydrosphere, atmosphere, and the solid Earth. Remembering the scientific method, why do you think that scientists tend to categorize and classify various features, phenomena, and characteristics of the natural world into groups or subdivisions? Also, are there potential pitfalls or problems if we only consider the natural world as individual groups or categories rather than as a whole?
Diff: 3

69) Label the layers of Earth's interior on the diagram below.

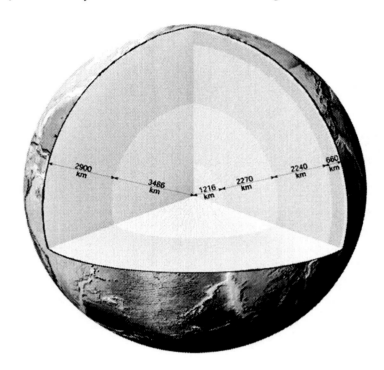

Answer: See Figure 1.13 in chapter 1 of the Essentials of Geology, 10e textbook
Diff: 1

70) On the seafloor profile below, fill in the blanks with the correct name of the feature that is labeled.

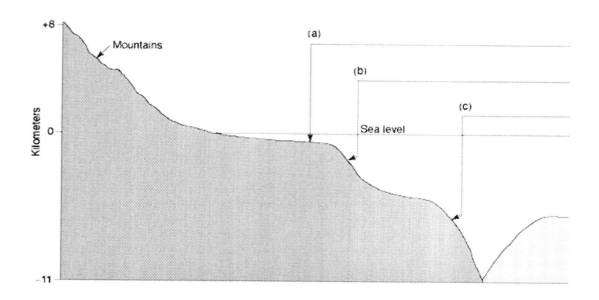

Answer: (a) continental shelf (b) continental slope (c) oceanic trench
Diff: 1

71) Fill in the blanks with the correct name of the feature that is labeled.

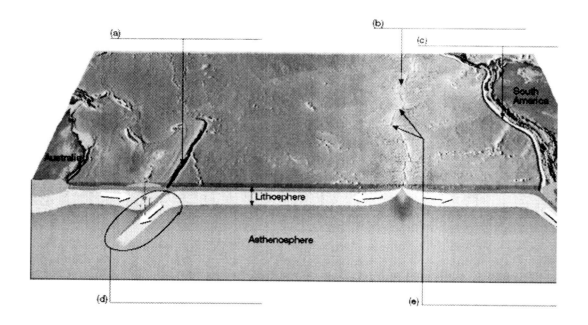

Answer: (a) oceanic trench (b) oceanic ridge (c) oceanic trench (d) subduction zone (e) transform faults
Diff: 1

Chapter 2 Matter and Minerals

1) Which of the following best defines a mineral and a rock?
   A) a rock has an orderly, repetitive, geometrical, internal arrangement of minerals; a mineral is a lithified or consolidated aggregate of rocks
   B) a mineral consists of its constituent atoms arranged in a geometrically repetitive structure; in a rock, the atoms are randomly bonded without any geometric pattern
   C) in a mineral the constituent atoms are bonded in a regular, repetitive, internal structure; a rock is a lithified or consolidated aggregate of different mineral grains
   D) a rock consists of atoms bonded in a regular, geometrically predictable arrangement; a mineral is a consolidated aggregate of different rock particles

Answer: C
Diff: 1

2) Which of the following is not a fundamental particle found in atoms?
   A) neutron
   B) selectron
   C) electron
   D) protons

Answer: B
Diff: 1

3) Atoms of the same element, zinc for example, have the same number of _____.
   A) electrons in the nucleus
   B) protons in the nucleus
   C) neutrons in the outer nuclear shell
   D) electrons in the valence bond level

Answer: B
Diff: 1

4) Which of the following is an accurate description of ionic bonding?
   A) nuclei of bonding atoms exchange electrons; the resulting ions are bonded together by the attractive forces between the negative and positive nucleons
   B) atoms of two different elements share electrons and protons; the resulting compound is bonded together by the strong, binding energy of shared protons
   C) nuclei of two different atoms share electrons, and the resulting compound is tightly bonded by the very strong, induced, electronuclear bonds
   D) atoms of different elements, having gained or lost electrons, form negative and positive ions that are bonded together by attractive forces between ions with opposite charges

Answer: D
Diff: 1

5) Which of the following is correct for isotopes of the same element?
   A) the atoms have different numbers of protons and the same number of neutrons
   B) the atoms have the same number of electrons and different numbers of protons
   C) the atoms have different numbers of neutrons and the same number of protons
   D) the atoms have different numbers of electrons but the same number of neutrons

Answer: C
Diff: 1

6) What mineral is the hardest known substance in nature?
   A) silicate
   B) native gold
   C) diamond
   D) muscovite

Answer: C
Diff: 1

7) Which carbonate mineral reacts readily with cool, dilute hydrochloric acid to produce visible bubbles of carbon dioxide gas?
   A) calcite
   B) quartz
   C) dolomite
   D) plagioclase

Answer: A
Diff: 1

8) Which mineral is composed of silicon dioxide (SiO_2)?
   A) calcite
   B) diamond
   C) olivine
   D) quartz

Answer: D
Diff: 1

9) Which of the following minerals is a silicate?
   A) hematite
   B) muscovite
   C) calcite
   D) halite

Answer: B
Diff: 1

10) A cubic centimeter of quartz, olivine, and gold weigh 2.5, 3.0, and 19.8 grams respectively. This
    indicates that _____.
    A) gold has a higher density and specific gravity than quartz and olivine
    B) gold is 6 to 7 times harder than olivine and quartz
    C) gold and olivine are silicates, quartz is elemental silicon
    D) olivine and quartz powders are harder than metallic gold

Answer: A
Diff: 2

11) Which one of the following is a sodium and calcium feldspar with twinning striations?
    A) orthoclase
    B) microcline
    C) plagioclase
    D) sanidine

Answer: C
Diff: 1

12) Which of the following minerals is a ferromagnesian silicate?
   A) quartz
   B) orthoclase
   C) hornblende
   D) muscovite
Answer: C
Diff: 1

13) Which of the following minerals is in the mineral group known as mica?
   A) orthoclase
   B) muscovite
   C) augite
   D) olivine
Answer: B
Diff: 1

14) Which of the following best characterizes ferromagnesian silicates?
   A) they contain iron and magnetite, are black in color, and they have metallic lusters
   B) they are black to dark-green, silicate minerals containing iron and magnesium
   C) they contain magnetite and ferroite and they are clear to light green
   D) they are mostly clear, colorless, and rich in the elements magnesium and ferrium
Answer: B
Diff: 1

15) Which one of the following mineral groups exhibits a sheet-like silicate structure?
   A) carbonates
   B) pyroxenes
   C) clays
   D) feldspars
Answer: C
Diff: 1

16) Which one of the following is a typical product of weathering?
   A) micasmicas
   B) ferromagnesians
   C) feldspars
   D) clays
Answer: D
Diff: 1

17) The ion at the center of a silicate tetrahedron is surrounded by _____.
   A) 4 oxygen ions
   B) 6 oxygen ions
   C) 4 sodium ions
   D) 6 sodium ions
Answer: A
Diff: 1

18) Which one of the following describes a mineral's response to mechanical impact?
   A) luster
   B) cleavage
   C) streak
   D) crystal form
Answer: B
Diff: 1

19) Chrysotile, crocidolite, and amosite are different mineralogical forms of what industrial commodity?
   A) gemstones
   B) metallic sulfide ores
   C) Portland cement
   D) asbestos
Answer: D
Diff: 1

20) Which of the following diseases has been linked directly to prolonged inhalation of asbestos dust?
   A) muscular dystrophy
   B) diabetes
   C) glaucoma
   D) lung cancer
Answer: D
Diff: 1

21) Which of the following is the unit of weight used for measuring diamonds (about 0.2 grams)?
   A) carat
   B) Troy ounce
   C) point
   D) kilo
Answer: A
Diff: 1

22) Which of the following denotes the purity of gold used in jewelry?
   A) carnot
   B) carette
   C) karat
   D) carlot
Answer: D
Diff: 1

23) Ruby and sapphire are red and blue forms of the mineral _____.
   A) diamond
   B) turquoise
   C) emerald
   D) corundum
Answer: D
Diff: 1

24) All silicate minerals contain which two elements?
   A) iron, silicon
   B) silicon, sodium
   C) oxygen, carbon
   D) silicon, oxygen
Answer: D
Diff: 1

25) Which mineral is easily soluble in water at room temperature conditions?
   A) diamond
   B) talc
   C) halite
   D) olivine
Answer: C
Diff: 1

26) What element is the most abundant in the Earth's crust by weight?
   A) carbon
   B) chlorine
   C) oxygen
   D) sodium
Answer: C
Diff: 1

27) The strong tendency of certain minerals to break along smooth, parallel planes is known as
   _____.
   A) streak
   B) cleavage
   C) cracking luster
   D) crystal form
Answer: B
Diff: 1

28) What in the name given to an atom that gains or loses electrons in a chemical reaction?
   A) molecule
   B) ion
   C) isotope
   D) nucleon
Answer: B
Diff: 1

29) An atom's mass number is 13 and its atomic number is 6. How many neutrons are in its nucleus?
   A) 19
   B) 7
   C) 13
   D) 6
Answer: B
Diff: 1

30) Which one of the following is not true for minerals?
  A) they have a specific, internal, crystalline structure
  B) they can be a liquid, solid, or glass
  C) they have a specific, predictable chemical composition
  D) they can be identified by characteristic physical properties
Answer: B
Diff: 1

31) In which type of chemical bonding are electrons shared between adjacent atoms?
  A) ionic
  B) subatomic
  C) covalent
  D) isotopic
Answer: C
Diff: 1

32) How do the electrons behave in a mineral with metallic bonding?
  A) they are tightly bound to certain atoms and cannot readily move
  B) they can move relatively easily from atom to atom inside the mineral
  C) they react with protons to make neutrons in the outer valence shells
  D) they move to adjacent negative ions, forming positive ions
Answer: B
Diff: 1

33) Which group of minerals are the most abundant in the Earth's crust?
  A) sulfides
  B) carbonates
  C) silicates
  D) chlorides
Answer: C
Diff: 1

34) Which the following denotes the massive, positively charged, nuclear particles?
  A) protons
  B) electrons
  C) isotrons
  D) neutrons
Answer: A
Diff: 1

35) What are the lightest or least massive of the basic atomic particles?
  A) uranium nuclei
  B) protons
  C) electrons
  D) neutrons
Answer: C
Diff: 1

36) Which of the following has the highest specific gravity?
   A) wood
   B) water
   C) gold
   D) quartz
   Answer: C
   Diff: 1

37) Which of the following will react readily with acids such as hydrochloric?
   A) calcite
   B) quartz
   C) diamond
   D) talc
   Answer: A
   Diff: 1

38) Which of the following describes the light reflecting and transmission characteristics of a mineral?
   A) luster
   B) color streak
   C) virtual absorption
   D) fluorescence
   Answer: A
   Diff: 1

39) What is the name of dark-colored mica?
   A) calcite
   B) biotite
   C) quartz
   D) olivine
   Answer: B
   Diff: 1

40) Hornblende and the other amphiboles have what type of silicate structure?
   A) metallic
   B) sheet
   C) 3-D framework
   D) double chains
   Answer: D
   Diff: 1

Word Analysis. Examine the words and/or phrases for each question below and determine the relationship among the majority of words/phrases. Choose the option which does not fit the pattern.

41) a. electron   b. atom   c. proton   d. neutron
   Answer: B
   Diff: 1

42) a. hardness   b. streak   c. luster   d. cleavage
   Answer: C
   Diff: 1

43) a. quartz   b. olivine   c. feldspar   d. calcite

Answer: D
Diff: 1

44) a. olivine   b. quartz   c. amphibole   d. pyroxene

Answer: B
Diff: 1

45) a. galena   b. calcite   c. gypsum   d. halite

Answer: A
Diff: 2

46) Calcite and dolomite are both carbonate minerals.

Answer: TRUE
Diff: 1

47) Graphite and diamond have the same chemical compositions and different crystalline structures.

Answer: TRUE
Diff: 1

48) Rocks are aggregates of one or more minerals.

Answer: TRUE
Diff: 1

49) Mineral luster is broadly classified as either being metallic or opaque.

Answer: FALSE
Diff: 1

50) Electrically neutral atoms have equal numbers of electrons and protons.

Answer: TRUE
Diff: 1

51) Rock–forming silicate minerals have higher specific gravities than water.

Answer: TRUE
Diff: 1

52) In a silicon–oxygen structural unit, silicon atoms occupy corners of a tetrahedron.

Answer: FALSE
Diff: 1

53) Calcite and halite react with dilute acids to evolve carbon dioxide.

Answer: FALSE
Diff: 2

54) All atoms of the same element have the same atomic number.

Answer: TRUE
Diff: 1

55) Orthoclase and plagioclase feldspars have quite different forms of cleavage.

Answer: FALSE
Diff: 1

56) Diamond and quartz are both minerals composed of a single element.

Answer: FALSE
Diff: 1

57) The micas, biotite and muscovite, both exhibit one direction of cleavage.

Answer: TRUE
Diff: 1

58) Nonmetallic minerals like quartz and gypsum have no industrial uses.

Answer: FALSE
Diff: 1

59) Ferromagnesian silicate minerals contain some magnesium and/or iron.

Answer: TRUE
Diff: 1

60) Positive ions are atoms that have gained electrons during a chemical reaction.

Answer: FALSE
Diff: 1

61) Isotopes of the same element have the same mass number.

Answer: FALSE
Diff: 1

62) Moh's hardness scale is a relative measure of which physical property of minerals?

Answer: hardness
Diff: 1

63) What physical property denotes the color of a powdered mineral?

Answer: streak
Diff: 1

64) The physical property denoting a mineral's tendency to crack along parallel, planar surfaces is known as what?

Answer: cleavage
Diff: 1

65) What is the hardest mineral known?

Answer: diamond
Diff: 1

66) What is the chemical composition of graphite and diamond?

Answer: carbon
Diff: 1

67) In atoms, which electrons are involved in chemical bonding?

Answer: valence
Diff: 1

68) A compound is a stable chemical substance composed of two or more what?

Answer: elements
Diff: 1

69) What is the dominant form of chemical bonding exhibited by minerals such as native gold, native copper and copper–rich sulfides?

Answer: metallic
Diff: 1

70) What two major characteristics differentiate minerals from natural glasses?

Answer: solid, internal arrangement of atoms
Diff: 1

71) Most glasses and some minerals exhibit a type of fracture characterized by nested and curved, crack surfaces. What term describes this property?

Answer: conchoidal
Diff: 1

72) Parallel, straight, linear imperfections visible on the cleavage surfaces of plagioclase feldspar are called what?

Answer: striations
Diff: 1

73) What is the smallest particle of matter that exhibits and defines the distinctive chemical characteristics of the individual elements?

Answer: atom
Diff: 1

74) What ferromagnesian silicate mineral is named for its green color?

Answer: olivine
Diff: 1

75) What mineral group forms by the breakdown and weathering of rock–forming silicate minerals and are important constituents of soils?

Answer: clays
Diff: 1

Critical thinking and discussion questions. Use complete sentences, correct spelling, and the information presented in Chapter 2 to answer the questions below.

76) Overall, the physical properties of minerals provide a reliable means to identify common minerals. However, certain properties can exhibit a range of characteristics or values making them less useful for identification purposes. Choose three physical properties that might vary considerably between samples of the same mineral and explain why such variability would exist.

Diff: 2

77) Based on the brief discussion of chemistry and chemical bonding in chapter 2, why do minerals rarely exhibit pure chemical compositions (100% always the same chemical composition)?

Diff: 2

78) Considering the composition and structure of Earth discussed in chapter 1, do you think all of the possible silicate (and even mineral) structures have been identified by scientists? Discuss why or why not. Also, does this same reasoning apply to all possible chemical elements of Earth?

Diff: 3

79) Label the various parts of an atom in the diagram below.

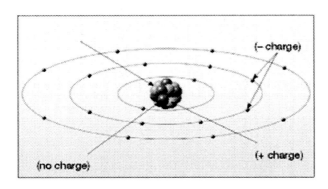

Answer: See Figure 2.5 A in chapter 2 of the Essentials of Geology, 10e textbook
Diff: 1

80) For each illustration below, note the number of cleavage directions.

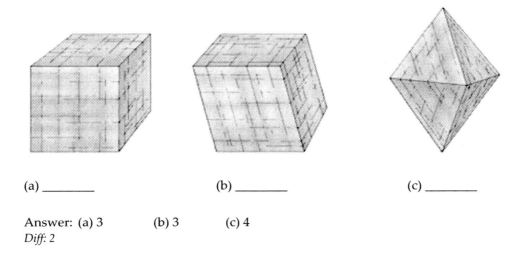

(a) _____   (b) _____   (c) _____

Answer: (a) 3   (b) 3   (c) 4
Diff: 2

81) Fill in the table below on silicate minerals.

Silicate structure	Oxygen to silicon ratio	mineral	cleavage
oxygen atoms → silicon atom	4:1	olivine	(a)
(b)		(c)	two planes at right angles
(d)		(e)	(f)

Answer: (a) none   (b) slightly more than 3:1   (c) pyroxene group –
        augite
        (d) slightly less than 3:1   (e) amphibole group– hornblende   (f) two planes at 60
        and 120 degrees
Diff: 2

Chapter 3 Igneous Rocks

1) Lava flows are typically finer grained than intrusive igneous rocks. Why?
   A) intrusive magma is cooler because it is well insulated by the surrounding rock
   B) intrusive magma flows onto the Earth's surface and cools very slowly, allowing many small mineral grains to grow
   C) the extrusive magma cools quickly so the mineral grains do not have time to grow
   D) the extrusive magma, because it is deep below the surface, cools very slowly producing very small mineral grains

   Answer: C
   Diff: 1

2) Which magma is most likely to quench (congeal) to a natural glass?
   A) highly viscous; cools quickly
   B) highly viscous; cools slowly
   C) highly fluid; cools slowly
   D) highly fluid; cools quickly

   Answer: A
   Diff: 1

3) The sizes, shapes, and arrangements of mineral grains in an igneous rock are known as _____.
   A) silica content
   B) texture
   C) mineral content
   D) Bowen's reaction series

   Answer: B
   Diff: 1

Match the description with the appropriate texture.
   a. aphanitic   b. porphyritic   c. phaneritic   d. glassy

4) magma cools and consolidates without growth of mineral grains

   Answer: d
   Diff: 1

5) mineral grains are of roughly equal size and coarse enough to be seen without a microscope or magnifying glass

   Answer: c
   Diff: 1

6) rock has two or more, distinctly different-sized populations of mineral grains

   Answer: b
   Diff: 1

7) a magnifying glass or microscope is needed to see individual mineral grains

   Answer: a
   Diff: 1

8) A _____ is an open cavity in a volcanic rock that was filled by a gas bubble when the lava was still mainly liquid.
   A) porphyrocryst
   B) vesicle
   C) phenocryst
   D) xenocryst

   Answer: B
   Diff: 1

9) Consider the Bowen's reaction series. Which mineral would you expect to see as a phenocryst in a porphyritic basalt?
   A) olivine
   B) quartz
   C) orthoclase
   D) sodium−rich plagioclase

   Answer: A
   Diff: 1

Match the following rocks to their equivalent aphanitic or phaneritic igneous rocks.
   a. andesite   b. gabbro   c. rhyolite

10) granite

   Answer: c
   Diff: 1

11) basalt

   Answer: b
   Diff: 1

12) diorite

   Answer: a
   Diff: 1

13) Which of the following igneous rocks exhibit aphanitic texture?
   A) granite, gabbro
   B) andesite, rhyolite
   C) andesite, diorite
   D) rhyolite, gabbro

   Answer: B
   Diff: 1

14) In a porphyritic volcanic rock, which mineral grains are the last to crystallize?
   A) phenocrysts
   B) vesicles
   C) pegmatites
   D) matrix or groundmass

   Answer: D
   Diff: 1

15) Visible quartz and potassium feldspar grains are the main constituents in a _____.
   A) granite
   B) gabbro
   C) basalt
   D) rhyolite

Answer: A
Diff: 1

16) Which of the following igneous rocks has a pyroclastic texture?
   A) rhyolitic tuff
   B) porphyritic basalt
   C) intrusive granite
   D) andesitic lava

Answer: A
Diff: 1

17) _____ is a volcanic rock that is extremely vesicular and glassy.
   A) Obsidian
   B) Pegmatite
   C) Tuff
   D) Pumice

Answer: D
Diff: 1

18) _____ is composed mainly of ferromagnesian minerals.
   A) Peridotite
   B) Rhyolite
   C) Andesite
   D) Granite

Answer: A
Diff: 1

19) Which of the following minerals crystallize early in Bowen's reaction series?
   A) biotite
   B) quartz
   C) olivine
   D) muscovite

Answer: C
Diff: 1

20) _____ is the dominant feldspar in basalt.
   A) Plagioclase
   B) Microcline
   C) Orthoclase
   D) Pyroxene

Answer: A
Diff: 1

21) Which of the following are used for studying rocks with a polarizing microscope?
   A) polished cubes
   B) broken chips
   C) thin sections
   D) grain karats
   Answer: C
   Diff: 1

22) _____ is characterized by very coarse mineral grains?
   A) Obsidian
   B) Pumice
   C) Pegmatite
   D) Granite
   Answer: C
   Diff: 1

23) In which of the following igneous rocks and environments would you expect to find unusually high concentrations of rare elements such as lithium, beryllium, and boron?
   A) basalt dike; fills a vertical fracture at shallow depth
   B) pumice lump; crystallized at depth in a mass of intrusive granite
   C) peridotite; crystallized at depth in the upper mantle
   D) pegmatite; crystallized from a water–rich, highly differentiated, residual magma
   Answer: D
   Diff: 1

24) A(n) _____ texture represents a single, long period of cooling and crystallization.
   A) glassy
   B) pyroclastic
   C) aphanitic
   D) phaneritic
   Answer: D
   Diff: 1

25) _____ has the same mineral composition as andesite?
   A) Basalt
   B) Granite
   C) Gabbro
   D) Diorite
   Answer: D
   Diff: 1

26) What do pumice and obsidian have in common?
   A) basaltic composition
   B) glassy texture
   C) ultramafic composition
   D) phaneritic texture
   Answer: B
   Diff: 1

27) Which of the following best describes an aphanitic texture?
  A) the rock is crystalline; mineral grains are too small to be visible without a magnifying
     lens or microscope
  B) the mineral grains have glassy textures
  C) the rock consists of broken, volcanic–rock and mineral fragments
  D) the rock is crystalline; mineral grains are of distinctly different sizes
Answer: A
Diff: 1

28) A(n) _____ texture would be most unlikely to occur in an extrusive igneous rock.
  A) pyroclastic
  B) glassy
  C) aphanitic
  D) phaneritic
Answer: C
Diff: 1

29) _____ is named for a prominent, volcanic mountain range in western South America.
  A) Basalt
  B) Andesite
  C) Pegmatite
  D) Peridotite
Answer: B
Diff: 1

30) _____ is the dominant lava erupted from volcanoes on Hawaii and Iceland.
  A) Rhyolite
  B) Andesite
  C) Peridotite
  D) Basalt
Answer: D
Diff: 1

31) Which igneous rock or magma has the lowest silica (SiO_2) content?
  A) granite
  B) basalt
  C) andesite
  D) peridotite
Answer: B
Diff: 1

32) _____ is thought to be common in the Earth's mantle but rare in the crust?
  A) Pumice
  B) Granite
  C) Pegmatite
  D) Peridotite
Answer: D
Diff: 1

33) _____ often contain gem-quality crystals of minerals such as beryl and tourmaline and
    high concentrations of relatively rare elements such as lithium, boron, and beryllium?
        A) Welded tuff sheets
        B) Basaltic lavas
        C) Granitic pegmatites
        D) Diorite plutons
Answer: C
Diff: 1

34) The last minerals to crystallize on Bowen's Reaction Series result in igneous rocks with a
    _____ composition.
        A) felsic
        B) intermediate
        C) mafic
        D) ultramafic
Answer: A
Diff: 1

35) Changing the composition of magma by incorporating surrounding host rock is known as
    _____.
        A) magma mixing
        B) partial melting
        C) differentiation
        D) assimilation
Answer: D
Diff: 1

36) All of the following are factors that affect the generation of magma except for _____.
        A) heat
        B) pressure
        C) crystal size
        D) volatiles
Answer: C
Diff: 1

**Word Analysis. Examine the words and/or phrases for each question below and determine the
relationship among the majority of words/phrases. Choose the option which does not fit the pattern.**

37) a. granite   b. basalt   c. diorite   d. gabbro
    Answer: B
    Diff: 1

38) a. aphanitic   b. phaneritic   c. porphyritic   d. glassy
    Answer: D
    Diff: 2

39) a. biotite   b. hornblende   c. plagioclase   d. augite
    Answer: C
    Diff: 2

40) a. obsidian   b. rhyolite   c. pumice   d. welded tuff

Answer: B
Diff: 2

41) a. phenocrysts   b. crystals   c. groundmass   d. vesicles

Answer: B
Diff: 1

42) Bowen's reaction series predicts the sizes of the different mineral grains that grow from crystallizing magmas.

Answer: FALSE
Diff: 1

43) In an igneous rock with a phaneritic texture, the mineral grains are visible to the unaided eye.

Answer: TRUE
Diff: 1

44) Olivine and quartz commonly crystallize together from mafic or basaltic magmas.

Answer: FALSE
Diff: 1

45) Most lava crystallizes to form igneous rocks with phaneritic textures.

Answer: FALSE
Diff: 1

46) Pegmatites are smaller volume, intrusive bodies with glassy textures.

Answer: FALSE
Diff: 1

47) Basalt is the aphanitic or fine-grained equivalent of gabbro.

Answer: TRUE
Diff: 1

48) Plutonic rocks are intrusive and generally consist of mineral grains coarse enough to be readily visible in a hand sample.

Answer: TRUE
Diff: 1

49) A porphyritic texture includes two different sizes of mineral grains, the phenocrysts and the vesicles.

Answer: FALSE
Diff: 1

50) Olivine is an important mineral in peridotites and other ultramafic rocks.

Answer: TRUE
Diff: 1

51) The process of magmatic differentiation can generate residual, more felsic magmas from mafic magmas such as basalt.

Answer: TRUE
Diff: 2

52) Glassy igneous rocks form when magma cools too fast for mineral grains to grow.

Answer: TRUE
Diff: 1

53) Minerals, such as plagioclase feldspar, on the continuous branch of Bowen's Reaction Series react with the magma to form lower temperature, more stable minerals such as hornblende or biotite.

Answer: FALSE
Diff: 1

54) What term denotes the larger mineral grains in a porphyritic igneous rock?

Answer: phenocryst
Diff: 1

55) _____ is the name given to molten rock below the Earth's surface.

Answer: Magma
Diff: 1

56) Melting of rocks to form magma as a result of decreases pressure is known as _____.

Answer: decompression melting
Diff: 1

57) What type of magma, commonly erupted along oceanic ridge systems, originates by partial melting of mantle peridotite?

Answer: basalt
Diff: 1

58) Pegmatites consist of what size mineral grains?

Answer: coarse to very coarse
Diff: 1

59) A _____ texture refers to rocks composed mainly of mineral and volcanic fragments.

Answer: pyroclastic
Diff: 1

60) Pyroxene, hornblende, and biotite are all minerals found on the _____ series of Bowen's Reaction Series.

Answer: discontinuous
Diff: 1

61) Name two igneous rocks with glassy textures.

Answer: pumice, obsidian
Diff: 1

62) Technically, the process whereby ions arrange themselves into orderly patterns during the cooling of a liquid is called _____.

Answer: crystallization
Diff: 1

63) _____ refers to the removal and isolation of early–formed mineral grains that can cause the composition of the remaining magma to change.

Answer: Crystal settling

Diff: 1

64) Igneous rocks are classified on the basis of what two main characteristics?

Answer: texture and mineral composition

Diff: 1

Critical thinking and discussion questions. Use complete sentences, correct spelling, and the information presented in Chapter 3 to answer the questions below.

65) The size of crystals in igneous rocks is generally a function of the rate of cooling. However, within the same rock crystal size does not necessarily reflect the order of crystallization for individual minerals. Without using Bowen's Reaction Series, how might you determine the order of crystallization of minerals in an individual rock sample? (Hint: Think about the texture)

Diff: 3

66) All other factors being equal (geothermal gradient, pressure, composition, and heat from other sources such as friction), why is magma generally produced in association with subduction zones as opposed to areas away from subduction zones?

Diff: 2

67) In a series of basaltic lava flows on Hawaii, the top and bottom of each flow is difficult to distinguish just by looking at the layers of rock. What are some rock characteristics (texture, mineralogy, etc.) and other features that you might use to recognize individual lava flows?

Diff: 3

68) Fill in the missing rock names on the chart below.

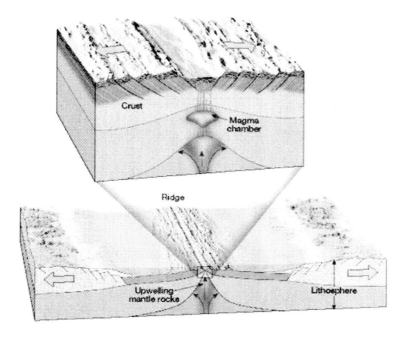

Answer: See Figure 3.6 in the Essentials of Geology, 10e textbook.
Diff: 1

69) What process is exhibited by the diagram below? When does this process take place?

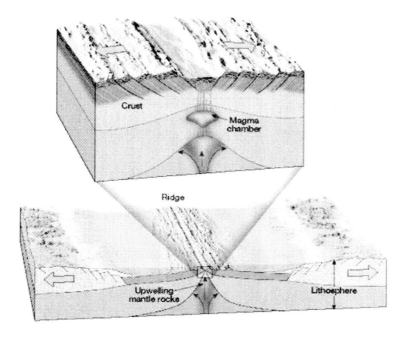

Answer: Decompression melting. This occurs when confining pressure drops enough to lower melting points. Such drops in pressure occur when rock ascends due to convective upwelling like that at divergent plate boundaries.
Diff: 1

70) In general, what happens in terms of composition as crystallization proceeds down the Bowen's reaction?

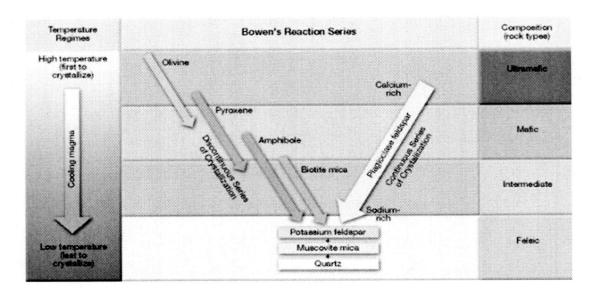

Answer: The early-formed silicates are enriched in iron and magnesium, resulting in such rocks as peridotite and basalt. As crystallization proceeds, the later-formed silicates are enriched in sodium, potassium, and silicon, resulting in andesite and granite.

Diff: 2

Chapter 4 Volcanoes and Other Igneous Activity

1) In 1980, _____ was the first Cascade Range volcano to erupt since Mt. Lassen, California, in 1915–16.
   A) Mt. Rainier
   B) Mt. Shasta
   C) Kilauea
   D) Mt. St. Helens
   Answer: D
   Diff: 1

2) Which type of basaltic lava flow has a fairly smooth, unfragmented, ropy surface?
   A) aa
   B) pegmatitic
   C) pahoehoe
   D) scoria
   Answer: C
   Diff: 1

3) _____ is a major dissolved volatile constituent in both magmas and volcanic gases?
   A) Water
   B) Carbon monoxide
   C) Hydrogen chloride
   D) Methane
   Answer: A
   Diff: 1

4) Volcanic bombs originate _____.
   A) as laser–guided, granite blocks launched from a supersonic jet
   B) as blocks of volcanic rock ejected from an erupting volcanic crater
   C) as erupted magma blobs that partly congeal before falling to the ground
   D) as ash particles that join together in the eruptive plume and fall as cobble–sized objects
   Answer: C
   Diff: 1

5) Which natural phenomenon occurs for many years after major explosive volcanic eruptions such as Tambora and Pinatubo?
   A) heavy falls of volcanic ash within 100 km of the volcano
   B) unusually warm weather in the tropics and subtropics
   C) a worldwide rise in sea level of one to three centimeters
   D) brilliantly colored sunrises and sunsets
   Answer: D
   Diff: 1

6) What fate befell the 'Lost City of Atlantis' mentioned in Plato's writings?
    A) it washed away in a giant sea wave about 79 A. D.
    B) it was obliterated by dust storms from North Africa in the fifth century A. D.
    C) it was buried by thick ash deposits from Mt. Vesuvius in 79 B. C.
    D) it disappeared as part of caldera collapse following a major, explosive, volcanic eruption
Answer: D
Diff: 1

7) _____ magma is the most abundant type of erupted at oceanic spreading centers.
    A) Basaltic
    B) Granitic
    C) Andesitic
    D) Pegmatitic
Answer: A
Diff: 1

8) The 1991 Pinatubo eruption in the Philippines caused brilliantly colored sunrises and sunsets to be seen for the next few years. What caused this phenomenon?
    A) the eruption added large amounts of carbon dioxide to the atmosphere
    B) the eruptive cloud destroyed parts of the Earth's protective ozone layer
    C) radioactive atoms blown into the atmosphere glowed red as they decayed
    D) sulfur dioxide and other erupted gases formed aerosols in the stratosphere
Answer: D
Diff: 1

9) The _____ ocean basin is rimmed by the most subduction zones.
    A) Atlantic
    B) Indian
    C) Pacific
    D) Arctic
Answer: C
Diff: 1

10) Which was the most powerful, explosive volcanic eruption of historic time?
    A) Mt. Pele, Martinique, 1902
    B) Vesuvius, Italy, 79 A. D.
    C) Tambora, Indonesia, 1815
    D) Nevado del Ruiz, Colombia, 1985
Answer: C
Diff: 1

11) Which of the following is associated with deep mantle hot spots?
    A) Vesuvius and the other volcanoes of Italy
    B) the volcanoes of Hawaii and Quaternary activity in Yellowstone National Park
    C) the very young cinder cones scattered across the southwestern United States
    D) Mt. St. Helens and other volcanoes of the Cascade Mountains
Answer: B
Diff: 1

12) Why would a plume of solid silicate rock rising slowly from deep in the mantle begin melting as it neared the base of the lithosphere?
    A) the rock heats up and expands at lower pressures, causing it to liquefy
    B) temperatures remain high as lowered pressures decrease melting temperatures
    C) the lowered pressures cause rapid heat loss accompanied by melting
    D) none of the above
Answer: B
Diff: 1

13) Which of the following best describes seamounts and islands of the deep ocean basins?
    A) huge granite batholiths intruded beneath the ocean floor
    B) piles of basaltic lava flows built up from the ocean floor by multiple, summit and flank eruptions
    C) andesitic pyroclastic rocks submerged when the mountains sank below sea level
    D) domed gabbro intrusions and massive, submarine, rhyolitic, pyroclastic cones
Answer: B
Diff: 1

14) Pockets of magmas can be formed by the melting of deep continental crust heated by the intrusion of other magmas. Which of the following correctly describes this process?
    A) intrusion of basaltic magma causes deep crustal rocks to melt, producing andesitic or rhyolitic magmas
    B) intruded rhyolite magma causes basalt magma to form by melting of granite
    C) intrusion of diorite magma causes basalt magma to melt from peridotite
    D) all of the above correctly describe the process
Answer: A
Diff: 2

15) Which of the following phenomena accompanied the year without a summer (1816) in parts of North America and northern Europe?
    A) ice jams on major rivers, such as the Nile and lower Mississippi during July
    B) snow falls and frosts in New England during July and August
    C) crop failures and vastly reduced crop yields
    D) shortened periods of daylight, such as normally occur only during winter months
Answer: B
Diff: 1

16) _____ are usually the most abundant gases emitted during basaltic volcanism.
    A) Chlorine and sodium
    B) Neon and ammonia
    C) Oxygen and nitrogen
    D) Water and carbon dioxide
Answer: D
Diff: 1

Please choose from one of the following answers.
    a. shield volcanoes   b. composite/stratovolcanoes   c. cinder cones

17) massive, gently sloping volcanoes built of successive, basaltic lava flows
Answer: a
Diff: 1

18) large, fairly steep-sided cones composed of lavas and pyroclastic layers

Answer: b
Diff: 1

19) small basaltic cones built during one, short, eruptive episode

Answer: c
Diff: 1

20) the volcanoes of southwestern Alaska and the Aleutian Islands

Answer: b
Diff: 1

21) the big volcanoes of Hawaii

Answer: a
Diff: 1

22) Which statement about the May, 1980, eruption of Mount St. Helens is false?
   A) during the eruptive period, the mountain peak was substantially built up by new lava
      flows and pyroclastic debris
   B) plumes of ash rose high into the atmosphere during the major eruptive events
   C) mudflows accompanied the major eruptive events
   D) the most powerful explosive event was preceded by a massive landslide

Answer: A
Diff: 1

23) _____ tend to increase the explosive potential of a magma body beneath a volcano.
   A) High viscosity and dissolved gas
   B) High viscosity; low dissolved gas content
   C) Low silica content, low viscosity
   D) Low viscosity; low dissolved gas content

Answer: A
Diff: 1

24) Which type of basaltic lava flow has its surface covered with sharp-edged, angular blocks and
rubble?
   A) scoria
   B) pahoehoe
   C) pillow lava
   D) aa

Answer: D
Diff: 1

25) Which one of the following statements concerning volcanic blocks and bombs is true?
   A) blocks are broken fragments of solid rocks; bombs have smaller sizes than lapilli
   B) bombs are guided to Earth by laser beams; blocks fall anywhere
   C) bombs are ejected as magma lumps; blocks are ejected as solid fragments
   D) bombs and blocks are both smaller than lapilli and cinders

Answer: C
Diff: 1

26) _____ destroyed the city of St. Pierre, Martinique in 1902.
    A) Mudflows
    B) Basaltic lava flows
    C) Heavy ashfall
    D) A nueé ardente

Answer: D
Diff: 1

27) Which one of the following statements concerning cinder cones is false?
    A) they are small volcanoes with fairly steep sides
    B) they are built mostly or entirely during one eruptive cycle
    C) the cinders and other pyroclastic particles are consolidated into welded tuff
    D) the cinders most commonly are basaltic

Answer: C
Diff: 1

28) The Columbia Plateau in Washington and Oregon is _____.
    A) a flood basalt plateau
    B) a thick stack of welded–tuff layers
    C) a caldera filled with rhyolite lava flows
    D) a field of large stratovolcanoes

Answer: A
Diff: 1

29) Which kind of eruptive activity is most likely to be highly explosive?
    A) lava flows from a large shield volcano on an oceanic island
    B) fissure eruptions feeding lava to flood basalt accumulations
    C) eruptions of big, continental margin, composite cones or stratovolcanoes
    D) lava flows from a large cinder cone complex

Answer: C
Diff: 1

30) Which one of the following statements is not true?
    A) melting temperatures of silicate rocks increase with increased pressure
    B) melting temperatures of silicate rocks are lowered by small amounts of water
    C) basalt magmas in general have higher temperatures than rhyolite magmas
    D) when magma reaches the surface, its dissolved gas content increases

Answer: D
Diff: 2

31) Which kind of volcanism is typical of mid–oceanic ridge systems?
    A) explosive; composite cones
    B) submarine; basaltic lava flows
    C) fissure eruptions; flood basalts fields
    D) explosive; rhyolitic, pyroclastic flows

Answer: B
Diff: 1

32) Kilauea and Mauna Loa are _____.
   A) explosive, rhyolitic volcanoes
   B) andesitic stratovolcanoes
   C) basaltic shield volcanoes
   D) small, basaltic cinder cones

   Answer: C
   Diff: 1

33) Mount St. Helens is _____.
   A) a basaltic cinder cone
   B) an explosive stratovolcano
   C) a basaltic shield volcano
   D) a small, welded tuff cone

   Answer: B
   Diff: 1

34) The 1943 eruption of Paricutin in Mexico was characterized by _____.
   A) mudflows and explosive ash eruptions
   B) welded–tuff deposition and caldera formation
   C) cinder cone building and basaltic lava
   D) pyroclastic eruptions and nueé ardente flows

   Answer: C
   Diff: 1

35) The average composition of rocks comprising a large composite cone or stratovolcano is similar to a (an) _____ magma.
   A) basaltic
   B) ultramafic
   C) andesitic
   D) rhyolitic

   Answer: C
   Diff: 1

36) A _____ volcano is a very large, gently sloping mound composed mainly of basaltic lava flows.
   A) composite
   B) stratospheric
   C) cinder cone
   D) shield

   Answer: D
   Diff: 1

37) Which of the following best describes Shiprock, a famous volcanic feature in New Mexico?
   A) a very recently active, basaltic cinder cone
   B) an extinct, highly symmetrical, composite volcanic cone
   C) the eroded remains of a volcanic pipe and radiating dikes
   D) an extinct, massive, rhyolitic shield volcano

   Answer: C
   Diff: 1

38) Which region has the greatest concentration of currently active volcanoes?
    A) the coastal plain of western Africa
    B) European Russia and Siberia
    C) the area surrounding the Red Sea
    D) the circum-Pacific area
Answer: D
Diff: 1

39) The recent (geologically) volcanic activity in Yellowstone National Park is _____.
    A) related to plate subduction
    B) related to a divergent plate boundary
    C) related to a transform plate boundary
    D) related to intraplate, hot spot volcanism
Answer: D
Diff: 1

40) The Icelandic volcanoes are related to plate tectonics because _____.
    A) they lie on a spreading center where two plates are converging
    B) they lie on a subduction zone where two plates are converging
    C) they lie on a spreading center where two plates are moving apart
    D) they lie along a subduction zone where two plates are diverging
Answer: C
Diff: 1

41) Which one of the following best describes volcanism in the Cascade Range, northwestern U.
S.?
    A) related to a mantle hot spot
    B) related to plate subduction
    C) related to a mid-oceanic ridge system
    D) related to deep, transform faults
Answer: B
Diff: 1

42) Which of the following statements best describes the big Hawaiian volcanoes?
    A) lie directly above a transform plate boundary that cuts deeply into the mantle
    B) lie directly above an active subduction zone where the Pacific plate is sinking into the
       mantle
    C) lie along the crest of the East Pacific Rise, a mid-ocean ridge or spreading center
    D) are situated in the interior of a large, Pacific plate above a hot spot deep in the mantle
Answer: D
Diff: 1

43) At low pressures and in the absence of water, rhyolites and granites begin to melt at about
_____.
    A) 300° C
    B) 500° F
    C) 800° C
    D) 6000° F
Answer: C
Diff: 1

44) What volcanic events formed Crater Lake, OR? When did they take place?
    A) a powerful explosion blew away the top of a stratovolcano; 10 million years ago
    B) the crater of a large, extinct cinder cone filled with water; 5 million years ago
    C) landslides and volcanic mudflows dammed the Mazama River; 500 years ago
    D) caldera collapse followed major ash and pyroclastic–flow eruptions; 6000 years ago
Answer: D
Diff: 1

45) Which one of the following shows the correct order (left to right) of decreasing magma viscosity?
    A) rhyolite, andesite, basalt
    B) andesite, rhyolite, basalt
    C) basalt, rhyolite, andesite
    D) basalt, andesite, rhyolite
Answer: A
Diff: 1

46) Why do magmas rise toward Earth's surface?
    A) magmas are more viscous than solid rocks in the crust and upper mantle
    B) most magmas are richer in silica than most crustal and upper mantle rocks
    C) magmas are mainly liquid and contain dissolved fluids such as water; most are less dense than the adjacent solid rock
    D) all of the above
Answer: C
Diff: 1

47) What is the largest, known volcano in the Solar System?
    A) Mauna Loa, Hawaii, Earth
    B) Mount Olympus, Greece, Earth
    C) Mauna Kea, southern hemisphere, Mars
    D) Olympus Mons, Mars
Answer: D
Diff: 1

48) A _____ is the largest, discordant body of intrusive, igneous rock.
    A) lopolith
    B) laccolith
    C) pluton
    D) batholith
Answer: D
Diff: 1

49) A _____ is an intrusive, igneous rock body that is tabular and concordant.
    A) laccolith
    B) dike
    C) pluton
    D) sill
Answer: D
Diff: 1

50) A _____ is a near surface, intrusive, igneous rock body that results from local inflation of a horizontal sill.
    A) batholith
    B) dike
    C) laccolith
    D) volcanic neck

Answer: C
Diff: 1

51) Which of the following best describes the bedrock in the Sierra Nevada Mountains in California?
    A) basalt; dikes
    B) gabbro; plutoliths
    C) andesite; laccoliths
    D) granite; batholiths

Answer: D
Diff: 1

52) Xenoliths are associated most closely with which magmatic process and igneous rock body?
    A) columnar jointing; lava flow
    B) vesiculation; pumice lump
    C) magmatic differentation; gabbro sill
    D) intrusion; granitic batholith

Answer: D
Diff: 1

Word Analysis. Examine the words and/or phrases for each question below and determine the relationship among the majority of words/phrases. Choose the option which does not fit the pattern.

53) a. silica content   b. temperature   c. dissolved gases   d. pressure

Answer: D
Diff: 1

54) a. pahoehoe   b. aa   c. volcanic bomb   d. pillow lava

Answer: C
Diff: 1

55) a. ash   b. crystals   c. lapilli   d. blocks

Answer: B
Diff: 1

56) a. caldera   b. pipe   c. crater   d. fumarole

Answer: A
Diff: 2

57) a. Mt. Vesuvius   b. Mt. Mazama   c. Mount Pelée   d. Kilauea

Answer: D
Diff: 1

58) a. sill   b. batholith   c. dike   d. laccolith

Answer: B
Diff: 1

59) Dissolved gases may comprise up to a few percent by weight of a magma.

Answer: TRUE
Diff: 1

60) Ash and lapilli are different sized pyroclastic particles.

Answer: TRUE
Diff: 1

61) The viscosities of magmas increase with increasing percentages of silica.

Answer: TRUE
Diff: 1

62) The eruptions of the Hawaiian volcanoes may be described as explosive in comparison to the 1980 Mount St. Helens eruption.

Answer: FALSE
Diff: 1

63) Powerful, explosive, volcanic eruptions can result in climatic cooling for millions of years following the eruption.

Answer: FALSE
Diff: 1

64) Magma generation at depth almost always involves partial melting, not complete melting of the source rock.

Answer: TRUE
Diff: 1

65) The active Hawaiian volcanoes are situated directly above a major boundary between two of the Earth's largest tectonic plates.

Answer: FALSE
Diff: 1

66) Most basaltic magmas are believed to form by partial melting of granite in the lower crust and upper mantle.

Answer: FALSE
Diff: 1

67) Basaltic lavas are generally hotter and more viscous than andesite lavas.

Answer: FALSE
Diff: 1

68) Small amounts of water can lower partial melting temperatures in silicate rocks.

Answer: TRUE
Diff: 1

69) Repeated eruptions of relatively fluid lava from fissures can eventually cause an area to be covered by flood basalts.

Answer: TRUE
Diff: 1

70) In general, cinder cones are much larger than shield volcanoes.

Answer: FALSE
Diff: 1

71) Crater Lake in Oregon actually occupies a caldera, not a crater.

Answer: TRUE
Diff: 2

72) Vents that emit only heated, volcanic gases and water are called fumaroles.

Answer: TRUE
Diff: 1

73) Aa flows are generally thinner and have smoother surfaces than pahoehoe flows.

Answer: FALSE
Diff: 1

74) Basalt is the most common magma erupted along oceanic rift systems.

Answer: TRUE
Diff: 1

75) Composite volcanic cones are also known as _____.

Answer: stratovolcanoes
Diff: 1

76) _____ is the most abundant gaseous component dissolved in most magmas.

Answer: H_2O
Diff: 1

77) Vents that emit only hot gases and vapors are called _____.

Answer: fumaroles
Diff: 1

78) Large, volcanic depressions formed by subsidence and collapse are known as _____.

Answer: calderas
Diff: 1

79) Which basaltic lava flow has a relatively smooth surface?

Answer: pahoehoe
Diff: 1

80) What term describes fragmental volcanic material?

Answer: pyroclastic
Diff: 1

81) _____ denotes a basaltic lava flow covered with angular, congealed lava rubble.

Answer: Aa
Diff: 1

82) _____ is a dangerous, fast moving, hot, turbulent cloud of volcanic gases and fine–sized, pyroclastic particles.

Answer: Nueé ardente
Diff: 1

83) A relatively small, summit depression on a volcano, marking a former eruptive vent, is a

_____.

Answer: crater
Diff: 1

84) Pyroclastic fragments intermediate in size between ash and bombs are known as _____.

Answer: lapilli
Diff: 1

85) What kind of volcanoes are Kilauea and the other big Hawaiian volcanoes?

Answer: shield
Diff: 1

86) Another term for a volcanic mudflow is a _____.

Answer: lahar
Diff: 1

87) Which kind of volcano is closely associated with convergent plate boundaries and subduction zones?

Answer: composite or stratovolcano
Diff: 1

88) Which tabular, discordant igneous rock body intrudes along a crack or fissure?

Answer: dike
Diff: 1

89) A very large, discordant pluton, commonly of composed of granite is a _____.

Answer: granite
Diff: 1

90) A small, igneous rock body emplaced at shallow depths by uplift and arching of the overlying, older strata is a _____.

Answer: laccolith
Diff: 1

Critical thinking and discussion questions. Use complete sentences, correct spelling, and the information presented in Chapter 4 to answer the questions below.

91) Aside from near oceanic trenches, most earthquakes originate at depths of 100 kilometers or less. Considering the physical properties of Earth's interior, what type of mechanical behavior (in rocks) must be necessary for earthquakes to occur? Explain.

Diff: 2

92) Catastrophism obviously influenced seventeenth and eighteenth century thought by implying that Earth only needed to be a few thousand years old to explain landscapes and geologic features. However, catastrophic and often sudden changes are at least a part of the rock record that geologist's attempt to interpret. List three geologic catastrophes that would most likely affect landscapes or features on Earth and be recorded in rocks. How might these events be explained in the rock record using only uniformitarianism (or the implication of slow, gradual change)?

Diff: 3

93) Earth's physical environment is traditionally divided in the hydrosphere, atmosphere, and the solid Earth. Remembering the scientific method, why do you think that scientists tend to categorize and classify various features, phenomena, and characteristics of the natural world into groups or subdivisions? Also, are there potential pitfalls or problems if we only consider the natural world as individual groups or categories rather than as a whole?

Diff: 3

94) What type of volcano is shown in the diagram below?

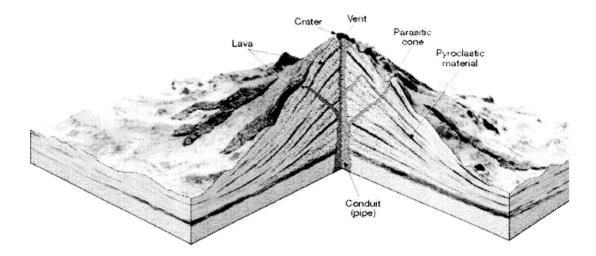

Answer: composite
Diff: 1

95) What type of volcano is shown in the diagram below?

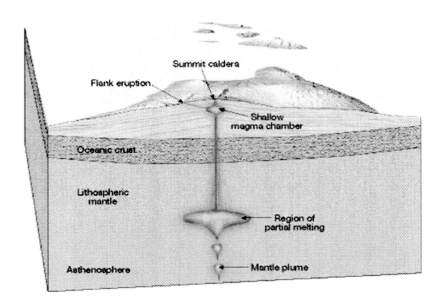

Answer: shield
Diff: 1

96) What type of volcano is shown in the diagram below?

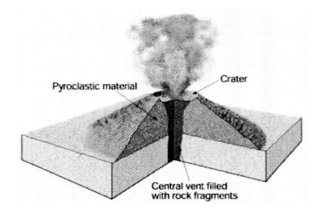

Answer: cinder cone
Diff: 1

97) What volcanic feature is shown in the diagram below?

Answer: lava dome
Diff: 1

98) On the blanks provided, write the name of the feature labeled. On the same blank, indicate with capital letters whether the feature is concordant (C) or discordant (D) and whether the feature is tabular (T) or massive (M).

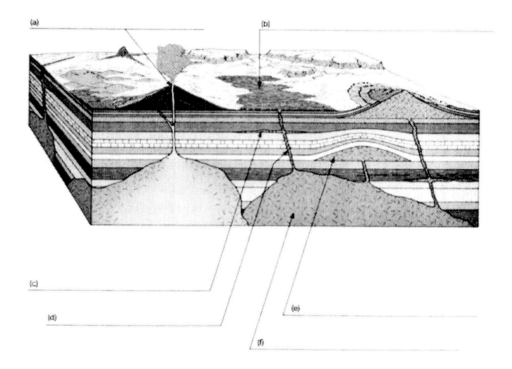

Answer: a. volcano, D, M
b. lava flow, C, T
c. sill, C, T
d. dike, D, T
e. laccolith, C, M
f. batholith, D, M

Diff: 2

99) What is the name of the chain of volcanoes below that forms at an oceanic to oceanic plate boundary?

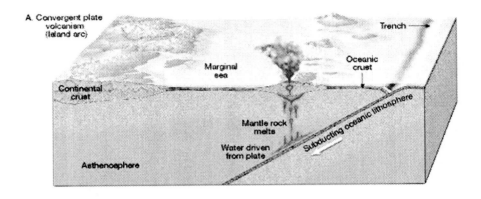

Answer: volcanic island arc
Diff: 1

100) What is the name of the chain of volcanoes below that forms at an oceanic to continental plate boundary?

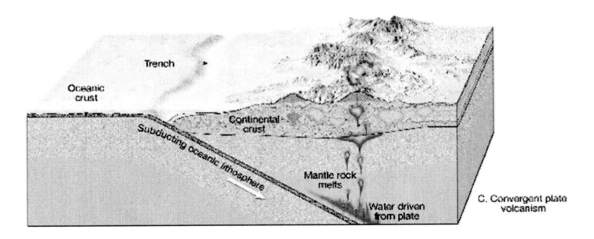

Answer: continental volcanic arc
Diff: 1

Chapter 5 Weathering and Soils

1) Clay minerals formed from gabbro or diorite bedrock illustrate which kind of weathering?
   A) chemical
   B) proactive
   C) syntropical
   D) mechanical
   Answer: A
   Diff: 1

2) Which of the following is/are most susceptible to chemical weathering by dissolution?
   A) quartz
   B) clay minerals
   C) iron oxides
   D) calcite
   Answer: D
   Diff: 1

3) Frost wedging is the major weathering process contributing to the formation of which regolith material?
   A) tropical laterites
   B) talus slopes
   C) C soil horizons
   D) mature pedalfers
   Answer: B
   Diff: 1

4) What portion of an angular, fracture-bounded granitic block shows the highest rate of weathering?
   A) the unfractured interior
   B) the edges and corners
   C) the crack surfaces not including edges and corners
   D) all of the above show equal rates
   Answer: B
   Diff: 1

5) Which of the following describes a characteristic process in the formation of a pedalfer soil?
   A) soil bacteria produce organic acids that precipitate calcium carbonate in the B-horizon
   B) iron oxides and aluminum-rich clays are precipitated in the B-horizon
   C) humus accumulates below the solum in the C-horizon
   D) clays are eluviated upward from the C-horizon
   Answer: B
   Diff: 1

6) Why is the humus layer typically thicker in a cool, temperate, forest soil than in a tropical rainforest soil?
   A) less humus is produced in the tropical rainforest because the B–horizon is so poorly developed
   B) less humus is produced in the cool, temperate forest but the rate of decay and oxidation is slower than in a tropical rainforest
   C) more humus is produced in the tropical rainforest, but it is quickly washed away by the heavy rains
   D) in a tropical rainforest, the forest–floor litter is often burned during the dry season

Answer: B
Diff: 2

7) Clay minerals, silica (SiO_2), and dissolved potassium bicarbonate in the soil water are products of which process?
   A) chemical weathering of olivine and plagioclase feldspar
   B) mechanical weathering of granite and rhyolite
   C) chemical weathering of orthoclase feldspar
   D) differential mechanical weathering of micas

Answer: C
Diff: 1

8) What two factors speed up rates of chemical reaction and weathering in rocks and soils?
   A) low temperatures; very dry
   B) low temperatures; very moist
   C) high temperatures; very dry
   D) warm temperatures; very moist

Answer: D
Diff: 1

9) In terrain with steep hill slopes, which crop and cultivation technique will minimize soil erosion?
   A) corn; rows trending straight down the slope, frequent cultivation
   B) apples; land between the trees is planted in grass and not cultivated
   C) winter wheat; after the harvest, the field is plowed and left idle until next fall
   D) bean, rows are spaced wider than on a level field

Answer: B
Diff: 2

10) In which area are pedocal soils most likely to be found?
   A) a tropical rainforest in the Amazon Basin of Brazil
   B) a bitterly cold, permafrost area in north–central Siberia
   C) a forested area of the southeastern United States
   D) a moderately dry to semiarid grassland such as the western Great Plains

Answer: D
Diff: 1

11) In the Rocky Mountain region of the United States, north-facing slopes (downhill direction is toward the north) are typically more moist and heavily forested than south-facing slopes. Why?
A) north-facing slopes receive more sunlight in the summer; snow melts faster and more soil moisture is available for the trees
B) south-facing slopes receive more moisture and sunlight; rock weathering is slower
C) north-facing slopes receive about the same amount of precipitation as south-facing slopes; less moisture evaporates from north-facing slopes
D) south-facing slopes receive less moisture, yet rock weathering is faster

Answer: C
Diff: 2

12) The finely divided, red, brown, and yellow soil-coloring minerals originate by what process?
A) mechanical weathering of very fine-grained, blue-gray clays
B) chemical weathering of quartz and feldspars
C) precipitation of iron oxides during the chemical weathering process
D) mechanical weathering of the feldspars and micas in granite and rhyolite

Answer: C
Diff: 1

13) Which of the following statements about acidic precipitation is likely to be false?
A) chemical weathering and deterioration of exposed rock and metal surfaces will accelerate if acidic precipitation increases
B) lowered taxes and relaxed governmental regulations will result in more private and public sector spending to reduce emissions of acid-forming gases to the atmosphere
C) fish and other aquatic species in acidified lakes will eventually die off and disappear due to the toxic effects of the acidic waters and increased levels of dissolved aluminum
D) damage to trees and plants, especially to tender new growth, will intensify if acidic precipitation worsens

Answer: B
Diff: 1

14) Which of the following statements about laterites or tropical rainforests is true?
A) laterite soils readily compact and hardened when dried and exposed to sunlight
B) rainforests regenerate quickly following clear cutting or clearing for agriculture
C) laterite soils are very rich in nutrients required for vigorous plant growth
D) laterites, with proper management, are very suitable for commercial agriculture

Answer: A
Diff: 1

15) Which of the following best describes the "Dust Bowl"?
A) the long drought preceding the Irish potato famine of the 1840s
B) the area covered by volcanic ash around Mt. Pinatubo, 1991
C) areas of severe wind erosion on the Great Plains, 1930s
D) a New Year's Day invitational soccer match in Tripoli, Libya

Answer: C
Diff: 1

16) Which one of the following is an important, mechanical weathering process for enlarging fractures and extending them deeper into large boulders and bedrock?
   A) oxidation
   B) eluviation
   C) hydrologic cycling
   D) frost wedging

Answer: D
Diff: 1

17) Which of the following best describes sets of fractures in relatively fresh bedrock, such as granite, that are roughly parallel to the land surface?
   A) thermal expansion cracks
   B) sheeting fractures
   C) hydrolytic failures
   D) columnar joints

Answer: B
Diff: 1

18) What two, chemical constituents cannot form by chemical weathering of the feldspar minerals?
   A) soluble sodium and potassium bicarbonates
   B) insoluble iron oxides and soluble magnesium bicarbonates
   C) silica and insoluble clay minerals
   D) silica and soluble calcium bicarbonate

Answer: B
Diff: 1

19) Under similar warm, moist climatic conditions, why would basalt and gabbro generally have higher chemical weathering rates than rhyolite and granite?
   A) the quartz in the gabbro and basalt decomposes very quickly
   B) the ferromagnesian minerals in the gabbro and basalt are subject to oxidation and chemical breakdown
   C) the plagioclase feldspars in the granite and rhyolite decompose readily to clay minerals and iron oxides
   D) the potassium feldspars and quartz in the rhyolite and granite are more susceptible to cracking by frost wedging

Answer: B
Diff: 2

20) Which one of the following statements concerning mechanical weathering is not true?
   A) reduces grain sizes of rock particles
   B) allows for faster rates of chemical weathering
   C) is important in the formation of talus slopes
   D) involves a major change in the mineral composition of the weathered material

Answer: D
Diff: 1

21) Which term describes a soil formed by weathering of the underlying bedrock?
    A) transformational
    B) residual
    C) relict
    D) transported
Answer: B
Diff: 1

22) Which one of the following statements best describes erosion?
    A) disintegration and decomposition of rocks and minerals at the surface
    B) movement of weathered rock and regolith toward the base of a slope
    C) the process by which weathered rock and mineral particles are removed from one area and transported elsewhere
    D) the combined processes of leaching, eluviation, and mass wasting
Answer: C
Diff: 1

23) Which term best describes those processes that move weathered rock materials and soils downslope?
    A) podzolization
    B) slope sheeting
    C) mass wasting
    D) talus transfer
Answer: C
Diff: 1

24) Assume that water filling a crack in a rock undergoes cycles of freezing and melting. Which of the following statement is true?
    A) water expands as it melts, causing the crack walls to be pushed apart
    B) water shrinks as it freezes, causing the crack walls to be drawn closer together
    C) water expands as it freezes, causing the crack walls to be pushed apart
    D) water shrinks as it melts, causing the crack walls to be pulled closer together
Answer: C
Diff: 1

25) Which of the following best describe the A soil horizon?
    A) regolith zone
    B) erosion zone
    C) residual zone
    D) leaching zone
Answer: D
Diff: 1

26) What mineral particles are the dominant coloring agents in reddish, brownish, and yellowish soils?
    A) soluble potassium and sodium bicarbonates
    B) humus and calcium carbonate
    C) very fine-sized, silica and calcite particles
    D) dust-sized grains of iron oxides
Answer: D
Diff: 1

27) Which term best describes an accumulation of angular rock fragments at the base of a steep, bedrock slope or cliff?
    A) trellis slope
    B) taliche slope
    C) tellus slope
    D) talus slope
Answer: D
Diff: 1

28) In which area would weathering by frost wedging probably be most effective?
    A) in a moist, tropical forest
    B) in cool high desert areas
    C) where the subsoil is permanently frozen
    D) in moist, temperate climates
Answer: D
Diff: 1

29) Which one of the following statements concerning soil erosion is not true?
    A) sheet erosion, rills, and gullies develop mainly during prolonged droughts
    B) soils form naturally by weathering; if protected from erosion, sound management can maintain or enhance their nutrient levels and textural characteristics
    C) rates of soil erosion exceed rates of soil formation in some parts of the world
    D) grasses and other vegetation, windbreaks, and contour cropping will help reduce losses of soil from cultivated lands
Answer: A
Diff: 1

30) Lateritic soils form under what climatic conditions?
    A) warm and moist as in a wet, tropical forest
    B) cool and relatively dry as in the northern Great Plains of the United States
    C) hot and dry as in the desert regions of North Africa and Arabia
    D) moist and temperate as in the northeastern United States
Answer: A
Diff: 1

31) Which of the following statements concerning humus is not true?
    A) is typically found above the B soil horizon
    B) consists of decaying and partly decayed leaves and other plant materials
    C) is readily leached from the B horizon in weakly acidic, soil solutions
    D) is less abundant in wet, tropical, forested areas than in temperate, forested areas
Answer: C
Diff: 1

32) Which of the following statements concerning lateritic soils is generally not true?
    A) they form in warm, moist, tropical climates
    B) they are mainly red in color
    C) they remain highly productive agriculturally without additions of fertilizers
    D) they consist of only the most insoluble, soil-forming minerals
Answer: C
Diff: 1

33) Caliche is an excessive accumulation of _____.
    A) calcite in the E horizon of a pedalfer
    B) clays in the A horizon of a laterite
    C) clays in hardpan layers of a pedocal
    D) calcium carbonate in the B-horizon of a pedocal
Answer: D
Diff: 1

34) Which of the following best describes the process of eluviation?
    A) removal of very fine-sized silt and clay particles from the A and E soil horizons
    B) buildup of calcite in the B-horizon of pedocal soils
    C) removal of soluble chemical constituents from the A and B soil horizons
    D) feldspar decomposition and leaching of the soluble products from the C soil horizon
Answer: A
Diff: 1

35) From the land surface downward to the unweathered bedrock, which of the following is the correct order of the different soil horizons?
    A) 0, A, E, B, C, bedrock
    B) A, B, C, D, E, bedrock
    C) E, A, B, C, 0, bedrock
    D) D, E, C, B, A, bedrock
Answer: A
Diff: 1

Word Analysis. Examine the words and/or phrases for each question below and determine the relationship among the majority of words/phrases. Choose the option which does not fit the pattern.

36) a. frost wedging   b. mass wasting   c. sheeting   d. oxidation
Answer: B
Diff: 1

37) a. oxidation   b. dissolution   c. hydrolysis   d. sheeting
Answer: D
Diff: 1

38) a. surface area   b. rock characteristics   c. geologic age   d. climate
Answer: C
Diff: 2

39) a. topography   b. time   c. parent material   d. elevation
Answer: D
Diff: 2

40) a. C-horizon   b. A horizon   c. E horizon   d. B-horizon
Answer: A
Diff: 1

41) Quartz weathers readily to aluminum-rich clay minerals.
Answer: FALSE
Diff: 1

42) Abundant moisture and warm temperatures result in high rates of chemical weathering.

Answer: TRUE
Diff: 1

43) Very fine-grained, iron oxide particles account for nearly all red, yellow, and brown soil colors.

Answer: TRUE
Diff: 1

44) In pedalfer soils, the B-horizon is enriched in calcite and humus.

Answer: FALSE
Diff: 1

45) Pedocal soils typically form by intense chemical weathering under very cold and wet climatic conditions.

Answer: FALSE
Diff: 1

46) Pedalfers form more readily than pedocals under conditions of low soil moisture content.

Answer: FALSE
Diff: 1

47) Oxidation of iron is an important chemical weathering process for ferromagnesian silicate minerals like olivine and biotite.

Answer: TRUE
Diff: 1

48) Sheeting is mainly a process of mechanical weathering.

Answer: TRUE
Diff: 1

49) Sheeting fractures and exfoliation domes commonly develop in areas with soft, highly fractured bedrock.

Answer: TRUE
Diff: 1

50) Quartz is quite resistant to weathering and is an important component of sands in riverbeds and on beaches.

Answer: TRUE
Diff: 1

51) Feldspars commonly decompose during weathering to clay minerals, silica, and soluble constituents.

Answer: TRUE
Diff: 1

52) Humus is a concentration of decaying, organic matter in the B-horizons of lateritic soils.

Answer: FALSE
Diff: 1

53) Calcite, a major component of some monumental and building stones, slowly dissolves in weakly acidic waters.

Answer: TRUE
Diff: 1

54) Like most other liquids, water decreases in volume when it freezes.

Answer: FALSE
Diff: 1

55) Chemical weathering in bedrock below the land surface often begins along joints and sheeting fractures.

Answer: TRUE
Diff: 1

56) Removal of soluble chemical constituents from a soil is termed leaching.

Answer: TRUE
Diff: 1

57) The material caliche represents an extensive, concrete-like accumulation of calcite in the B-horizon of a pedalfer soil.

Answer: FALSE
Diff: 1

58) The solum or true soil includes all horizons above the C-horizon.

Answer: TRUE
Diff: 1

59) Ferromagnesian minerals (like olivine and pyroxene) that crystallize at high temperatures in Bowen's reaction series are generally much less susceptible to chemical weathering than quartz.

Answer: FALSE
Diff: 1

60) Decomposition of pyrite is an important factor in generating acidic mine drainage.

Answer: TRUE
Diff: 1

61) What kind of weathering involves only a reduction in the sizes of bedrock, regolith, and mineral particles?

Answer: mechanical
Diff: 1

62) Half Dome in Yosemite National Park, California, and Stone Mountain in Georgia, are shaped mainly by what mechanical weathering process?

Answer: sheeting
Diff: 1

63) Which form of chemical weathering specifically affects the iron contained in ferromagnesian, rock-forming, silicate minerals?

Answer: oxidation
Diff: 1

64) What is the most abundant, naturally produced, weak acid involved in chemical weathering and soil formation?

Answer: carbonic
Diff: 1

65) The very fine-sized, clay mineral particles move downward from the A to the B-horizon of some soils. What is this process called?

Answer: eluviation
Diff: 1

66) Under most weathering conditions, which mineral component of granites and rhyolites would be most resistant to decomposition?

Answer: quartz
Diff: 1

67) What term describes the layer of partly decayed plant matter at the top of the soil profile in most forested areas?

Answer: humus
Diff: 1

68) What term refers to removal of soluble constituents from soils?

Answer: leaching
Diff: 1

69) Which term denotes the true soil above the zone of partly weathered bedrock?

Answer: solum
Diff: 1

70) What term describes a soil that has developed from silt and clay deposited by a flooding river?

Answer: transported
Diff: 1

71) Would you call the loose, unconsolidated, surface material on Mars regolith or soil?

Answer: regolith
Diff: 1

Critical thinking and discussion questions. Use complete sentences, correct spelling, and the information presented in Chapter 5 to answer the questions below.

72) Based on the examples and discussion in Chapter 5, what is the relationship of climate to weathering, both chemical and mechanical? Also, are certain climates more susceptible to certain types of weathering? Why or why not?
Diff: 2

73) Briefly discuss the classification of soils. What parameters are important? What characteristics or features are evaluated for distinguishing between different types of soils?
Diff: 2

74) How does weathering and the development of soils influence the topography and landforms in a given region? Are certain landforms indicative of the particular bedrock geology of a region or is that determined more by weathering?
Diff: 3

75) What process does the diagram below illustrate?

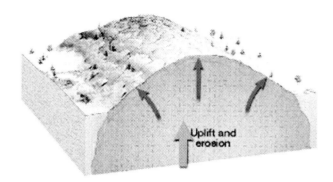

Answer: sheeting
Diff: 1

76) Carefully examine the illustration below and the features labeled A through D. Give a letter (A, B, C, or D) for each answer below.

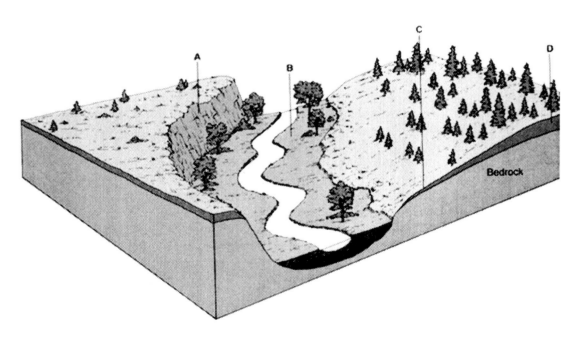

At which location would the thickest residual soil develop? (a) _____
At which location would the greatest amount of frost wedging occur? (b) _____
At which location would the thickest transported soil develop? (c) _____
At which location would there be the most unconsolidated deposits? (d) _____

Answer: (a) D (b) A (c) B (d) B
Diff: 2

77) Fill in the blanks on the diagram below with the names of the soil "layers" that are labeled.

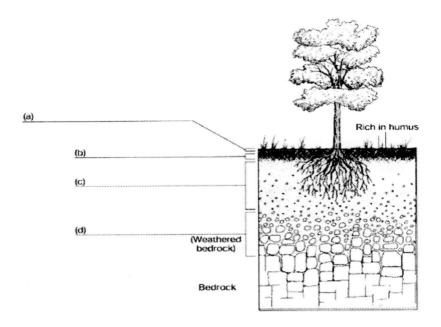

Answer: (a) O horizon (b) A horizon (c) B horizon (d) C horizon
Diff: 1

Chapter 6 Sedimentary Rocks

1) _____, a common mineral found in igneous rocks, is the most abundant mineral in detrital sedimentary rocks.
   A) Calcite
   B) Orthoclase
   C) Quartz
   D) Biotite

   Answer: C
   Diff: 1

2) Which major component of detrital sedimentary rocks only rarely occurs as a primary mineral in igneous rocks?
   A) clays
   B) carbonates
   C) quartz
   D) ferromagnesian minerals

   Answer: A
   Diff: 1

3) Zircon and tourmaline are dense, highly insoluble, chemically stable, minor minerals of igneous and metamorphic rocks. In which sedimentary rock might you expect to find these minerals concentrated?
   A) sandstone lithified from quartz–rich beach sand
   B) limestone representing lithified coral–reef carbonates
   C) a thin, upper, mudstone portion of a thick graywacke bed with graded bedding
   D) evaporite deposits of gypsum and salt

   Answer: A
   Diff: 1

Match the sediment with the appropriate rock name.
   a. sand   b. clay and fine silt   c. gravel   d. all clay sediment

4) sandstone

   Answer: a
   Diff: 1

5) shale

   Answer: d
   Diff: 1

6) conglomerate

   Answer: c
   Diff: 1

7) mudstone

   Answer: b
   Diff: 1

8) Compaction is a very important part of the lithification process for which of the following sediments?
    A) gravel
    B) sand
    C) mud
    D) cobble
Answer: C
Diff: 1

9) A cherty limestone would contain which major constituents?
    A) iron oxide, calcite
    B) silica; iron oxide
    C) clay minerals
    D) silica; calcite
Answer: D
Diff: 1

10) Which of the following best describes bedded gypsum and halite?
    A) detrital sedimentary rocks
    B) varieties of dolostone
    C) varieties of coal and peat
    D) evaporates; chemical, sedimentary rocks
Answer: D
Diff: 1

11) _____ sandstone contains abundant feldspar, suggesting that the sand was derived by weathering and erosion of granitic bedrock.
    A) Quartz–rich
    B) Lignitic
    C) Arkosic
    D) Oolitic
Answer: C
Diff: 1

12) _____ cement produces bright–red and yellow colors in some sandstone.
    A) Clay
    B) Calcite
    C) Quartz
    D) Iron oxide
Answer: D
Diff: 1

13) What is probably the single most important, original, depositional feature in sedimentary rocks?
    A) sizes of the sand grains
    B) degree of lithification
    C) bedding or stratification
    D) compaction of the mud and clay
Answer: C
Diff: 1

14) Which of the following would retain the most detailed impressions of fossilized organisms?
    A) very fine-grained volcanic ash deposited in an ancient lake
    B) an ancient, rainforest lateritic soil buried by basalt lava flows
    C) quartz-rich sand deposited in shallow, beachfront environment
    D) gravel and sand stream deposits laid down during flash floods
Answer: A
Diff: 1

15) What is a bittern?
    A) an evaporate sedimentary rock rich in gypsum and halite
    B) the dark-gray, clay-rich matrix of an arkose
    C) residual brine left after precipitation of halite
    D) an algal limestone mound deposited in an atoll lagoon
Answer: C
Diff: 1

16) _____ are further concentrated in a residual brine after NaCl is crystallized.
    A) Iron, sodium, and chlorine
    B) Magnesium, calcium, and sulfur
    C) Calcium, sulfur, and titanium
    D) Potassium, magnesium, and bromine
Answer: D
Diff: 1

17) Studies of deep-sea sediment cores have contributed greatly to scientific knowledge of
_____.
    A) climatic changes during the last four million years
    B) how soft-bodied organisms are carbonized
    C) the origin of oscillation ripple marks in deep-sea muds
    D) the biological impacts of pollution on parts of the continental shelves
Answer: A
Diff: 1

18) What is the main difference between a conglomerate and a sedimentary breccia?
    A) breccia clasts are angular; conglomerate clasts are rounded
    B) a breccia is well stratified; a conglomerate is poorly stratified
    C) breccia clasts are the size of baseballs; conglomerate clasts are larger
    D) breccia has a compacted, clay-rich matrix; conglomerate has no matrix
Answer: A
Diff: 1

19) Which of the following describes the correct order for relative solubility of minerals in sedimentary rocks?
    A) evaporate minerals are more soluble than quartz and less soluble than calcite
    B) evaporate minerals are less soluble than quartz and calcite
    C) evaporate minerals are more soluble than calcite and quartz
    D) evaporate minerals, quartz, and calcite all have the same relative solubility
Answer: C
Diff: 1

20) A graywacke is _____.
    A) a limestone with abundant, sand-sized, quartz grains
    B) a sandstone with the sand grains embedded in a clay-rich matrix
    C) a dark-gray, calcite-rich mudstone or shale containing pyrite
    D) a dark, organic-rich, chemical sedimentary rock containing small crystals of halite

Answer: B
Diff: 1

21) Which statement concerning sedimentary rocks is not true?
    A) they may contain fossils that provide clues about ancient life forms
    B) they probably show some evidence of stratification
    C) they were originally deposited at depth below the bottom of the sea
    D) they are composed of particles and constituents derived from weathering and erosion of
       other rocks

Answer: C
Diff: 1

22) Which type of limestone consists mainly of tiny, marine fossils composed of calcite?
    A) dolostone
    B) chert
    C) coquina
    D) chalk

Answer: D
Diff: 1

23) _____ is not a common cementing agent for sandstones.
    A) Quartz
    B) Calcite
    C) Fluorite
    D) Iron oxides

Answer: C
Diff: 1

24) Detrital sedimentary rocks are classified (named) based on the _____.
    A) colors of the cementing minerals
    B) grain sizes of the detrital particles
    C) compositions of soluble minerals
    D) degree of compaction and lithification

Answer: B
Diff: 1

25) Which of the following applies to the basic constituents of halite, gypsum, and sylvite?
    A) transported as dissolved ions; deposited as detrital mud
    B) transported as detrital mud; deposited by evaporation
    C) transported as dissolved ions; deposited by evaporation
    D) transported and deposited as mud-sized particles

Answer: C
Diff: 1

26) Flint, chert, and jasper are microcrystalline forms of _____.
   A) quartz; (SiO_2)
   B) hematite ($Fe2O_3$)
   C) halite (NaCl)
   D) calcite ($CaCO_3$)

   Answer: A
   Diff: 1

27) Sedimentary rocks account for about what percentage of the Earth's outermost 10 kilometers of rock (first percentage). Also, what percentage of the Earth's continental area is covered by sedimentary rocks (second percentage)?
   A) 5% & 75%
   B) 3.5% & 100%
   C) 65% & 10%
   D) 85% & 100%

   Answer: A
   Diff: 1

28) Which of the following sedimentary rocks would you expect to have originally been deposited by fast-moving streams?
   A) mudstone
   B) oolitic limestone
   C) greywacke
   D) conglomerate

   Answer: D
   Diff: 2

29) Which type of sediment undergoes the most compaction as it lithifies to sedimentary rocks?
   A) marine mud
   B) desert dune sand
   C) reef limestone
   D) coarse gravel

   Answer: A
   Diff: 1

30) Detrital grains of which mineral(s) are extremely rare in detrital sediments? Why?
   A) calcite; it is soft and relatively soluble
   B) clays; they are rare in soils and regolith
   C) quartz; it is very hard and insoluble
   D) feldspars; they occur only in granites

   Answer: A
   Diff: 2

31) Which of the following sedimentary features would typically be found in shales but not in sandstones?
   A) mud cracks
   B) cross stratification
   C) ripple marks
   D) bedding

   Answer: A
   Diff: 1

32) _____ is the most common type of chemical sedimentary rock.
   A) Limestone
   B) Chert
   C) Phosphate rock
   D) Quartz sandstone
Answer: A
Diff: 1

33) _____ is a form of calcium carbonate.
   A) Travertine
   B) Chert
   C) Lignite
   D) Gypsum
Answer: A
Diff: 1

34) Which one of the following is not a chemical sedimentary rock or evaporite?
   A) shale
   B) bedded gypsum
   C) cherty dolostone
   D) oolitic limestone
Answer: A
Diff: 1

35) Which of the following is not a type of limestone?
   A) arkose
   B) coquina
   C) chalk
   D) travertine
Answer: A
Diff: 1

36) Oolitic limestone is most likely to form in what type of depositional environment?
   A) quiet, muddy, lagoons and bays
   B) shallow, clear, marine waters with vigorous current activity
   C) deep, marine waters below most wave action
   D) acidic, organic-rich waters in freshwater swamps and bogs
Answer: B
Diff: 2

37) What is the chemical formula for dolomite, the major mineral in dolostones?
   A) NaCl
   B) $CaSO_4 \cdot 2H20$
   C) SiO_2
   D) $CaMg(CO_3)_2$
Answer: D
Diff: 1

38) Which of the following sedimentary features can each be used to determine paleocurrent directions?
    A) mud cracks and ripple marks
    B) ripple marks and cross stratification
    C) fossils and mud cracks
    D) grain size sorting and ripple marks
Answer: B
Diff: 1

39) Coal beds originate in _____.
    A) shallow lakes in a dry, desert region
    B) channels of fast-moving streams
    C) deep, marine basins below wave action
    D) freshwater coastal swamps and bogs
Answer: D
Diff: 1

40) Which characteristic is absolutely necessary for a sedimentary rock to have potential as a possible reservoir rock for oil or gas?
    A) high porosity
    B) clastic texture
    C) chemical origin
    D) good stratification
Answer: A
Diff: 1

41) Nonclastic textures are common in which of the following sedimentary rocks?
    A) sandstones
    B) limestones
    C) boulder breccias
    D) cherty conglomerates
Answer: B
Diff: 1

Word Analysis. Examine the words and/or phrases for each question below and determine the relationship among the majority of words/phrases. Choose the option which does not fit the pattern.

42) a. lithification   b. cementation   c. weathering   d. compaction
    Answer: C
    Diff: 1

43) a. shale   b. sandstone   c. breccia   d. conglomerate
    Answer: A
    Diff: 2

44) a. limestone   b. chert   c. coquina   d. travertine
    Answer: B
    Diff: 1

45) a. floodplain   b. alluvial fan   c. playa lakes   d. lagoon

Answer: D

Diff: 1

46) a. graded bedding   b. ripple marks   c. mud cracks   d. cross-bedding

Answer: A

Diff: 1

47) Clay and muddy sediments lithify to form shales and mudstones.

Answer: TRUE

Diff: 1

48) Detrital sedimentary rocks have clastic textures.

Answer: TRUE

Diff: 1

49) Peat is thought to be the original material from which coals are formed.

Answer: TRUE

Diff: 1

50) Graywacke sandstones are typically better sorted than sandstones lithified from ancient beach sands.

Answer: FALSE

Diff: 1

51) Clastic particles in a sedimentary breccia are rounded and are about the same size as fine-grained sand.

Answer: FALSE

Diff: 1

52) Many limestones are of biochemical origin.

Answer: TRUE

Diff: 1

53) Boulder conglomerates suggest deposition by strong winds in a desert.

Answer: FALSE

Diff: 1

54) Mud cracks in a shale or mudstone indicate that the mud or clay was deposited in deep waters of an offshore marine environment.

Answer: FALSE

Diff: 1

55) Chalk, coquina, and ancient coral reefs are primarily composed of microcrystalline quartz.

Answer: FALSE

Diff: 1

56) Water is gradually expelled from compacting clay and mud sediments.

Answer: TRUE

Diff: 1

57) The mineral dolomite, which is the major mineral of the sedimentary rock dolostone, is a carbonate of calcium and magnesium.

Answer: TRUE
Diff: 1

58) The chemical sedimentary rock, conglomerate, is composed of gravel–size, rounded, calcite oolites.

Answer: FALSE
Diff: 1

59) Detrital sedimentary rocks are classified according to clastic particle size; chemical sedimentary rocks are named according to the most abundant minerals.

Answer: TRUE
Diff: 1

60) A feldspar–rich sandstone is called an arkose.

Answer: TRUE
Diff: 1

61) What is the most abundant mineral in detrital sedimentary rocks?

Answer: quartz
Diff: 1

62) Which variety of limestone consists mainly of sand–sized, mostly spherical grains of calcium carbonate precipitated in shallow, marine waters?

Answer: oolitic
Diff: 1

63) Which is the most common, chemical, sedimentary rock?

Answer: limestone
Diff: 1

64) What is the general name for microcrystalline quartz in sedimentary rocks?

Answer: chert
Diff: 1

65) Which evaporite sedimentary rock, composed of calcium sulfate, is an important component of plasters and wallboard?

Answer: gypsum
Diff: 1

66) Red, brown and yellow sandstones are cemented by oxides of _____.

Answer: iron
Diff: 1

67) What are the three, most common, cementing agents for sandstones?

Answer: silica, calcite, iron oxide
Diff: 1

68) Sandstones are lithified mainly by cementation. What is the major process involved in the lithification of shales?

Answer: compaction
Diff: 1

69) Which property of sediment describes the range of different grain sizes in a detrital sedimentary rock?

Answer: sorting
Diff: 1

70) The sedimentary rocks salt and gypsum are deposited by what process?

Answer: evaporation
Diff: 1

71) Flint and jasper are microcrystalline forms of _____.

Answer: quartz
Diff: 1

72) What is the most characteristic, original, depositional feature preserved in sedimentary rocks?

Answer: stratification
Diff: 1

73) What term describes the complex, original stratification pattern seen in sandstones deposited in ancient sand dunes?

Answer: cross–bedding
Diff: 1

74) _____ is composed mainly of lithified, organic debris that accumulated in ancient, heavily forested swamps?

Answer: coal
Diff: 1

Critical thinking and discussion questions. Use complete sentences, correct spelling, and the information presented in Chapter 6 to answer the questions below.

75) Fossils often provide valuable information about climatic conditions of the geologic past. How else might a geologist infer ancient climatic conditions using sedimentary rocks ? (Hint: Think in terms of the conditions necessary to form certain rocks and also features/structures found in sedimentary rocks.)

Diff: 3

76) Considering the factors, which influence the formation of sedimentary rocks, how might sedimentary rocks be different on another planet such as Mars or Venus? What about similarities?

Diff: 3

77) The study of depositional environments in sedimentary rocks is critical to understanding Earth's history. What features or characteristics of sedimentary rocks are unique to particular environments? What features are found in a variety of environments and are therefore less definitive for interpreting paleoenvironments?

Diff: 3

78) Fill in the missing sediment names on the following table.

Table 7.1	Particle Size Classification for Dentrital Rocks		
Size Range (millimeters)	Particle Name	Common Sediment Name	Dentrital Rock
< 256	Boulder		
64-256	Cobble		Conglomerate
4-64	Pebble		or breccia
2-4	Granule		
1/16-2	Sand		Sandstone
1/256-1/16	Silt		Shale. mudstone or
<1/256	Clay		siltstone

Answer: See Table 6.1 in the Essentials of Geology, 10e textbook.
Diff: 1

79) Label the various sedimentary facies on the diagram below.

Answer: See Figure 6.16 in the Essentials of Geology, 10e textbook.
Diff: 2

80) What kind of sedimentary structure is pictured in the photograph below? (a) _____
Explain how this kind of sedimentary structure forms. (b) _____

Answer: (a) mud cracks (b) Mud shrinks and cracks as it dries (as in an evaporating mud puddle).

Diff: 2

81) Carefully observe each of the photographs below of sedimentary rocks. To the right of each sample, name the rock and describe its origin (how it formed).

 (a) _____

 (b) _____

 (c) _____

Answer: (a) conglomerate. Origin: A poorly sorted mixture of rounded grains of sand and gravel was lithified.

(b) biochemical limestone or coquina. Origin: A mass of calcareous seashells and broken shells was cemented together.

(c) breccia. Origin: A poorly sorted mixture of angular grains of sand and gravel was lithified.

Diff: 2

Chapter 7 Metamorphic Rocks

1) Which of the following forms at the highest grade of regional metamorphism?
   A) hornfels
   B) schist
   C) slate
   D) phyllite

   Answer: B
   Diff: 1

2) What platy, parallel, mineral grains are the most visual aspect of foliated metamorphic rocks?
   A) micas
   B) feldspars
   C) carbonates
   D) quartz

   Answer: A
   Diff: 1

3) What major change occurs during metamorphism of limestone to marble?
   A) calcite grains grow larger and increase in size
   B) clays crystallize to micas, forming a highly foliated, mica-rich rock
   C) limestone grains react to form quartz and feldspars
   D) calcite grains are dissolved away leaving only marble crystals

   Answer: A
   Diff: 1

4) Which low-grade metamorphic rock, composed of extremely fine-sized mica and other mineral grains, typically exhibits well-developed rock cleavage?
   A) schist
   B) hornfels
   C) quartzite
   D) slate

   Answer: D
   Diff: 1

Please match the rock with the appropriate description.
   a. hornfels   b. marble   c. gneiss   d. phyllite

5) forms by contact metamorphism of mudstones and shales

   Answer: a
   Diff: 1

6) foliated, fine-grained metamorphic rock formed from mudstone and shale

   Answer: d
   Diff: 1

7) nonfoliated metamorphic rock consisting mostly of calcite

   Answer: b
   Diff: 1

8) coarse-grained, metamorphic rock with alternating bands or stringers of light and dark minerals

Answer: c
Diff: 1

9) _____ is thought to form by partial melting and in situ crystallization of the melted portion.
   A) Magmatite
   B) Magnetite
   C) Migmatite
   D) Megatite

Answer: C
Diff: 1

10) Tektites originate in what metamorphic environment?
    A) low pressure and high temperature associated with volcanism
    B) high temperatures associated with meteorite impacts
    C) very high pressures and temperatures associated with deep subduction
    D) high temperatures and shearing stresses in an oceanic–crust transform fault

Answer: B
Diff: 1

11) Which one of the following is not likely to be genetically associated with impact of an asteroid or large meteorite?
    A) tektites
    B) blueschists
    C) coesite
    D) impact crater

Answer: B
Diff: 1

12) Which of the following statements concerning slate is not true?
    A) forms from shales and mudstones
    B) has abundant, coarse–grained mica
    C) rock cleavage is common
    D) sedimentary features may be visible

Answer: B
Diff: 1

13) _____ is a strong, parallel alignment of coarse mica flakes and/or of different mineral bands in a metamorphic rock.
    A) Rock cleavage
    B) Foliation
    C) Stress streaking
    D) Marbleizing

Answer: B
Diff: 1

14) _____ is a nonfoliated rock formed by contact metamorphism of a shale or mudstone.
   A) Schist
   B) Marble
   C) Gneiss
   D) Hornfels

Answer: D
Diff: 1

15) Which of the following would exhibit sheared and mechanically fragmented rocks?
   A) fault movements at shallow depths
   B) intense compression in a deep-seated, regional metamorphic zone
   C) heating of shales and mudstones near a pluton
   D) regional metamorphism of pyroclastic volcanic rocks

Answer: A
Diff: 1

16) Which of the following best describes the conditions of contact metamorphism?
   A) pressures are very high, the rock is deeply buried, and temperatures are raised by the Earth's internal heat
   B) pressures are fairly low, the rock is in the upper part of the crust, and heat is supplied from a nearby magma body
   C) heat is generated by shearing and mechanical movements along faults
   D) depths are fairly shallow, but temperatures and pressures are so high that the rocks begin to partially melt

Answer: B
Diff: 1

17) _____ forms from the metamorphism of limestone or dolostone.
   A) Migmatite
   B) Amphibolite
   C) Marble
   D) Quartzite

Answer: C
Diff: 1

18) What foliated, metamorphic rock is texturally intermediate between slate and schist?
   A) fault breccia
   B) phyllite
   C) quartzite
   D) gneiss

Answer: B
Diff: 1

19) _____ is characterized by the segregation of light- and dark-colored minerals into thin layers or bands.
   A) Garnet hornfels
   B) Granitic gneiss
   C) Slate
   D) Quartzite

Answer: B
Diff: 1

20) What type of foliation results from the parallel alignment of abundant, coarse-grained, mica flakes in a metamorphic rock?
   A) schistosity
   B) gneissic banding
   C) slaty cleavage
   D) phyllitic structure

Answer: A
Diff: 1

21) Which of the following metamorphic rocks could be used to neutralize acidic mine waters?
   A) granite gneiss
   B) quartzite
   C) slate
   D) marble

Answer: D
Diff: 1

22) Which of the following lists the rocks in the order of increasing grain size and increasing grade of metamorphism?
   A) phyllite, slate, schist
   B) schist, slate, phyllite
   C) slate, phyllite, schist
   D) slate, schist, phyllite

Answer: C
Diff: 1

23) _____ is typically formed by metamorphism of a sandstone.
   A) Marble
   B) Slate
   C) Amphibolite
   D) Quartzite

Answer: D
Diff: 1

24) Which of the following rocks would exhibit visible, textural evidence of having undergone some partial melting?
   A) fault breccia
   B) migmatite
   C) slate
   D) foliated hornfels

Answer: B
Diff: 1

25) What is the major source of heat for contact metamorphism?
   A) deep burial and heat from the Earths interior
   B) heat from grinding and shearing on faults
   C) heat from the spontaneous decomposition of micas and feldspars
   D) heat from a nearby magma body

Answer: D
Diff: 1

26) In which setting would regional metamorphism be most likely?
    A) at shallow depths below an oceanic ridge or rift zone
    B) at shallow depths along major transform faults in the continental crust
    C) at great depths in the crust where two continents are colliding
    D) at shallow depths beneath the seafloor where water pressures are immense
Answer: C
Diff: 2

27) Graphite is identified in a particular schist. Which one of the following conclusions is justified?
    A) the rock also contains diamonds; both are crystalline forms of the element carbon
    B) the schist formed from a quartz–rich, sedimentary limestone
    C) the graphite lubricated shearing movements along a fault, causing a schist to form
    D) the pre–metamorphic rock was a shale or mudstone containing organic matter
Answer: D
Diff: 2

28) Amphibolite is a foliated metamorphic rock composed principally of hornblende and plagioclase. How does it form?
    A) by contact metamorphism of sandstone along the contact with a granitic batholith
    B) by regional metamorphism of volcanic rocks such as andesite and basalt
    C) by gouging and crushing of limestone along a fault
    D) by the impact of an asteroid on interbedded sandstone and shale
Answer: B
Diff: 1

29) What term describes the zone of contact metamorphism surrounding an intrusive magma body?
    A) aura
    B) auricle
    C) oracle
    D) aureole
Answer: D
Diff: 1

30) During metamorphism, what is the major effect of chemically active fluids?
    A) increase the pressures in deeply buried, regional–metamorphic zones
    B) aid in the movement of dissolved silicate constituents and facilitate growth of the mineral grains
    C) prevent partial melting so solid rocks can undergo very high temperature regional metamorphism
    D) facilitate the formation of schistosity and gneissic banding in hornfels and slates
Answer: B
Diff: 1

31) What two, metamorphic rocks are composed predominantly of single minerals?
    A) mica schist and granitic gneiss
    B) fault breccia and graphitic schist
    C) garnet schist and hornfels
    D) marble and quartzite
Answer: D
Diff: 1

32) A _____ forms at very high pressures but moderately low temperatures associated with subduction of oceanic crust and sediments.
   A) mylonite
   B) migmatite
   C) biotite marble
   D) blueschist
   Answer: D
   Diff: 1

Word Analysis. Examine the words and/or phrases for each question below and determine the relationship among the majority of words/phrases. Choose the option which does not fit the pattern.

33) a. pressure   b. recrystallization   c. melting   d. chemical fluids
   Answer: C
   Diff: 1

34) a. porphyroblastic   b. slaty cleavage   c. schistosity   d. gneissic texture
   Answer: A
   Diff: 1

35) a. aureole   b. hornfels   c. skarn   d. schist
   Answer: D
   Diff: 2

36) a. phyllite   b. quartzite   c. slate   d. schist
   Answer: B
   Diff: 1

37) Partial melting is an important process in the formation of migmatites.
   Answer: TRUE
   Diff: 1

38) Slate and schist are both derived by metamorphism of shales and mudstones.
   Answer: TRUE
   Diff: 1

39) Hornfels are metamorphic rocks produced at great depths and high temperatures associated with regional metamorphism.
   Answer: FALSE
   Diff: 1

40) Calcite is the main mineral constituent of the sedimentary rock limestone and of the metamorphic rock marble.
   Answer: TRUE
   Diff: 1

41) Metamorphic rocks formed during episodes of mountain building typically show textural characteristics indicative of shearing stress and deformation.
   Answer: TRUE
   Diff: 1

42) Amphibolites have gneissic textures and form by regional metamorphism of granites and rhyolites.

Answer: FALSE
Diff: 1

43) At high pressures and elevated temperatures of regional metamorphism, silicate rocks are more resistant to flowage and deformation than at low temperatures and pressures.

Answer: FALSE
Diff: 1

44) Foliated metamorphic rocks are composed largely of equidimensional grains of minerals such as quartz and calcite.

Answer: FALSE
Diff: 1

45) Rock cleavage or slaty cleavage in slates is largely a consequence of abundant, parallel-aligned, very fine-grained mica flakes in the rock.

Answer: TRUE
Diff: 1

46) Muscovite, biotite, and chlorite are common minerals found in phyllites and schists.

Answer: TRUE
Diff: 1

47) The distinctive layers or bands of different minerals in gneisses may be complexly folded.

Answer: TRUE
Diff: 1

48) Quartzites and metaconglomerates are formed along faults by intensive fracturing and fragmentation of conglomerate beds and quartz veins.

Answer: FALSE
Diff: 1

49) High-grade, regional metamorphism produces significant and recognizable changes in the textures and mineral compositions of rocks.

Answer: TRUE
Diff: 1

50) Talc and graphite are very soft minerals found in some schists.

Answer: TRUE
Diff: 1

51) Three major factors involved in metamorphism are elevated temperature, elevated pressure, and the chemical action of hot fluids.

Answer: TRUE
Diff: 1

52) During metamorphism, most rock is composed of solid mineral grains, but small amounts of hot fluids or partial melting may facilitate the metamorphic process.

Answer: TRUE
Diff: 1

53) Give the name of a rock formed by regional metamorphism of a conglomerate.

Answer: metaconglomerate
Diff: 1

54) Which type of metamorphism occurs specifically in the heated zone around a pluton or other body of magma?

Answer: contact
Diff: 1

55) List the three most important agents of metamorphism.

Answer: heat, pressure, chemically active fluids
Diff: 1

56) What type of sedimentary rock is typically metamorphosed to form slates or phyllites?

Answer: shale or mudstone
Diff: 1

57) Foliation in metamorphic rocks is mainly evident in the parallel alignment of certain mineral grains. What are they?

Answer: micas
Diff: 1

58) Which metamorphic rock or rocks exhibit alternating layers or bands of different light- and dark-colored minerals?

Answer: gneiss
Diff: 1

59) Which metamorphic rock, widely used for monuments and buildings, would deteriorate significantly in contact with acid rain?

Answer: marble
Diff: 1

60) What strongly banded, metamorphic rocks show good evidence for having formed by partial melting?

Answer: migmatite
Diff: 1

61) What metamorphic rock forms by intense ductile deformation along fault zones at depth in the Earth?

Answer: mylonite
Diff: 1

Critical thinking and discussion questions. Use complete sentences, correct spelling, and the information presented in Chapter 7 to answer the questions below.

62) Is it always possible to determine the original parent rock (called a protolith) prior to metamorphism? Why or why not? List three protoliths and give a possible metamorphic equivalent for each one.

Diff: 3

63) Briefly outline how regional metamorphism is related to plate boundaries. Are certain types of metamorphic rocks indicative of particular plate boundaries or tectonic settings? Give two or three examples of such rocks and indicate the tectonic environment they represent.
Diff: 3

64) Is the texture of a metamorphic rock always indicative of the conditions (degree of metamorphism) under which it formed? (Hint: Think about the protolith and how it may influence the resulting metamorphic rock.)
Diff: 2

65) What type of stress (pressure) is illustrated in the diagram below?

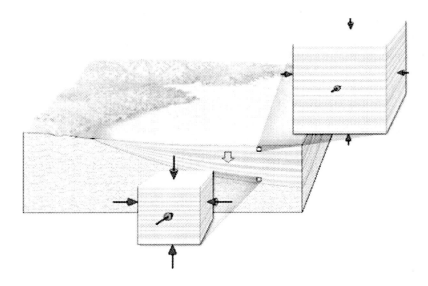

Answer: confining pressure
Diff: 1

66) What type of stress (pressure) is illustrated in the diagram below?

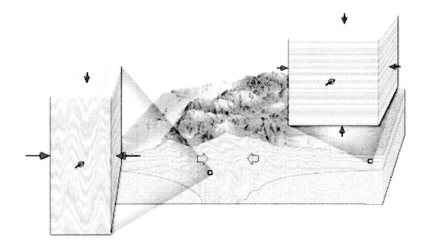

Answer: differential stress
Diff: 3

67) Carefully examine the photograph below of a metamorphic rock sample. The sample is shown as its actual size.

Is this rock foliated or nonfoliated? (a) _____
What is the name of this metamorphic rock? (b) _____
Consider how this rock got its texture. Was it compressed from top to bottom or from side to side? (c) _____

Answer: (a) foliated (b) gneiss (c) top to bottom
Diff: 1

68) Carefully examine the cross section below of a subduction zone, and note the areas labeled A, B, and C.

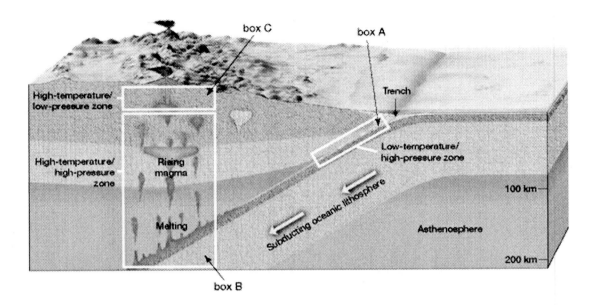

At which location (A, B, or C) would a metamorphic regime occur that is characterized by high temperature and high pressure? (a) _____
At which location (A, B, or C) would a metamorphic regime occur that is characterized by high temperature and low pressure? (b) _____
At which location (A, B, or C) would a metamorphic regime occur that is characterized by low temperature and high pressure? (c) _____
At which location (A, B, and C) would blueschist form? (d) _____

Answer: (a) B (b) C (c) A (d) A
Diff: 2

Chapter 8 Mass Wasting: The Work of Gravity

1) Which one of the following materials has the maximum, sustainable, slope angle, as determined by the angle of repose?
   A) dry silt
   B) moist, sandy soil with a clay-rich matrix
   C) dry sand
   D) moist, clay-rich shale layers

Answer: C
Diff: 2

2) _____ denotes the exposed, crescent-shaped rupture surface at the head of a slump.
   A) Scoop
   B) Sole
   C) Toe
   D) Scarp

Answer: D
Diff: 1

3) Consider a weathered rock or soil particle lying on a slope. How will the gravitational force pulling the particle downward along the land surface vary with the inclination of the slope?
   A) it will increase as the slope angle is lessened
   B) it will decrease as the slope angle is lessened
   C) it is not affected by the slope angle
   D) it will possibly increase or decrease as slope angle is lessened, depending upon other factors

Answer: B
Diff: 1

4) How do the strength and cohesion of clay-rich regolith or soil change with the addition of water?
   A) water does not affect the cohesion but lowers the strength
   B) water reduces the strength of clays but raises the cohesion of the soil
   C) water increases the strength and cohesion
   D) water lowers the strength and cohesion

Answer: D
Diff: 2

5) _____ involves movement on a zone of compressed air.
   A) A slump
   B) A mudflow
   C) A rock avalanche
   D) Soil creep

Answer: C
Diff: 1

6) Of the following, which one would most likely be triggered by an earthquake?
   A) solifluction
   B) soil creep
   C) slump
   D) rock avalanche

Answer: D
Diff: 2

7) Which one of the following operates primarily in areas of permafrost?
   A) rock avalanche
   B) solifluction
   C) soil creep
   D) mudflow

Answer: B
Diff: 2

8) Consider a steep highway cut made by removing slightly weathered to fresh, fractured, granite bedrock. Which of the following situations is most stable against rockslides?
   A) one set of widely spaced, sub-horizontal fractures
   B) two sets of fractures, one inclined toward the road cut and the other away
   C) two sets of fractures, one widely spaced and sub-horizontal, the other inclined away from the highway cut
   D) one set of widely spaced fractures inclined towards the road cut

Answer: A
Diff: 2

9) Which of the following was a major factor leading to the Gros Ventre, WY slide?
   A) erosion by the river had undercut the slope-forming shale and exposed the underlying sandstone
   B) soils and shallow bedrock were very wet and locally saturated
   C) a strong earthquake caused the unstable rock layers to move
   D) dry weather caused the clay-rich strata to compact, allowing the overlying sandstone to slide into the valley

Answer: B
Diff: 1

10) What caused the mudflows (1985) on the Nevado del Ruiz volcano?
   A) hot ash fell onto snow near the summit
   B) a crater lake was broken during an eruption
   C) warm weather caused rapid melting of snow and ice near the summit
   D) all of the above

Answer: A
Diff: 1

11) Why was the Alaskan pipeline built above ground and insulated?
    A) to protect the pipeline against damage due to thawing ground and to keep the crude oil hot and fluid
    B) to keep the crude oil cool and highly fluid
    C) to protect against damage from herds of elk and deer
    D) to protect against damage from roots of large trees uprooted in windstorms

Answer: A
Diff: 1

12) A geologist wants to locate a horizontal coal bed on a soil-covered slope where soil creep is active. A distinctive sandstone bed underlies the coal bed. On the basis of weathered sandstone fragments in the soil, where is the coal bed?
    A) just below the lowest piece of sandstone seen in the soil
    B) just above the highest piece of sandstone seen in the soil
    C) just below the highest piece of sandstone seen in the soil
    D) just above the lowest piece of sandstone seen in the soil

Answer: B
Diff: 2

13) Which disaster was triggered by a huge mass of soil and rock that suddenly slid into a water-filled reservoir?
    A) Nevado del Ruiz, Colombia, 1985
    B) Vaiont Canyon, Italy, 1963
    C) Sherman Glacier rock avalanche, AK, 1964
    D) Yungay-Ranrahirca, Peru, 1970

Answer: B
Diff: 1

14) Which statement best describes slumping, a mass wasting process?
    A) a block or blocks of unconsolidated regolith slide downhill along a curved slip surface
    B) blocks of hard bedrock rapidly slide downhill along fracture surfaces
    C) the soil and regolith move downhill very slowly
    D) a mass of soil or regolith becomes saturated with water and suddenly flows downhill to the base of the slope

Answer: A
Diff: 1

15) Which mass wasting process has the slowest rate of movement?
    A) slump
    B) rock avalanche
    C) solifluction
    D) creep

Answer: D
Diff: 1

16) All of the following are factors affecting mass wasting except for _____.
    A) gravity
    B) water
    C) slope angle
    D) geologic age
    Answer: D
    Diff: 1

17) The most rapid type of mass movement is a _____.
    A) slump
    B) lahar
    C) rock avalanche
    D) debris flow
    Answer: C
    Diff: 1

18) As an erosional process, how is mass wasting unique from wind, water, and ice?
    A) mass wasting affects particles of all sizes whereas the others affect only smaller particles
    B) mass wasting does not require a transporting medium
    C) mass wasting affects much larger geographic areas than does wind, water, and ice
    D) all of the above make mass wasting unique compared to wind, water, and ice
    Answer: B
    Diff: 1

19) Which of the following mass movements is most likely to occur in a geologic setting where the rock strata are inclined?
    A) debris flow
    B) slump
    C) creep
    D) rockslide
    Answer: D
    Diff: 1

20) Which of the following statements concerning mudflows is not true?
    A) mudflows may be caused by heavy rains or melting snow
    B) in hilly areas, mudflows move down the canyons and stream valleys
    C) mudflows deposit talus slopes
    D) mudflows can move and carry very large boulders and other coarse debris
    Answer: C
    Diff: 1

21) During wet weather or times when snow is melting, sometimes the downhill toe of a slump _____.
    A) turns into a rock avalanche
    B) becomes an earthflow
    C) stops moving because water makes the clay sticky
    D) collapses and is deposited as talus at the base of the slope
    Answer: B
    Diff: 1

22) How do freezing, thawing, wetting, and drying contribute to soil creep?
    A) the soil becomes much weaker when dry and frozen
    B) gravity exerts a much stronger force when the soil is wet and thawed
    C) the soil expands and contracts, lifting particles and dropping them a slight distance downslope
    D) eventually, these cause the soil and regolith to suddenly slide down the slope
    Answer: C
    Diff: 1

23) All of the following are possible indicators that creep is occurring except for _____.
    A) tilted fences or power line poles
    B) an extremely thick soil profile
    C) curved tree trunks
    D) cracks in roads or sidewalks
    Answer: B
    Diff: 1

Word Analysis. Examine the words and/or phrases for each question below and determine the relationship among the majority of words/phrases. Choose the option which does not fit the pattern.

24) a. wind   b. water   c. mass wasting   d. ice
    Answer: C
    Diff: 1

25) a. slope angle   b. water   c. vegetation   d. earthquake
    Answer: D
    Diff: 1

26) a. rockslide   b. debris flow   c. creep   d. slump
    Answer: C
    Diff: 1

27) a. solifluction   b. fall   c. slide   d. flow
    Answer: A
    Diff: 1

28) a. earthquake   b. lahar   c. liquefaction   d. landslide
    Answer: B
    Diff: 2

29) Slump describes the very slow, downhill movement of soil and regolith.
    Answer: FALSE
    Diff: 1

30) The steepest, stable, slope angle possible in unconsolidated, granular materials like sand and gravel is called the angle of retention.
    Answer: FALSE
    Diff: 1

31) Solifluction occurs during the warmer summer months.

Answer: TRUE
Diff: 1

32) The Gros Ventre slide of 1925 was actually a mudflow triggered by an earthquake.

Answer: FALSE
Diff: 1

33) Repeated freezing and thawing can be important in soil creep movements.

Answer: TRUE
Diff: 1

34) Lahars are essentially mudflows associated with volcanoes and volcanism.

Answer: TRUE
Diff: 1

35) Solifluction is an important mass wasting process in areas of permafrost.

Answer: TRUE
Diff: 1

36) A triggering mechanism, such as heavy rains or an earthquake, are necessary for mass wasting to occur.

Answer: FALSE
Diff: 1

37) A scarp is the exposed portion of the rupture surface beneath a slump block.

Answer: TRUE
Diff: 1

38) Earthflows and slumps generally involve movement of unconsolidated or weakly consolidated soil and regolith.

Answer: TRUE
Diff: 1

39) Bedding planes and fractures can both act as slip surfaces for rockslides.

Answer: TRUE
Diff: 1

40) The very destructive, mass wasting event that wiped out Yungay and Ranrahirca, Peru was caused by hot, volcanic ash falling on deep snow in the summit region of a volcano.

Answer: FALSE
Diff: 1

41) Submarine landslides are generally much smaller than similar mass wasting events on land.

Answer: FALSE
Diff: 1

42) _____ denotes the downslope movement of soils and regolith.

Answer: Mass wasting
Diff: 1

43) _____ is the basic force that moves or accelerates soil and regolith down a slope.

Answer: Gravity
Diff: 1

44) What is another name for volcanic mudflows, like those formed during the Mount St. Helens and Nevado del Ruiz eruptions?

Answer: lahars
Diff: 1

45) Which process of mass wasting occurs primarily in permafrost regions?

Answer: solifluction
Diff: 1

46) Talus blocks or piles are associated with what of motion — a fall, a slide, or a flow?

Answer: fall
Diff: 1

47) _____ involves the downslope movement of a block or blocks of unconsolidated soil and regolith along a curved, slip surface.

Answer: Slump
Diff: 1

48) What is the fastest moving of the mass wasting processes?

Answer: rock avalanche
Diff: 1

49) Unconsolidated, granular materials such as gravel and sand will support maximum slope angles of about 33 to 35 degrees. What is the name for this maximum slope angle?

Answer: angle of repose
Diff: 1

50) _____ denotes the exposed portion of the slip surface beneath a slump block.

Answer: Scarp
Diff: 1

51) _____ is the fan-shaped pile of broken rock fragments at the base of a steep, bedrock slope or cliff.

Answer: Talus
Diff: 1

Critical thinking and discussion questions. Use complete sentences, correct spelling, and the information presented in Chapter 8 to answer the questions below.

52) As a geologist working in a foreign country for the first time, you are asked to assess the potential for mass wasting in a particular region. What aspects or characteristics (geologic, geographic, biologic, etc.) of the region are you interested in for your assessment? Also, how could you possibly determine if mass wasting has been active in the recent geologic past (100's or 1000's of years)?

Diff: 3

53) Although it was not discussed in chapter 8, what are some preventive measures that can be done to reduce or lessen the impact of mass wasting? (Hint: Think about the controls and triggers of mass wasting.)
Diff: 2

54) Based on the examples and discussion in chapter 8, what is the relationship of climate to mass wasting? Also, are certain climates more susceptible to mass wasting? Why?
Diff: 2

55) In the diagram below, match the letter of each illustration to the correct form of mass wasting.
   a) debris flow   b) slump   c) earthflow   d) rockslide

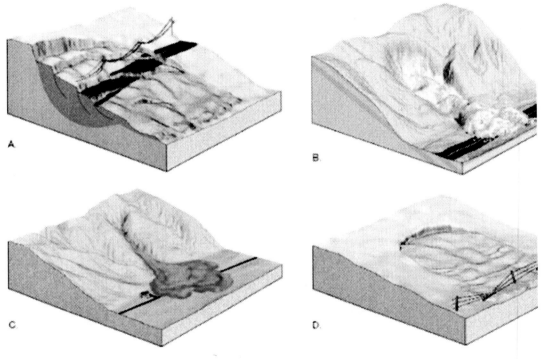

A = _____, B = _____, C = _____, D = _____
Answer: A = b, B = d, C = a, D = c
Diff: 1

56) What process of mass wasting is illustrated in the diagram below?

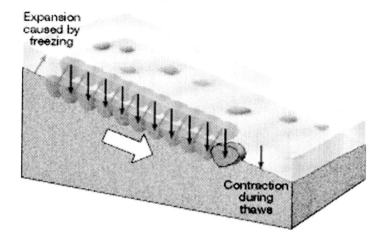

Expansion caused by freezing

Contraction during thaws

Answer: creep
Diff: 1

Chapter 9 Running Water

1) _____ is not part of the hydrologic cycle.
   A) Water evaporating from a lake
   B) Water infiltrating into the soil and bedrock
   C) Calcium carbonate dissolving in soil water and groundwater
   D) Water moving into creeks and streams following a rainstorm

Answer: C
Diff: 1

2) Which one of the following statements is correct?
   A) sea level drops when water is stored in expanding ice sheets and continental glaciers
   B) sea level rises when water is added to the oceans through increased rainfall and
      increased inflow from rivers
   C) sea level drops when evaporation rates increase over the oceans and when this extra,
      atmospheric moisture falls on land as rain
   D) sea level rises when water is stored in expanding ice sheets and continental glaciers

Answer: A
Diff: 1

3) Which of the following is the correct definition of stream gradient?
   A) the distance traveled by water in a channel times a drop in elevation
   B) the drop in elevation of a stream divided by the distance the water travels
   C) the water pressure at the bottom of the stream divided by the stream's width
   D) the increase in discharge of a stream per unit drop in elevation

Answer: B
Diff: 1

4) A natural, meandering, river channel is modified into a more or less straight and smooth,
   canal-like channel. Which of the following statements is correct?
   A) the natural channel had a lower gradient and less friction than the modified channel
   B) the straight channel has a higher gradient and more friction than the natural channel
   C) the natural channel had a lower gradient and higher friction than the straight channel
   D) all of the above statements are true

Answer: C
Diff: 2

5) How does urbanization (paving, etc.) affect runoff and infiltration in a small, previously
   forested, drainage basin?
   A) both decrease
   B) runoff decreases; infiltration increases
   C) both increase
   D) infiltration decreases; runoff increases

Answer: D
Diff: 1

6) Which of the following must result in a lower base level for rivers and streams?
   A) sea level drops; land subsides
   B) sea level falls; land rises
   C) sea level rises; land subsides
   D) sea level rises; land rises
   Answer: B
   Diff: 2

7) _____ make up the suspended loads of most rivers and streams.
   A) Dissolved ions and sand
   B) Dissolved salts
   C) Silt and clay-sized, detrital grains
   D) Sand and gravel that move during floods
   Answer: C
   Diff: 1

8) _____ describes the total sediment load transported by a stream.
   A) Capacity
   B) Discharge
   C) Competence
   D) Hydro-load factor
   Answer: A
   Diff: 1

9) At the head of a delta, the major channel splits into smaller channels that follow different paths to the sea. These smaller channels are known as _____.
   A) endotributaries
   B) exotributaries
   C) distributaries
   D) cotributaries
   Answer: C
   Diff: 1

10) Why is a bird-foot delta like that of the present-day Mississippi below New Orleans likely to change naturally toward one with the shape of an equilateral triangle like the upper-case, Greek letter delta (Δ)?
   A) present-day distributaries have higher gradients than potential new ones
   B) potential, new, major distributary channels have steeper gradients than existing channels
   C) potential, new, distributary channels have higher gradients, causing downcutting of the existing channels
   D) increased sediment loads since the mid-19th century have caused the major distributaries to be filled with sand
   Answer: B
   Diff: 2

11) In the absence of cutoff, how does a river meander loop behave over time?
    A) the gradient is raised as the loop lengthens, and the channel migrates toward the cut or inner bank of the loop
    B) the gradient is raised as the loop shortens, and the channel migrates away from the cut or outer bank of the loop
    C) the gradient is lowered as the channel lengthens and migrates toward the cut or outer bank of the loop
    D) the gradient is lowered as the loop shortens, and the channel migrates toward the cut or inner bank of the loop
    Answer: C
    Diff: 2

12) A _____ stream pattern is developed only on growing mountains like volcanoes or where the land surface is tectonically doming upward.
    A) radial
    B) dendritic
    C) boreal
    D) trellis
    Answer: A
    Diff: 1

13) A _____ stream pattern develops on lands underlain by tilted or folded, alternating hard and soft, sedimentary strata.
    A) dendritic
    B) radial
    C) trellis
    D) boreal
    Answer: C
    Diff: 1

14) _____ is an abandoned, cutoff, meander loop.
    A) A builtrail
    B) An oxbow
    C) A cowhock
    D) A gatorback
    Answer: B
    Diff: 1

15) _____ are characteristics of downcutting streams and a youthful stage of valley evolution.
    A) Rapids and lots of whitewater
    B) Wide floodplains
    C) A U-shaped, cross-valley profiles
    D) Meandering channels and natural levees
    Answer: A
    Diff: 1

16) Many larger rivers in the Colorado Plateau region meander in deep, narrow canyons and have no floodplains. How could this happen?
    A) original, youthful streams continued to downcut as the land rose
    B) original, old age streams downcut as the land gradually rose
    C) as sea level dropped, the original youthful streams matured into old-age streams
    D) as sea level rose, the original, old age streams were rejuvenated
Answer: B
Diff: 1

17) A water gap is _____.
    A) a low sag between adjoining segments of a natural levee
    B) the narrow strip of land separating two meander loops
    C) a vertical-walled canyon resulting from very rapid stream downcutting
    D) a short segment of canyon formed where a river flows across the outcrop area of a resistant, ridge-forming rock layer
Answer: D
Diff: 1

18) Which of the following is the only correct response concerning the location and causes of the extraordinarily severe, 1993, flooding on the Mississippi River and tributaries?
    A) lower basin; heavy rains in late spring and early summer
    B) upper basin; rapid melting of an unusually deep snow pack in early spring
    C) lower basin; very heavy, late summer rains associated with a severe hurricane
    D) upper basin; very heavy, sustained rainfall in the late spring and early summer
Answer: D
Diff: 1

19) Which one of the following statements correctly describes how stream terraces can form?
    A) base level drops; the stream aggrades its channel, and the former floodplain is left below the present elevation of the stream
    B) a temporary base level is eliminated; the stream downcuts upstream from the old temporary base level, and the former floodplain is left well above the present elevation of the stream
    C) base level rises; the stream downcuts, and the old floodplain is left well above the elevation of the present-day channel
    D) a temporary base level is eliminated; the stream aggrades its channel upstream from the old temporary base level, and the former floodplain is left well above the present elevation of the stream
Answer: B
Diff: 2

20) _____ are components of the hydrologic cycle that release water vapor directly to the atmosphere.
    A) Runoff and infiltration
    B) Evaporation and transpiration
    C) Precipitation and runoff
    D) Discharge and transportation
Answer: B
Diff: 1

21) What is the drop in water surface elevation divided by the distance the water flows?
   A) stream discharge
   B) hydraulic capacity
   C) hydrologic resistance
   D) stream gradient

   Answer: D
   Diff: 1

22) The _____ river has the largest discharge of any in the world.
   A) Nile
   B) Mississippi
   C) Congo
   D) Amazon

   Answer: D
   Diff: 1

23) Which one of the following does not apply to stream turbulence and average velocity?
   A) channel shape; bed roughness
   B) laminar flow; dissolved load
   C) discharge; stream gradient
   D) stream gradient; channel roughness

   Answer: B
   Diff: 1

24) Which one of the following is true concerning a major river system?
   A) upstream tributaries generally have lower gradients than the major river
   B) channel bed roughness and turbulence generally increase downstream
   C) upstream tributaries generally have higher competencies than the major river
   D) discharge decreases below junctions with perennial tributaries

   Answer: C
   Diff: 1

25) _____ generally constitutes the highest percentage of the annual sediment load moved by a stream.
   A) Bed load
   B) Dissolved load
   C) Suspended load
   D) Saltation load

   Answer: C
   Diff: 1

26) Where is erosion concentrated along a meandering stream?
   A) on the straight channel segments that connect the meander loops
   B) on the outer parts of the meander loops or bends
   C) at the unconsolidated point bars
   D) on the inner banks of the meander loops

   Answer: B
   Diff: 1

27) Which one of the following would cause stream rejuvenation?
    A) sea level rises
    B) a shift from downcutting to lateral cutting
    C) the land is uplifted
    D) when unstable distributaries in a delta are abandoned
Answer: C
Diff: 1

28) Which one of the following statements is true concerning natural levees?
    A) depositional features formed at times of low discharge
    B) mostly fine sand and silt that build up during floods
    C) erosional features left behind when meander cutoff occurs
    D) form the high, steep banks of a downcutting stream
Answer: B
Diff: 1

29) In a _____ drainage pattern that is generally developed in areas underlain by tilted or folded strata, tributary streams flow along outcrop areas of the softer strata.
    A) trellis
    B) dendritic
    C) coparallel
    D) radial
Answer: A
Diff: 1

30) A _____ drainage pattern is common in the Appalachian Valley and Ridge Province.
    A) dendritic
    B) polygonal
    C) circular
    D) trellis
Answer: D
Diff: 1

31) A stream begins at an elevation of 200 meters and flows a distance of 400 kilometers to the ocean? What is the average gradient?
    A) 2m/km
    B) 2km/m
    C) 0.5m/km
    D) 0.5 km/in
Answer: C
Diff: 1

32) _____ in a delta are essentially cross strata inclined toward deeper water.
    A) Backset beds
    B) Topset beds
    C) Foreset beds
    D) Bottomset beds
Answer: C
Diff: 1

33) The _____ describes the movement of water through Earth's hydrosphere.
   A) aqualytic cycle
   B) aquatic cycle
   C) precipitation cycle
   D) hydrologic cycle

   Answer: D
   Diff: 1

34) _____ describes the particle transport mode in streams intermediate between suspension and rolling along the bottom?
   A) Siltation
   B) Alluviation
   C) Impact leaping
   D) Saltation

   Answer: D
   Diff: 1

35) Which of the following features characterize wide streams and valleys?
   A) natural levees; broad floodplains
   B) rapids; channel bed potholes
   C) waterfalls; entrenched meanders
   D) V-shaped valley cross-sections

   Answer: A
   Diff: 1

36) Entrenched meanders are evidence for what sequence of geologic events?
   A) land uplift was followed by stream downcutting
   B) lateral cutting by streams was followed by subsidence of the land
   C) a sea level rise was followed by stream downcutting
   D) stream downcutting was followed by a rise in base level

   Answer: A
   Diff: 1

37) Which one of the following best describes how urbanization affects small-stream watersheds?
   A) infiltration is reduced; lag time between storms and peak runoff is increased
   B) infiltration increases slightly; lag time between storms and peak runoff decreases
   C) infiltration decreases; lag time between storms and peak runoff is shortened
   D) infiltration and lag time between storms and peak runoff increase

   Answer: C
   Diff: 2

38) A dam and reservoir are constructed on a graded river. What will happen?
   A) deposition upstream from the dam; channel downcutting below
   B) channel downcutting upstream from the dam; deposition below
   C) deposition upstream and downstream from the dam
   D) channel downcutting upstream and downstream from the dam

   Answer: A
   Diff: 1

Word Analysis. Examine the words and/or phrases for each question below and determine the relationship among the majority of words/phrases. Choose the option which does not fit the pattern.

39) a. natural levees   b. rapids   c. backswamps   d. yazoo tributaries

Answer: B
Diff: 1

40) a. gradient   b. velocity   c. capacity   d. discharge

Answer: C
Diff: 2

41) a. abrasion   b. pothole   c. cut bank   d. natural levee

Answer: D
Diff: 1

42) a. cut bank   b. point bar   c. natural levee   d. delta

Answer: A
Diff: 1

43) a. artificial levees   b. dams   c. floodplains   d. channelization

Answer: C
Diff: 1

44) Alluvial fans develop at unusual locations where stream gradients abruptly increase for a short distance.

Answer: FALSE
Diff: 1

45) Gradients usually decrease downstream in a major river system.

Answer: TRUE
Diff: 1

46) Alluvium refers to stream deposits, mainly sand and gravel.

Answer: TRUE
Diff: 1

47) The lowest base level for most streams is sea level.

Answer: TRUE
Diff: 1

48) Natural levees are constructed of machine–compacted sand and mud; artificial levees are made of concrete.

Answer: FALSE
Diff: 1

49) Point bars are depositional features located along the outer portions of meander bends.

Answer: FALSE
Diff: 1

50) Rapids and waterfalls are characteristic of laterally cutting streams.

Answer: FALSE

Diff: 1

51) After a meander is cut off, the gradient through the newly formed cutoff is steeper than the gradient along the abandoned meander loop.

Answer: TRUE

Diff: 1

52) The lower Mississippi River has the largest discharge of any river in North America.

Answer: TRUE

Diff: 1

53) Stream discharge is defined as the quantity of water flowing past a specific channel location per unit time.

Answer: TRUE

Diff: 1

54) Urbanization lowers peak discharges on small streams by routing the runoff directly to the stream.

Answer: FALSE

Diff: 1

55) A stream flowing out from a lake cannot downcut below the water surface elevation of the lake.

Answer: FALSE

Diff: 1

56) Evapotranspiration and average velocity are both important components of the hydrologic cycle.

Answer: FALSE

Diff: 1

57) Most precipitation in land areas originates by transpiration and by evaporation from lakes and rivers.

Answer: FALSE

Diff: 1

58) A V-shaped valley and no floodplain indicate a youthful, downcutting stream.

Answer: TRUE

Diff: 1

59) Lateral cutting and deposition are important factors in floodplain development.

Answer: TRUE

Diff: 1

60) With the passage of time, deposition and erosion gradually shorten the channel length of a meander loop.

Answer: FALSE

Diff: 1

61) Foreset beds are part of a deltaic, depositional sequence.

Answer: TRUE
Diff: 1

62) For the same discharge, gradient, and channel cross section, a stream with a boulder–strewn bed would be more turbulent than one with a sandy bed.

Answer: TRUE
Diff: 1

63) The lowermost distal portion of the modern Mississippi Delta is a typical bird–foot delta.

Answer: TRUE
Diff: 1

64) The lowest elevation limiting stream erosion is called _____.

Answer: base level
Diff: 1

65) _____ is the boundary line separating adjacent, stream drainage basins

Answer: A stream divide
Diff: 1

66) _____ is the release of water vapor to the atmosphere by plants.

Answer: Evapotranspiration
Diff: 1

67) _____ is defined as the drop in elevation of the stream surface divided by the distance the water flows.

Answer: Gradient
Diff: 1

68) _____ is the total quantity of sediment carried by a river.

Answer: Capacity
Diff: 1

69) _____ is the sediment transport mode in which sand grains alternately bounce up into the water column, sink, and roll or skip along the bottom before bouncing again.

Answer: Saltation
Diff: 1

70) _____ is the quantity of water flowing past a certain stream cross section per unit time.

Answer: Discharge
Diff: 1

71) What stream characteristic is measured by the size of the largest particle that a stream can move?

Answer: competence
Diff: 1

72) _____ refers to sediments deposited from streams.

Answer: Alluvium
Diff: 1

73) Which component of the hydrologic cycle describes the recharge of water to the soil and groundwater systems?

Answer: infiltration
Diff: 1

Critical thinking and discussion questions. Use complete sentences, correct spelling, and the information presented in Chapter 9 to answer the questions below.

74) A city located on a large river has a history of moderate flooding over its 150-year history. However, the severity and magnitude of flooding has increased dramatically in the past 30 years. Give some possible reasons, both natural and human-induced, as to why such increased flooding might occur.

Diff: 3

75) Briefly compare those stream characteristics that decrease in a downstream direction with those that increase downstream. Also, indicate whether these changing stream characteristics tend to favor erosion or deposition of sediments.

Diff: 3

76) What generalizations can you make regarding the geology of a given area by examining stream drainage patterns on a topographic map? Give some examples. Also, are there limitations to such generalizations?

Diff: 3

77) Label the cut bank and the point bar on the diagram below.

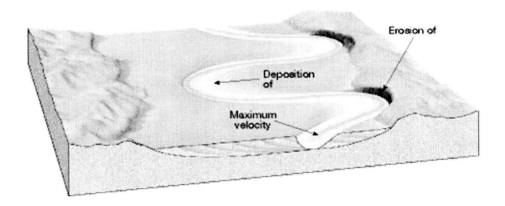

Answer: See Figure 9.7 in the Essentials of Geology, 10e textbook.
Diff: 1

78) Label the oxbow lake on the diagram below.

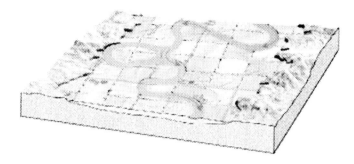

Answer: See Figure 9.8 in the Essentials of Geology, 10e textbook.
Diff: 1

79) On the blanks provided beside each illustration, name the type of drainage pattern that is illustrated.

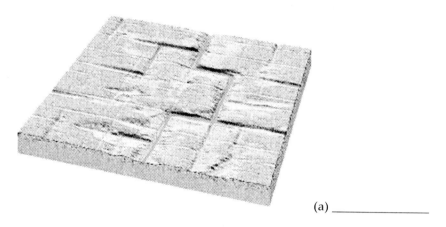

(a) _____

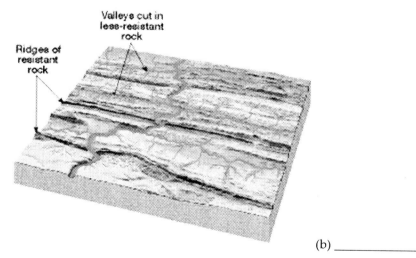

(b) _____

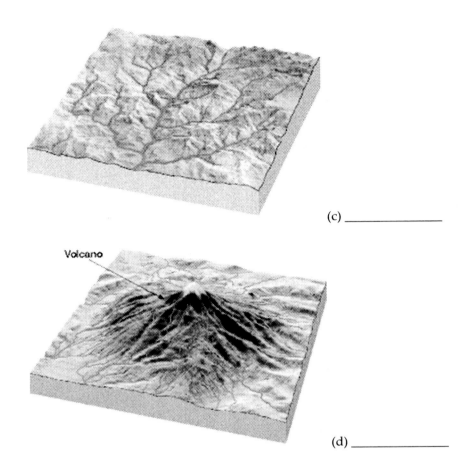

(c) _____

(d) _____

Answer: (a) rectangular (b) trellis (c) dendritic (d) radial
Diff: 2

Chapter 10 Groundwater

1) After ice sheets and glaciers, _____ contains the next highest percentage of Earth's freshwater.
   A) the atmosphere
   B) lakes and rivers
   C) groundwater
   D) rocks & minerals

Answer: C
Diff: 1

2) Which common, rock-forming mineral or mineral group is most readily dissolved by groundwater?
   A) calcite
   B) quartz
   C) feldspars
   D) clay minerals

Answer: A
Diff: 1

3) Which of the following is not a general characteristic of groundwater?
   A) constant temperature year round
   B) rarely contains dissolved constituents
   C) rarely contains suspended sediment
   D) supply is independent of short droughts

Answer: B
Diff: 1

4) A stream is said to be perennial and effluent when _____.
   A) the channel bottom is above the local water table year round
   B) the local water table is above the channel bottom year round

Answer: B
Diff: 1

5) The water table is _____.
   A) a boundary between unsaturated bedrock and an underground river
   B) a boundary between unsaturated bedrock below and saturated bedrock above
   C) an underground mass of partly saturated rock
   D) a boundary between saturated rock below and unsaturated rock above

Answer: D
Diff: 1

6) _____ controls the ease (or difficulty) of groundwater transmission through a porous material.
   A) Potability
   B) Portability
   C) Permeosity
   D) Permeability

Answer: D
Diff: 1

7) _____ are characteristics found in all good aquifers.
   A) High porosity and high permeability
   B) Low permeability and high potability
   C) High potability and high portability
   D) Low porosity and low permeability

Answer: A
Diff: 1

8) A perched water table develops when _____.
   A) a horizontal aquitard above the regional water table lies below an aquifer
   B) an aquifer above the regional water table is overlain by a horizontal aquitard
   C) an aquifer below the regional water table is underlain by a horizontal aquitard
   D) an aquitard below the regional water table lies above a horizontal aquifer

Answer: A
Diff: 1

9) An artesian well is one in which _____.
   A) the water is warm, fairly saline, and recharged by an affluent stream
   B) pressurized groundwater rises from a deep, unsaturated aquifer
   C) water rises above the top of the aquifer without any pumping
   D) the well is horizontal and the water table is perched

Answer: C
Diff: 1

10) Which one of the following statements is true for an artesian aquifer?
   A) the water table in the recharge area is at a higher elevation than the top of the aquifer in the subsurface
   B) upward flow from a permeable aquitard is prevented by a confining aquifer
   C) the pressure at any point in the aquifer is considerably less than the weight of the water column between the point and the top of the aquifer
   D) in deep, stream-cut valleys, many springs are fed from artesian aquifers

Answer: A
Diff: 1

11) Excessive groundwater withdrawals can cause _____.
   A) the water table drops or declines in elevation
   B) an influent stream becomes an effluent stream
   C) expansion of the dewatered aquifer
   D) porosity in the aquifer increases as the water is removed

Answer: A
Diff: 1

12) Which of the following geologic materials would have the highest groundwater velocities and be least effective in removing unwanted pollutants from the water?
   A) unconsolidated medium-grained sand; sand grains are coated with clay minerals
   B) sandstone; well-cemented with a few, widely spaced vertical fractures
   C) lakebeds; unconsolidated very fine-grained sand and silt
   D) limestone; numerous solution channels and fractures widened by dissolution
   Answer: D
   Diff: 1

13) Which one of the following logically explains why parts of some cavern systems are aerated?
   A) the caves formed and later the water table rose
   B) a nearby, downcutting stream lowered the water table after the caves had formed
   C) streams formerly flowing on the surface were diverted into the groundwater system through sinkholes
   D) the main water table is perched above the cavern roofs, allowing air to enter
   Answer: B
   Diff: 1

14) How would hazardous substances behave that accidentally entered a groundwater system?
   A) gasoline and kerosene would float on the water table; ethyl alcohol would dissolve and disperse in the groundwater
   B) gasoline and kerosene would float on the water table, but most pesticides break down chemically when they reach the water table
   C) sulfuric and nitric acids would sink to the bottom of the aquifer; kerosene would accumulate as a layer just below the water table
   D) all of the above hazardous substances would dissolve into the groundwater
   Answer: A
   Diff: 1

15) A _____ is the icicle-like speleothem that grows down from the roof of a cavern.
   A) stalandite
   B) stalactite
   C) stalagmite
   D) slagdite
   Answer: B
   Diff: 1

16) _____ are specific features of karst topography.
   A) Streams flowing into depressions and continuing underground
   B) Perched water table springs on hillsides
   C) Numerous artesian wells in a given area
   D) Perennial, influent streams fed by large springs
   Answer: A
   Diff: 1

17) Which of the following can logically be concluded by speleothems/dripstone hanging from a cave roof?
   A) the cave roof was below the water table when the speleothems formed
   B) the cave floor was above the water table and the roof was below the water table when the speleothems formed
   C) the cave roof was above the water table when the speleothems formed
   D) the cave roof was below the water table sometime after the speleothems had formed

Answer: C
Diff: 2

18) _____ account for the largest usage of groundwater in the United States.
   A) Water for livestock and poultry
   B) Domestic and municipal supplies
   C) Industrial uses
   D) Agriculture and irrigation

Answer: D
Diff: 1

19) What is the relationship between drawdown and the cone of depression associated with a pumping well?
   A) the drawdown is the diameter of the cone of depression measured at the elevation of the original water table
   B) the drawdown is the percentage of available water in the aquifer that has already been used
   C) drawdown is the distance between the original water table and the water level in the well
   D) there is no relationship between drawdown and the cone of depression

Answer: C
Diff: 1

20) The hot spring deposits at Mammoth Hot Springs, Yellowstone National Park, are travertine. What rock probably lies somewhere beneath the hot springs?
   A) shale
   B) rhyolite
   C) limestone
   D) quartzite

Answer: C
Diff: 1

21) Which of the following statements concerning unconfined aquifers on barrier islands and atolls is correct?
   A) wells drilled below sea level will produce only saline water
   B) the water table must be 40 feet above sea level to keep the salty water in the aquifer below sea level
   C) any salty water in the aquifer will rise if the water table is lowered by pumping
   D) pumping freshwater from one, large capacity well is much less likely to cause salty water to rise in the aquifer than pumping from several, widely spaced, smaller capacity wells

Answer: C
Diff: 1

22) The aerated zone _____.
    A) lies above the water table
    B) pore spaces are filled with water
    C) is a well-oxygenated, shallow aquifer
    D) lies below the capillary fringe zone

    Answer: A
    Diff: 1

23) For unconfined aquifers, what hydrologic factor is approximated by the slope of the water table?
    A) porosity head
    B) hydro competency
    C) affluent decline
    D) hydraulic gradient

    Answer: D
    Diff: 1

24) An aquifer is _____.
    A) the porous and permeable, saturated cone of depression in an aquitard
    B) a layer or stratum in which groundwater flows downward to the water table
    C) a saturated, porous, and permeable layer or stratum
    D) an unsaturated, influent-flow bed or stratum below a spring

    Answer: C
    Diff: 1

25) A lens of fresh groundwater in an unconfined aquifer overlies deeper, salty groundwater. If the water table elevation drops by one foot, how far will the interface between the freshwater and salty water rise?
    A) 10 feet
    B) 30 meters
    C) 20 meters
    D) 40 feet

    Answer: D
    Diff: 1

26) _____ would have the largest capacity to naturally remove sewage pollutants.
    A) Fractured granite
    B) Well-sorted, coarse gravel
    C) Slightly clayey sand
    D) Limestone with solution channels and caverns

    Answer: C
    Diff: 1

27) What force pushes groundwater from pore to pore below the water table?
    A) integrated saturation impulse
    B) permeability steepness
    C) pressure gradient or hydraulic gradient
    D) seepage affluence actor

    Answer: C
    Diff: 1

28) Which of the following describes the configuration of an unconfined water table around a pumping well?
   A) depressional withdrawal
   B) upside-down siphon
   C) cone of depression
   D) inverted cone head

Answer: C
Diff: 1

29) A disappearing (sinking) creek is _____.
   A) an influent stream in a karst area
   B) a stream that downcuts below the water table
   C) a creek that originates as a large spring flowing from a cave
   D) a small creek flowing downslope to the top of a perched water table

Answer: A
Diff: 1

30) Which one of the following concerning stalactites and stalagmites is not true?
   A) stalactites are deposited from water dripping from the ceiling of an aerated cavern
   B) both are composed of calcium carbonate
   C) both are forms of dripstone; stalactites hang from the ceiling, stalagmites grow upward from the cavern floor
   D) stalagmites form on the floors of caves below the water table

Answer: D
Diff: 1

31) Which one of the following concerning artesian wells is not true?
   A) the well penetrates an aquifer overlain by an aquitard
   B) the well penetrates an aquifer underlain by an impermeable bed
   C) the aquifer is generally inclined, and it is saturated to an elevation above the point where the well penetrates the aquifer
   D) when the well penetrates the aquifer, the water rises to the bottom of the aquitard above the aquifer

Answer: D
Diff: 1

32) _____ is the volume of voids or open space in a rock or unconsolidated material.
   A) Permeability
   B) Space yield
   C) Porosity
   D) Saturation index

Answer: C
Diff: 1

33) The term karst topography was first used in _____.
   A) the Republic of Slovenia, a province of the former Yugoslavia
   B) eastern Canada in areas of fractured igneous and metamorphic rocks
   C) India near the southern foothills of the Himalayan Mountains
   D) Australia for the extremely dry interior area near Ayres Rock and Alice Springs

Answer: A
Diff: 1

34) Which one of the following is not a speleothem?
   A) geyserite
   B) dripstone
   C) stalactite
   D) stalagmite
   Answer: A
   Diff: 1

35) An unconfined water table is the _____.
   A) boundary between the saturated zone above and partly saturated zone below
   B) bottom boundary surface of the saturated zone above an aquitard
   C) boundary between the aerated zone above and saturated zone below
   D) boundary between the aerated and unsaturated zones
   Answer: C
   Diff: 1

36) Which of the following best describes how geysers erupt?
   A) water suddenly boils in disconnected voids and cracks above the water table, causing the aquifer to explosively fragment
   B) water slowly boils in a network of vertical cracks above the water table, sending up a plume of steam and hot water
   C) water below the water table slowly boils in a vertical crack or natural conduit, causing a plume of condensed water vapor to rise above the vent
   D) with a slight reduction in pressure, water in a saturated, natural conduit suddenly boils, sending a plume of steam and hot water into the air above the vent
   Answer: D
   Diff: 1

37) Where are the most extensive geothermal features in the world?
   A) Yosemite National Park, U. S.
   B) Geysers Artesian Park, Japan
   C) Iceland's Groundwater Preserve
   D) Yellowstone National Park, U. S.
   Answer: D
   Diff: 1

Word Analysis. Examine the words and/or phrases for each question below and determine the relationship among the majority of words/phrases. Choose the option which does not fit the pattern.

38) a. zone of saturation   b. belt of soil moisture   c. capillary fringe   d. zone of aeration
   Answer: A
   Diff: 1

39) a. porosity   b. permeability   c. aquitard   d. aquifer
   Answer: C
   Diff: 2

40) a. spring   b. aquitard   c. perched water table   d. zone of saturation
   Answer: D
   Diff: 2

115

41) a. stalagmite   b. soda straw   c. sinkhole   d. stalactite

Answer: C
Diff: 1

42) Water infiltrates down to the water table from influent streams.

Answer: TRUE
Diff: 1

43) Porosity is a measure of the volume of open space in rocks and unconsolidated, geological materials like alluvium and soils.

Answer: TRUE
Diff: 1

44) Permeability is the physical force that pushes water below the water table through a porous, rock material.

Answer: FALSE
Diff: 1

45) The water table is a surface separating the saturated and unsaturated zones.

Answer: TRUE
Diff: 1

46) In humid areas and for unconfined, groundwater conditions, the water table generally slopes toward the valley of a perennial stream.

Answer: TRUE
Diff: 1

47) Most caves and caverns originate by solution of limestone.

Answer: TRUE
Diff: 1

48) Speleothems generally form below the water table by water dripping from the roofs of caverns.

Answer: FALSE
Diff: 1

49) A perched water table develops in hilly terrain where an aquitard underlies an aquifer and both are above the elevation of the main water table.

Answer: TRUE
Diff: 1

50) Water-saturated muds have low permeabilities but can have greater porosities than well-cemented sandstone.

Answer: TRUE
Diff: 1

51) Warm springs in the eastern United States are mainly heated by geologically young, igneous rocks below the surface.

Answer: FALSE
Diff: 1

52) In areas of karst topography, rare surface streams typically flow into sinkholes and continue flowing underground for some distance.

Answer: TRUE
Diff: 1

53) Yosemite National Park in California is world famous for its hot springs, geysers, and other geothermal phenomena.

Answer: FALSE
Diff: 1

54) In areas underlain by unconsolidated or weakly consolidated strata, lowering of the water table can cause the land to subside.

Answer: TRUE
Diff: 1

55) Lowering of the water table around a pumping well results in a cone of infiltration.

Answer: FALSE
Diff: 1

56) On a coastal barrier island, the interface between the freshwater and salty water generally lies 40 feet below the top of the freshwater lens.

Answer: FALSE
Diff: 1

57) In general, contaminated groundwater will be naturally cleaned faster by circulation through porous and permeable sands than by circulation through fractured, crystalline igneous and metamorphic rocks.

Answer: TRUE
Diff: 1

58) A geyser can erupt because the boiling temperature of water decreases with depth below the water table.

Answer: FALSE
Diff: 1

59) Artesian groundwater conditions can develop in an inclined aquifer with aquitards above and below.

Answer: TRUE
Diff: 1

60) The _____ is the upper boundary surface of the saturated zone.

Answer: water table
Diff: 1

61) What property describes how readily groundwater will flow through a saturated porous material?

Answer: permeability
Diff: 1

62) Highly impermeable layers such as compacted clay or shale are known as _____.

Answer: aquitards
Diff: 1

63) What term denotes the percentage of open space or voids in a material?

Answer: porosity
Diff: 1

64) What feature originates where the water table intersects the land surface?

Answer: spring
Diff: 1

65) In three words, describe the shape of the water table around a pumping well.

Answer: cone of depression
Diff: 1

66) What term describes a groundwater system in which water in a well rises above the top of the aquifer without use of a pump?

Answer: artesian
Diff: 1

67) Which term denotes the physical force that pushes water though a saturated porous material?

Answer: pressure gradient
Diff: 1

68) What term describes a stream from which water is infiltrating downward to the water table?

Answer: losing stream
Diff: 1

69) Which slender, conical speleothem grows from water dripping from the ceiling of a cavern?

Answer: stalactite
Diff: 1

70) A terrain exhibiting many distinctive features related to subsurface solution of limestone is known as _____.

Answer: karst topography
Diff: 1

71) A stream flowing into a sinkhole is called a _____.

Answer: disappearing stream
Diff: 1

72) A hydrothermal vent that periodically or occasionally erupts a column of steam and hot water is called a _____.

Answer: geyser
Diff: 1

73) A _____ is a circular to elliptical, closed depressions in karst areas.

Answer: sinkhole
Diff: 1

74) Which speleothem grows upward from the floor of a cavern?

Answer: stalagmite
Diff: 1

75) What hydrogeological condition describes a local zone of saturated soil or rock above the elevation of the regional water table?

Answer: perched water table
Diff: 1

76) The unsaturated zone above the water table is also known as the _____.

Answer: zone of aeration
Diff: 1

77) Dripstone and travertine are composed of _____.

Answer: calcium carbonate ($CaCO_3$)
Diff: 1

Critical thinking and discussion questions. Use complete sentences, correct spelling, and the information presented in Chapter 10 to answer the questions below.

78) "The drinking water in our town is always cold, clear, and pure because it comes from an artesian well." Briefly discuss the geologic validity of this statement. Although this idea wasn't specifically discussed in chapter 10, give a possible reason or two as to why such statements are often made.

Diff: 2

79) When examining the geology of a region for potential aquifers, what characteristics or factors would you consider? Also, what areas (based on natural and human) factors would you avoid?

Diff: 3

80) How would you recognize areas of karst topography on a topographic map without knowing the local bedrock geology? Also, what features of karst topography on a topographic map might be misinterpreted as some other geologic feature?

Diff: 3

81) One the blanks provided beside each cross section below, describe what type of stream is represented. Arrows indicate direction of groundwater flow.

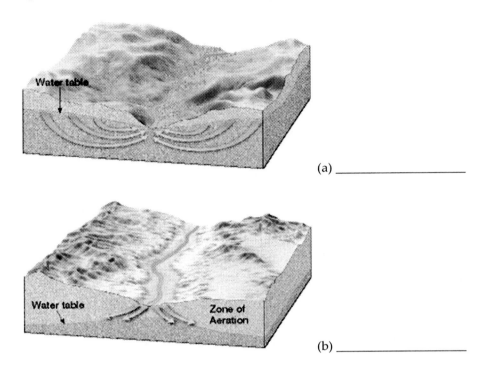

(a) _____

(b) _____

Answer: (a) gaining stream (b) losing stream
Diff: 1

82) On the cutaway sides of the illustration below, areas shaded dark represent the zone of aeration, and areas that are lightly shaded represent the zone of saturation. All rock types are aquifers except for the labeled aquitard. On the blanks provided, fill in the name of the labeled features.

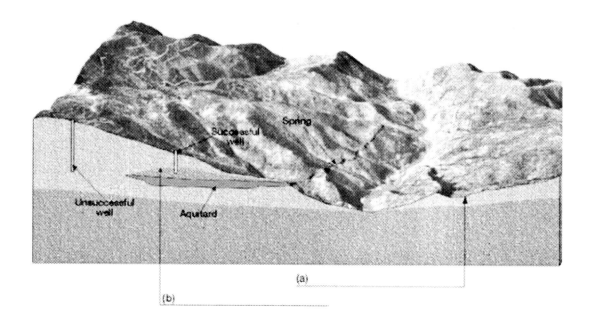

Answer: (a) water table (b) perched water table
Diff: 1

83) What is the name of the localized lowering of the water table shown in the diagram below?

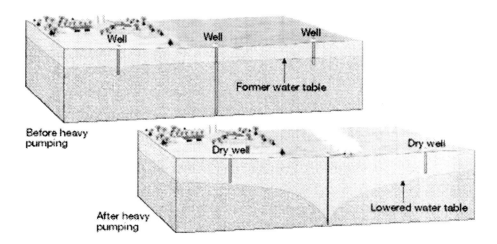

Answer: cone of depression
Diff: 1

84) What type of topography is illustrated in the diagram below?

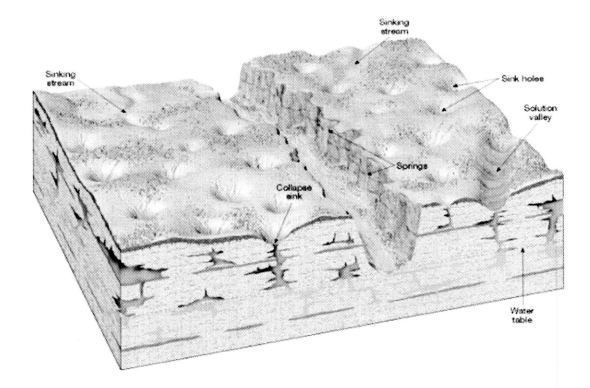

Answer: karst topography
Diff: 1

Chapter 11 Glaciers and Glaciation

1) The _____ is not the name of a Pleistocene glacial episode in North America.
   A) Dakotan
   B) Kansan
   C) Illinoian
   D) Nebraskan

   Answer: A
   Diff: 1

2) The _____ was the most recent Pleistocene glacial episode in North America.
   A) Dakotan
   B) Kansan
   C) Indianan
   D) Wisconsinan

   Answer: D
   Diff: 1

3) _____ is one of the two major flow mechanism in a glacier.
   A) Basal slip
   B) Crevassal slip
   C) Frost heaving
   D) Morainal sliding

   Answer: A
   Diff: 1

4) Where is the world's largest ice sheet located today?
   A) Greenland
   B) Russia, Siberia
   C) Iceland
   D) Antarctica

   Answer: D
   Diff: 1

5) Approximately how long ago did the last of the great North American ice sheets melt?
   A) 1500 yrs
   B) 1.5 million yrs
   C) 15,000 yrs
   D) 150,000 yrs

   Answer: C
   Diff: 1

6) _____ has speeds comparable to those of a flowing alpine glacier.
   A) Soil creep
   B) Streams
   C) Mudflows
   D) Basaltic lava flows

   Answer: A
   Diff: 1

7) The bottom or downward tip of a crevasse marks the _____.
   A) boundary between parts of the glacier moving by basal sliding and crevassal slip
   B) boundary between the basal sliding and external flowage zones
   C) bottom of the basal sliding zone
   D) top of the internal deformation and flowage zone
   Answer: D
   Diff: 1

8) Which one of the following applies to a valley glacier that lengthens (extends its terminus downslope) over a period of many years?
   A) wastage exceeds accumulation
   B) accumulation exceeds wastage
   C) accumulation and wastage are about equal
   D) none of the above
   Answer: B
   Diff: 1

9) Abrasion and plucking generally involve what part of a glacier?
   A) the internal, flowage zone
   B) the snout zone
   C) the surface, brittle zone
   D) the basal, sliding zone
   Answer: D
   Diff: 1

10) A _____ cross-valley profile is typical of canyons and valleys eroded and deepened by alpine or valley glaciers.
    A) U
    B) Y
    C) V
    D) S
    Answer: A
    Diff: 1

11) _____ are erosional features produced by valley/alpine glaciers.
    A) Moraines
    B) Cirques
    C) Eskers
    D) Drumlins
    Answer: B
    Diff: 1

12) A(n) _____ is a depositional feature composed of till and only associated with continental glaciation, not with alpine glaciers.
    A) cirque
    B) moraine
    C) drumlin
    D) outwash deposit
    Answer: C
    Diff: 1

Match the feature with the appropriate material.
   a. till   b. outwash   c. solid rock

13) moraine

   Answer: a
   Diff: 1

14) erratic

   Answer: c
   Diff: 1

15) cirque

   Answer: c
   Diff: 1

16) esker

   Answer: b
   Diff: 1

17) horn

   Answer: c
   Diff: 1

18) drumlin

   Answer: a
   Diff: 1

19) _____ first developed the theory that small variations in the Earth–Sun distance were
   responsible for short term, climatic oscillations (1000 to 100,000 years).
      A) H. Goering
      B) H. Marcee
      C) G. Zukhov
      D) M. Milankovitch

   Answer: D
   Diff: 1

20) The great, Southern Hemisphere glaciation that affected parts of Africa, South America, India,
   Australia, and Antarctica occurred _____.
      A) in late Paleozoic time
      B) in late Proterozoic time
      C) in early Cenozoic time
      D) in middle Mesozoic time

   Answer: A
   Diff: 1

21) Which of the following glacial features would typically be found in close proximity?
    A) cirque and terminal moraine
    B) outwash plain and horn
    C) hanging valley and truncated spur
    D) drumlin and fiord
Answer: C
Diff: 1

22) A(n) _____ represents a former meltwater channel or tunnel in glacial ice that was filled with sand and gravel.
    A) esker
    B) yazoo ridge
    C) valley plain
    D) kettle
Answer: A
Diff: 1

23) What type of moraine would be most useful for tracing diamond –bearing kimberlite fragments directly to their bedrock source area?
    A) terminal, valley or alpine glacier
    B) terminal, continental ice sheet
    C) recessional, continental ice sheet
    D) lateral, valley or alpine glacier
Answer: D
Diff: 1

24) Which one of the following samples and experimental measurements would provide the most information about the Earth's climate over the last 100,000 years or so?
    A) cores from sea ice in the Arctic Ocean; NaCl content
    B) sediment cores from a terminal moraine in Ohio sand to clay ratio
    C) sediment cores from a Pleistocene loess deposit in the state of Mississippi; SiO_2 content
    D) cores from the Greenland ice sheet; ratios of the oxygen isotopes (0–18/0–16)
Answer: D
Diff: 1

25) _____ is the best explanation for a glacial surge.
    A) The climate cools suddenly and a retreating glacier begins to advance
    B) Heavy snowfalls resulting in avalanches in the zone of accumulation
    C) Melting at the base of the glacier resulting in increased rates of basal slip
    D) Crevasses opening suddenly near the snout of a glacier
Answer: C
Diff: 1

26) All of the following descriptions apply to stratified drift (not glacial till) except for _____.
    A) deposited directly from melting ice
    B) sand and gravel beds
    C) deposits are often layered and well–sorted
    D) deposited by glacial meltwater streams
Answer: B
Diff: 1

27) A(n) _____ is similar in appearance to a sinkhole of a karst area.
   A) moraine
   B) esker
   C) cirque
   D) kettle

   Answer: D
   Diff: 1

28) Which one of the following prominent landforms, located from the Wasatch Range, UT, westward to the Sierra Nevada, CA, formed during the Pleistocene glacial episodes?
   A) terminal moraines of continental ice sheets that moved south from Canada
   B) old shorelines of large, pluvial lakes
   C) erosional features produced by continental glaciation
   D) subaerial deltas submerged by the post-glacial rise in sea level

   Answer: B
   Diff: 1

29) A fiord is _____.
   A) a stream valley, deepened by glacial erosion, that floods as sea level rises
   B) a glacier-cut valley that is dammed by an end moraine and a large lake is formed
   C) a glacier-cut valley which sinks below sea level due to glacial rebound after the ice melts
   D) a large, kettle-pocked moraine left as an island when sea level rises following melting of the ice

   Answer: A
   Diff: 1

30) Which process occurs where a glacier enters the sea?
   A) kaming
   B) calving
   C) surging
   D) drowning

   Answer: B
   Diff: 1

31) The _____ of the geologic time scale represents the time of the most recent "Ice Age."
   A) Pleistocene era
   B) Pliocene epoch
   C) Pleistocene epoch
   D) Pliocene era

   Answer: C
   Diff: 1

32) Which of the following is the correct listing of the North American glacial stages from older to younger?
   A) Indianan, Kansan, Nebraskan, Ohioan
   B) Kansan, Illinoian, Iowan, Dakotan
   C) Nebraskan, Indianan, Illinoian, Wisconsinan
   D) Nebraskan, Kansan, Illinoian, Wisconsinan

   Answer: D
   Diff: 1

33) Which one of the following statements concerning glaciers is not true?
   A) ice sheets are larger than ice caps
   B) piedmont glaciers form on lowlands at the base of mountainous terrain
   C) the volume of water tied up in the Antarctic ice sheet is about the same as the total discharge of the Amazon River in one year
   D) long, extended, alpine glaciers occupied valleys in most high, mountainous areas in the United States, Canada, and Europe at one or more times during the past two million years

Answer: D
Diff: 1

34) A _____ is an erosional feature specifically produced by alpine glaciation.
   A) lateral moraine
   B) drumlin
   C) crevasse spur
   D) U-shaped valley

Answer: D
Diff: 1

35) A(n) _____ is likely to host a waterfall or steep rapids today.
   A) outwash plain
   B) hanging valley
   C) striated drumlin
   D) horn peak

Answer: B
Diff: 1

36) A _____ is a glacier–cut valley that partly flooded as sea level rose.
   A) till crevasse
   B) fiord
   C) hanging cirque
   D) kettle trough

Answer: B
Diff: 1

37) A drumlin is a _____.
   A) smooth, tapering ridge of till; formed and shaped beneath a continental ice sheet
   B) bowl–shaped depression eroded largely by frost action and glacial plucking
   C) till mound of outwash deposited by meltwater streams at the snout of a glacier
   D) smooth, striated, bedrock ridge shaped and polished by a glacier

Answer: A
Diff: 1

38) _____ are both deposited by meltwater streams.
   A) Terminal moraines and cirques
   B) Outwash plains and valley trains
   C) Valley moraines and ice sheet trains
   D) Recessional kettles and erratics

Answer: B
Diff: 1

39) Where is the world's second largest continental ice sheet?
   A) Iceland
   B) Greenland
   C) Antarctica
   D) Siberian Russia
   Answer: B
   Diff: 1

40) How do icebergs in the North Atlantic Ocean originate?
   A) by calving of large piedmont glaciers in Greenland
   B) as large masses of sea ice that float northward from Antarctica
   C) as masses of sea ice that float southward from the Arctic Ocean
   D) as calved blocks of glacial ice that float northward from Antarctica
   Answer: A
   Diff: 1

41) Which of the following best describes the term glacial drift?
   A) floating of icebergs southward from the north polar seas
   B) slow, plastic flow movement in the brittle zone of a glacier
   C) the sedimentary materials outwash and till
   D) the slow, southward advance of the continental ice sheets over Canada and North America during the Pleistocene
   Answer: C
   Diff: 1

42) Which one of the following statements concerning glacial deposits is not true?
   A) till is deposited directly from the ice; outwash is deposited by meltwater streams
   B) glacial erratics are blocks of rock that are too large for the glacier to move
   C) tills are poorly sorted and the fragments are mostly angular
   D) outwash is mainly stratified sand and gravel
   Answer: B
   Diff: 1

43) What type of moraine is formed by the merging of two lateral moraines at a junction of two valley glaciers?
   A) medial
   B) recessional
   C) ground
   D) kettle
   Answer: A
   Diff: 1

44) A _____ forms when stagnant, glacial ice melts after being buried by drift.
   A) tarn
   B) kettle
   C) drumlin
   D) pluvial delta
   Answer: B
   Diff: 1

45) Which one of the following could not have significantly affected climatic variations and advances and retreats of ice sheets during the Pleistocene epoch?
   A) movements of Earth's tectonic plates
   B) variations in the Sun's energy output
   C) precession of Earth's orbit
   D) wobbling of Earth's rotational axis

Answer: A
Diff: 1

46) _____ was a very large, pluvial lake in Utah during the Pleistocene Epoch.
   A) Lake Caspian
   B) Lake Aral
   C) Lake Mead
   D) Lake Bonneville

Answer: D
Diff: 1

47) A _____ would logically be situated next to a large end moraine or terminal moraine.
   A) cirque
   B) fiord
   C) pluvial lake
   D) outwash plain

Answer: D
Diff: 1

48) Which of the following is often associated with a cirque basin in high, mountainous terrain?
   A) loon lake
   B) kettle pond
   C) tarn lake
   D) arête pond

Answer: C
Diff: 1

49) _____ is an irregular, usually thin till layer laid down by a retreating glacier.
   A) Terminal moraine
   B) Outwash blanket
   C) Kame sheet
   D) Ground moraine

Answer: D
Diff: 1

50) All of the following are thought to possibly contribute to the formation of glaciers except for _____.
   A) eccentricity
   B) precession
   C) comets
   D) plate tectonics

Answer: C
Diff: 1

Word Analysis. Examine the words and/or phrases for each question below and determine the relationship among the majority of words/phrases. Choose the option which does not fit the pattern.

51) a. drumlin   b. cirque   c. esker   d. moraine

    Answer: B
    Diff: 1

52) a. horn   b. arête   c. lateral moraine   d. drumlin

    Answer: D
    Diff: 1

53) a. calving   b. zone of accumulation   c. melting   d. zone of wastage

    Answer: B
    Diff: 1

54) a. truncated spur   b. glacial trough   c. hanging valley   d. pater noster lake

    Answer: D
    Diff: 2

55) a. drumlin   b. kame   c. kettle   d. esker

    Answer: A
    Diff: 2

56) When a glacier is retreating, the upstream ice is still moving forward toward the downstream terminus of the glacier.

    Answer: TRUE
    Diff: 1

57) Crevasses are short, narrow cracks in the plastic flow zone of a glacier that alternately open and close as the ice flows along.

    Answer: FALSE
    Diff: 1

58) The downstream end or snout of a glacier advances over periods of time during which ablation exceeds accumulation.

    Answer: FALSE
    Diff: 1

59) Till is an unsorted sediment deposited directly from the melting glacial ice; stream action is not involved.

    Answer: TRUE
    Diff: 1

60) The recessional moraine is the largest of many terminal moraines laid down by a retreating glacier.

    Answer: FALSE
    Diff: 1

61) Melting and evaporation are two forms of ablative calving.

    Answer: FALSE
    Diff: 1

62) Fiords are glacier-cut valleys that flooded as sea level rose in post-glacial times.

Answer: TRUE
Diff: 1

63) A cirque represents an erosional feature formed in what was an important accumulation zone for snow and ice at the upstream head of a glacier.

Answer: TRUE
Diff: 1

64) The volume of the Antarctic ice sheet is about equal to the total volume of ice in all alpine glaciers of the world.

Answer: FALSE
Diff: 1

65) The Pleistocene epoch of geological time began about 6 million years ago.

Answer: FALSE
Diff: 1

66) Because ice floats on seawater, coastal piedmont glaciers seldom erode much below the elevation of sea level at the times the glaciers are active.

Answer: TRUE
Diff: 1

67) The great, Southern Hemisphere glaciation left Jurassic tills on parts of South America, India, and South Africa.

Answer: FALSE
Diff: 1

68) Rapid surge movements of the Earth's tectonic plates offer a convincing explanation for the advances and retreats of the Pleistocene ice sheets.

Answer: FALSE
Diff: 1

69) Great Salt Lake in Utah is the shrunken, salty remnant of a much larger, Pleistocene, pluvial lake called Lake Bonneville.

Answer: TRUE
Diff: 1

70) Arêtes, horns, and U-shaped valleys are erosional features carved from bedrock by glaciers.

Answer: TRUE
Diff: 1

71) Sand and gravel deposited by glacial meltwater streams are known as outwash till or stratified till.

Answer: FALSE
Diff: 1

72) In the north-central United States, much of the land north of the Ohio and Missouri Rivers was covered by one or more of the Pleistocene ice sheets.

Answer: TRUE
Diff: 1

73) Surges in glacial movement are probably related to unusually fast rates of basal sliding.

Answer: TRUE

Diff: 1

74) Rock flour consists of silt–sized, rock and mineral particles produced by glacial abrasion.

Answer: TRUE

Diff: 1

75) Eskers and kames are deposited by meltwater streams; they are composed of stratified sand and gravel.

Answer: TRUE

Diff: 1

76) Drumlins are believed to represent deltas built into pluvial lakes by meltwater streams.

Answer: FALSE

Diff: 1

77) Eccentricity, obliquity, and precession are three factors involved in the Milankovitch astronomical explanation of why the Pleistocene continental ice sheets alternately grew and shrank in size.

Answer: TRUE

Diff: 1

78) The upper 40 meters or so of a glacier is known as the zone of _____.

Answer: fracture

Diff: 1

79) Unusually rapid, forward movements of glaciers are called _____.

Answer: surges

Diff: 1

80) List the two, major mechanisms of glacial flow.

Answer: plastic flow; basal slip

Diff: 1

81) What term describes open fissures in the brittle, surface ice of a glacier?

Answer: crevasse

Diff: 1

82) What general term denotes wastage of a glacier?

Answer: ablation

Diff: 1

83) Bridal Veil Falls in Yosemite National Park is an example a _____.

Answer: hanging valley

Diff: 1

84) Bowl-shaped depressions in bedrock at upstream ends of alpine glacial valleys are called _____.

Answer: cirque

Diff: 1

85) The wobbling motion of a spinning object is known as _____.

Answer: precession
Diff: 1

86) During the Pleistocene glacial epoch, pluvial lakes were common in valley regions of what part of the United States?

Answer: Basin & Range
Diff: 1

87) What is the name for the very large, pluvial lake that once existed in northwestern Utah?

Answer: Lake Bonneville
Diff: 1

88) _____ are smoothly tapered, elongated hills of till shaped by an overriding, continental ice sheet.

Answer: drumlins
Diff: 1

89) What is the oldest, Pleistocene, glacial stage in North America?

Answer: Nebraskan
Diff: 1

90) A(n) _____ is a closed depression formed by melting of an ice block buried in a moraine or outwash plain.

Answer: kettle
Diff: 1

91) A(n) _____ is a narrow, winding ridge composed of outwash deposited in a tunnel or channel cut into stagnant, glacial ice.

Answer: esker
Diff: 1

92) Valleys deeply eroded by alpine glaciers have what characteristic, cross–valley profile?

Answer: U–shaped
Diff: 1

93) What term denotes a glacial valley that was partly flooded as sea level rose?

Answer: fiord
Diff: 1

Critical thinking and discussion questions. Use complete sentences, correct spelling, and the information presented in Chapter 11 to answer the questions below.

94) Would most features of alpine glaciation be preserved in the geologic record? Why or why not? What about continental glaciation?

Diff: 3

95) Glacial ice is very effective as an agent of erosion. How would you identify glacial sediments from alluvial (stream) sediments? Also, could certain glacial sediments be mistaken for alluvium?

Diff: 3

96) Briefly discuss the indirect effects of glaciation. Indicate whether such changes would occur in conjunction with glaciation or at some time later?
   Diff: 3

97) Label the zones of ice movement on the glacier in the diagram below.

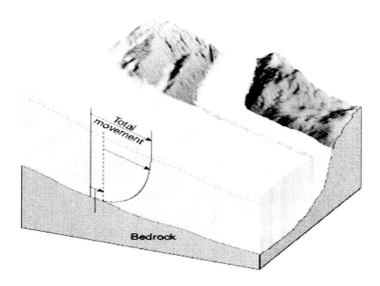

   Answer: See Figure 11.4 in the Essentials of Geology, 10e textbook.
   Diff: 1

98) Label the zone of accumulation and the zone of wastage on the diagram below.

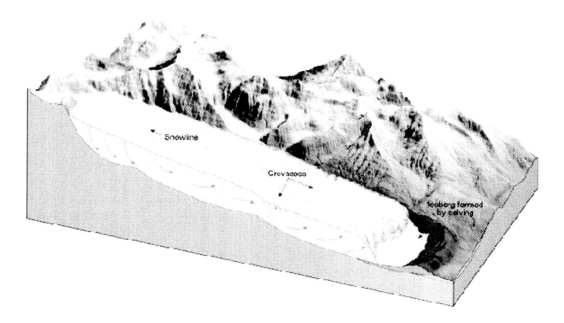

   Answer: See Figure 11.6 in the Essentials of Geology, 10e textbook.
   Diff: 1

99) On the blanks provided below, fill in the name of the labeled features that formed as a product of alpine glaciation.

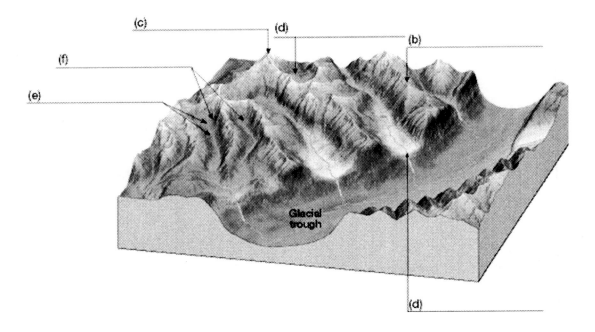

Answer: (a) hanging valley   (b) arête   (c) horn
        (d) tarn   (e) pater noster lake   (f) cirques
Diff: 2

100) Match the features on the illustration below to the correct answer for each one.

A) ground moraine B) outwash plain C) esker

D) end moraine E) drumlin F) kettle hole/lake

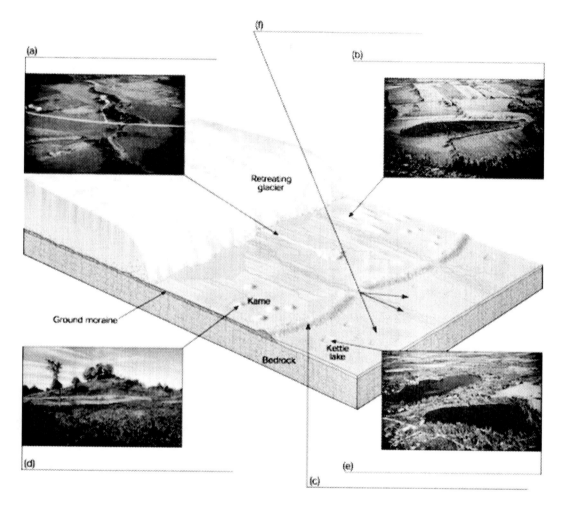

Answer: (a) C, (b) E, (c) D, (d) A, (e) F, (f) B
Diff: 2

Chapter 12 Deserts and Wind

1) Which one of the following statements is true?
   A) desert landscapes are monotonous, relatively flat areas covered to various depths with sand
   B) deserts and dry lands are concentrated in areas of ascending air masses and relatively low atmospheric pressures
   C) despite infrequent rainfalls, erosional and depositional features of running water are important in desert landscapes
   D) rainshadow deserts occur where air masses descend after first having risen to cross a mountain range

   Answer: C
   Diff: 1

2) _____ have rainfall amounts and soil moisture contents between those of true deserts and humid lands.
   A) Tundras
   B) Steppes
   C) Sundras
   D) Sabkhas

   Answer: B
   Diff: 1

3) Most dry lands lie between _____ degrees north and south of the equator.
   A) 40 and 50
   B) 20 and 30
   C) 5 and 10
   D) 0 and 5

   Answer: B
   Diff: 1

4) Which one of the following statements concerning rock weathering is true?
   A) warm temperatures and high soil moisture contents accelerate chemical weathering
   B) low temperatures and high soil moisture contents accelerate chemical weathering but inhibit mechanical weathering
   C) warm temperatures and low soil moisture contents both promote rapid rates of mechanical weathering
   D) temperature has no effect on rock weathering

   Answer: A
   Diff: 1

5) A _____ is an intermittent stream channel in the dry land areas of the western United States.
   A) rivulet
   B) playa
   C) rill
   D) wash

   Answer: D
   Diff: 1

6) _____ refers to the "bouncing" mode of sand transport in a windstorm or stream.
  A) Saltation
  B) Ventifaction
  C) Siltation
  D) Deflation

Answer: A
Diff: 1

7) Which one of the following will effectively limit further deflation in a given area?
  A) sea level
  B) desert pavement
  C) a hanging valley
  D) the repose level

Answer: B
Diff: 1

8) Which one of the following statements is correct?
  A) alluvial fans typically rim desert valleys; playas form in the lowest, interior parts of the valleys
  B) inselbergs are low, circular depressions on gently sloping pediments and bajadas
  C) playas are typically covered with gravel–sized desert pavement and loess deposits
  D) saline sediments and evaporites are common in inselbergs and pediments of desert landscapes

Answer: A
Diff: 1

9) In which area would surface water most effectively infiltrate into the local groundwater system?
  A) a stream in a steep–sided, bedrock canyon in the mountains
  B) streams flowing in the numerous channels of an alluvial fan
  C) a playa lake with a thick mud bottom
  D) all of the above would promote infiltration

Answer: B
Diff: 1

10) Which of the following characteristics would suggest recent, fault uplift of a desert mountain range?
  A) flat, upland surfaces, steep slopes and small alluvial fans
  B) extensive pediments and bajadas and small, deep playas
  C) inselbergs, extensive pediments and flat valley floors
  D) steep playas with extensive, bedrock alluvial fans and numerous sand dunes

Answer: A
Diff: 2

11) How is desert pavement formed?
   A) deflation removes the coarse fragments leaving behind a layer of loess
   B) alluvial fans are eroded to form inselbergs with rocky surfaces
   C) groundwater in an alluvial fan evaporates, leaving behind a surface layer of hard–baked mud
   D) runoff and deflation carry off the silt and clay, leaving coarser particles behind
   Answer: D
   Diff: 1

12) Which one of the following is determined by the angle of repose for dry sand?
   A) longitudinal dune gradient angle
   B) slope of an alluvial fan
   C) a vertical cut bank in loess
   D) inclination angle of a dune slip face
   Answer: D
   Diff: 1

13) Which one of the following statements about sand dunes is correct?
   A) a dune migrates in the direction of inclination of the slip face
   B) the more gently sloping surface is the leeward slope of the dune
   C) sand is blown up the slip face and rolls down the more gently sloping flank of the dune
   D) in a sand dune, the more gently inclined strata lie parallel to the slip face
   Answer: A
   Diff: 1

14) Deposition of glacial rock flour from blowing winds is responsible for _____.
   A) deflation ventifacts
   B) blowout pavement
   C) star steppes
   D) loess deposits
   Answer: D
   Diff: 1

15) Which one of the following is the one best measure of the wetness or dryness of a region?
   A) total annual precipitation
   B) mean annual temperature
   C) difference between annual precipitation and evaporation potential
   D) percentage of precipitation that falls during the summer months
   Answer: C
   Diff: 1

16) Which one of the following concerning desert lands is false?
   A) less than 30 percent is covered with dunes and drifting sand
   B) wind erosion and deposition are important processes
   C) running water has little effect on shaping the landscape
   D) most desert areas are characterized by descending wind patterns
   Answer: C
   Diff: 1

17) Desertification has been particularly well documented over the past 50 years in _____.
    A) the Empty Quarter of the Arabian Peninsula
    B) the Sahel along the southern margin of the Sahara Desert
    C) the Dust Bowl states of the Great Plains
    D) the steppe lands of southern Russia, Ukraine, and Kazakhstan
    Answer: B
    Diff: 1

18) All of the following statements concerning dry lands are true except for?
    A) precipitation totals are low; dew points are lower in the summer than winter
    B) evaporation potential exceeds actual precipitation
    C) storms are infrequent and rainfall amounts are highly variable
    D) wind is the dominant agent of erosion and sediment transport
    Answer: D
    Diff: 2

19) How are sand grains transported by the wind?
    A) high in the moving air column as suspended load
    B) by saltation in the first few meters above the land surface
    C) by deflation of abraded desert pavement
    D) by being picked up in swirling dust clouds and carried to distant blowouts
    Answer: B
    Diff: 1

20) Which of the following best describes the climatic factors that cause low latitude deserts like the Sahara in Africa?
    A) cool, dry air aloft is descending; surface winds are blowing toward the equator
    B) warm, humid air aloft is descending; surface winds blow away from the equator
    C) warm, humid air is rising; surface winds are calm
    D) cool, dry air at the surface is rising causing winds to blow away from the equator
    Answer: A
    Diff: 1

21) How is desert pavement formed?
    A) deflation and sheet wash remove fine-sized materials leaving coarse, weathered, rock fragments concentrated at the surface
    B) blowing wind removes fine-size soil particles; coarser particles abrades to sand size
    C) running water deposits gravel and sand over the finer-sized soil particles
    D) intense chemical weathering removes the sand- and silt-sized particles, leaving coarse rock debris covering the land surface
    Answer: A
    Diff: 1

22) Loess deposits in the central United States _____.
    A) blew in from the dry areas in the Great Plains and southwestern desert areas
    B) originated as rock flour in Pleistocene glacial streams and rivers
    C) accumulated from flooding of the Mississippi River
    D) were originally deposited as barchanoid dunes and later redeposited by glaciers
    Answer: B
    Diff: 1

23) Assume that the central slip face of a barchan dune slopes downhill toward the east. What is the direction of the prevailing wind?
   A) east to west
   B) north to south
   C) south to north
   D) west to east
   Answer: D
   Diff: 1

24) Desert and steppe lands cover about what percentage of Earth's land area?
   A) 10%
   B) 66%
   C) 30%
   D) 3%
   Answer: C
   Diff: 1

25) Inselbergs are _____.
   A) insulated icebergs floating in a hot spring
   B) blowouts cut from bedrock in mountainous areas
   C) lithified rock formed by cementation of wind-deposited, dune sands
   D) bedrock hills in a highly eroded desert landscape
   Answer: D
   Diff: 1

26) A _____ is formed by abrasion of rocks by windblown sand.
   A) playa
   B) ventifact
   C) pediment
   D) desert pavement
   Answer: B
   Diff: 1

27) Which one of the following would probably not affect the size and depth of a blowout?
   A) a rise in sea level
   B) the near surface water table
   C) type and density of vegetation
   D) areas of desert pavement
   Answer: A
   Diff: 1

28) What mature, desert landscape feature consists of coalesced alluvial fans?
   A) balda
   B) bajada
   C) bahia
   D) baja
   Answer: B
   Diff: 1

29) A _____ is a crescent-shaped dune whose tips point downwind.
   A) parabarcal
   B) transverse
   C) barchan
   D) star

Answer: C
Diff: 1

30) During a typical sandstorm, saltating sand grains reach a maximum height of _____ above the land surface.
   A) 1 inch
   B) 2 meters
   C) 10 centimeters
   D) 40 feet

Answer: B
Diff: 1

31) Rainshadow deserts are common in _____.
   A) vast, dry, steppe lands like the Great Plains
   B) north central Africa
   C) the dry valleys of eastern California and Nevada
   D) Europe north of the Alps

Answer: C
Diff: 1

32) _____ are both dry land, erosional features cut from bedrock.
   A) Inselbergs and barcanoids
   B) Pediments and playas
   C) Bajadas and blowouts
   D) Pediments and inselbergs

Answer: D
Diff: 1

33) _____ dunes result from persistent, onshore winds in certain coastal areas.
   A) Diabolic
   B) Barchanoid
   C) Parabolic
   D) Staroid

Answer: C
Diff: 1

34) _____ dunes are long, high, sand dunes parallel with the prevailing wind direction.
   A) Transducinal
   B) Longitudinal
   C) Latitudinal
   D) Transversal

Answer: B
Diff: 1

35) Which one of the following is a low-latitude desert characterized by high atmospheric pressures and descending air masses (not rain shadow deserts).
   A) Sahara Desert; northern Africa
   B) Atacama Desert in Chile, South America
   C) Gobi Desert, China and Mongolia
   D) desert valleys of the Great Basin, U.S.

Answer: A
Diff: 1

Match the sand dune with the appropriate description.
   a. star   b. barchan   c. parabolic
   d. barchanoid   e. transverse   f. longitudinal

36) complexly shaped dunes formed in response to different, seasonal, wind directions

   Answer: a
   Diff: 1

37) linear sand ridges at right angles to the prevailing wind direction

   Answer: e
   Diff: 1

38) linear sand ridges parallel to the prevailing wind direction

   Answer: f
   Diff: 1

39) multiple, connected, crescent-shaped coastal dunes with the tips pointing toward the beach

   Answer: d
   Diff: 1

40) sand ridges at right angles to prevailing winds with crescent-shaped slip faces pointing downwind

   Answer: d
   Diff: 1

41) single, crescent-shaped dune with the tips pointing downwind

   Answer: b
   Diff: 1

Word Analysis. Examine the words and/or phrases for each question below and determine the relationship among the majority of words/phrases. Choose the option which does not fit the pattern.

42) a. pothole   b. glacial striation   c. ventifact   d. steppe stone

   Answer: D
   Diff: 1

43) a. arroyo   b. wadi   c. inselberg   d. nullah

   Answer: C
   Diff: 1

44) a. ventifact   b. alluvial fan   c. playa   d. inselberg
   Answer: A
   Diff: 2

45) a. sand dune   b. deflation   c. blowout   d. desert pavement
   Answer: A
   Diff: 2

46) a. barchan dune   b. star dune   c. transverse dune   d. parabolic dune
   Answer: B
   Diff: 2

47) Running water is an important erosional agent in many arid lands despite infrequent rainfalls.
   Answer: TRUE
   Diff: 1

48) Sand dunes cover more than 50 percent of most desert lands.
   Answer: FALSE
   Diff: 1

49) Deserts between 30 and 45 degrees of latitude are more extensive in the southern hemisphere than in the northern hemisphere.
   Answer: FALSE
   Diff: 1

50) The loess in western China was derived from windblown, glacial rock flour.
   Answer: FALSE
   Diff: 1

51) Bajadas develop from coalescence of alluvial fans along fronts of mountain ranges in arid lands.
   Answer: TRUE
   Diff: 1

52) About one-third of the Earth's land areas have arid to semiarid climates.
   Answer: TRUE
   Diff: 1

53) The Basin and Range Province of the southeastern United States is well known for it's numerous and diverse arid region landforms.
   Answer: TRUE
   Diff: 1

54) A playa is an intermittent lake on the floor of a desert valley.
   Answer: TRUE
   Diff: 1

55) Steppes are the driest of the true desert lands.
   Answer: FALSE
   Diff: 1

56) Intermittent streams in dry areas of the western United States are called washes.

Answer: TRUE
Diff: 1

57) Windblown loess, like sand, typically accumulates as mound-like dunes.

Answer: FALSE
Diff: 1

58) In North America, loess deposits are found mainly in the dry to semiarid lands of southwestern United States and northern Mexico.

Answer: FALSE
Diff: 1

59) Sand is transported by saltation in running water and blowing winds.

Answer: TRUE
Diff: 1

60) Blowouts are broad, shallow depressions excavated by deflation.

Answer: TRUE
Diff: 1

61) Ventifacts are wind-abraded blowouts exceeding one kilometer in diameter.

Answer: FALSE
Diff: 1

62) The steeper, lee slope of a sand dune is called the slip face.

Answer: TRUE
Diff: 1

63) Loess consists mainly of silt-sized particles.

Answer: TRUE
Diff: 1

64) Saltation refers to evaporation of shallow, muddy waters from a playa lake.

Answer: FALSE
Diff: 1

65) Desert pavement accelerates deflation of bedrock pediments in alluvial fans.

Answer: TRUE
Diff: 1

66) Inselbergs and small, steep, alluvial fans are characteristic of recently faulted, basin and range terrain in dry lands.

Answer: TRUE
Diff: 1

67) Wind turbines 10 meters above the ground surface are subjected to relatively little abrasion by blowing sand.

Answer: TRUE
Diff: 1

68) _____ dunes are long, sand ridges that develop at right angles to the prevailing wind direction.

Answer: Transverse
Diff: 1

69) A _____ is an intermittent lake on the floor of a desert basin.

Answer: playa
Diff: 1

70) _____ is the skipping and bouncing transport of sand in blowing wind and running water.

Answer: Saltation
Diff: 1

71) In dry lands, _____ is the covering of coarse particles left on the surface after the finer particles are carried away by wind and running water.

Answer: desert pavement
Diff: 1

72) _____ are rocks with one or more flat surfaces abraded by windblown sand.

Answer: Ventifacts
Diff: 1

73) The leeward slope of a sand dune is also known as the _____.

Answer: slip face
Diff: 1

74) _____ are solitary, crescent-shaped dunes whose tips face downwind.

Answer: Barchan
Diff: 1

75) _____ describes the complex, internal stratification or bedding in a sand dune.

Answer: Cross bedding
Diff: 1

76) Deposits of windblown silt are called _____.

Answer: loess
Diff: 1

77) _____ dunes form in areas where the prevailing wind directions change with the seasons.

Answer: Star
Diff: 1

78) The low, bedrock ridges and peaks of a highly eroded, basin and range, desert landscape are called _____.

Answer: inselbergs
Diff: 1

Critical thinking and discussion questions. Use complete sentences, correct spelling, and the information presented in Chapter 12 to answer the questions below.

79) Wind is included along with gravity, water, and ice as an agent of erosion. In many national parks and other areas of natural beauty, statements are often made that credit wind as having sculpted the landscape. Briefly discuss the importance of wind as an agent of erosion and explain why such statements are probably geologically inaccurate.
Diff: 3

80) What features or characteristics would distinguish a Paleozoic sandstone formation as being eolian (wind–blown) in origin rather than having formed from an ancient stream or coastal environment?
Diff: 3

81) Label the alluvial fans and playa lakes on the diagram below.

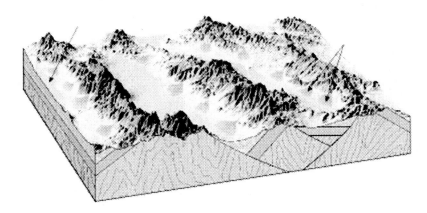

    Answer: See Figure 12.6 in the Essentials of Geology, 10e textbook.
Diff: 1

82) Label the bajadas and playa on the diagram below.

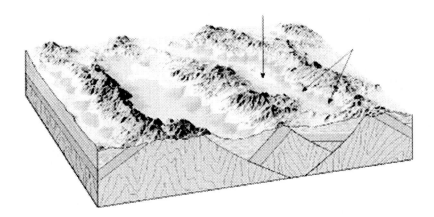

    Answer: See Figure 12.6 in the Essentials of Geology, 10e textbook.
Diff: 1

83) On the blank spaces provided beside each illustration, write the name of the type of dunes shown in the illustration.

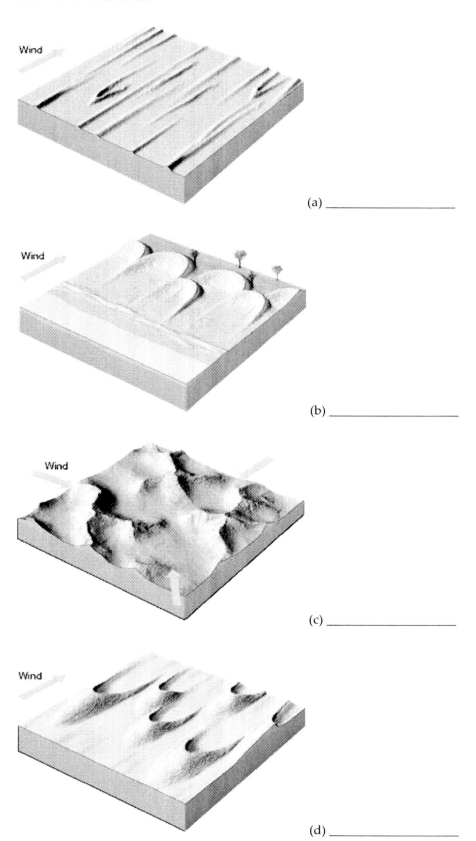

(a) _____

(b) _____

(c) _____

(d) _____

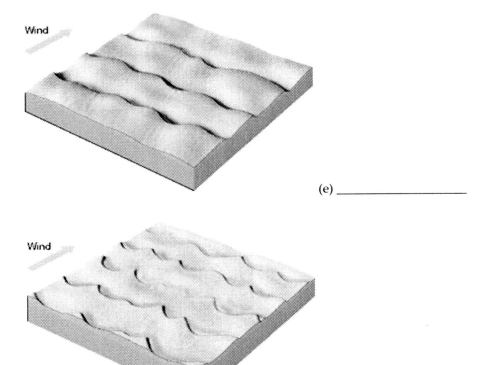

Wind

(e) _____

Wind

(f) _____

Answer: (a) longitudinal dunes   (b) parabolic dunes   (c) star dunes
             (d) barchan dunes   (e) transverse dunes   (f) barchanoid dunes

Diff: 1

Chapter 13 Shorelines

1) The height, length, and period of a wave depend upon _____.
   A) the length of time the wind has blown
   B) the wind speed
   C) the fetch
   D) all of these

   Answer: D
   Diff: 1

2) Which of the following is correct regarding a wave in the open ocean?
   A) Water particles move in an almost circular path.
   B) Such waves are called waves of oscillation.
   C) Waves do not exist in the open ocean — only near the coast..
   D) none of these

   Answer: D
   Diff: 1

3) Waves begin to "feel bottom" when the depth of water is _____.
   A) equal to one–half the wavelength
   B) equal to the wavelength
   C) twice as great as the wavelength
   D) three times as great as the wavelength

   Answer: A
   Diff: 1

4) When waves reach shallow water, they are often bent and tend to become parallel to the shore.
   This process is termed _____.
   A) oscillation
   B) refraction
   C) translation
   D) reflection

   Answer: B
   Diff: 1

5) The movement of water within the surf zone that parallels the shore is termed _____.
   A) tidal current
   B) salinity current
   C) beach drift
   D) longshore current

   Answer: D
   Diff: 1

6) The presence of which one of the following would indicate that the land had been uplifted or that sea level had fallen?
   A) an estuary
   B) a sea stack
   C) elevated marine terrace
   D) a tombolo

Answer: C
Diff: 1

7) Which one of the following is a landform created by wave erosion?
   A) spit
   B) estuary
   C) tombolo
   D) sea arch

Answer: D
Diff: 1

8) Chesapeake Bay and Delaware Bay are _____.
   A) associated with a submergent coast
   B) former river valleys that were flooded by a rise in sea level
   C) excellent examples of large estuaries
   D) all of the above

Answer: D
Diff: 1

9) The movement of sand parallel to the shore _____.
   A) is created by waves approaching at an oblique angle
   B) may create spits
   C) is achieved by longshore currents
   D) all of the above

Answer: D
Diff: 1

10) One result of wave refraction is that wave energy is concentrated _____.
    A) on headlands projecting into the water
    B) in the recessed areas between headlands
    C) in estuaries
    D) none of the above

Answer: A
Diff: 1

11) The zigzag movement of sand grains along a beach is _____.
    A) caused by obliquely breaking waves
    B) called beach drift
    C) very unusual and seldom occurs
    D) both A and B

Answer: D
Diff: 1

12) A sandbar that completely crosses a bay, sealing it off from the open ocean is a _____.
    A) sea stack
    B) tombolo
    C) coastal barrier
    D) none of these

Answer: D
Diff: 1

13) A ridge of sand projecting into a bay and often having a hooked end is a _____.
    A) spit
    B) jetty
    C) groin
    D) sea stack

Answer: A
Diff: 1

14) An isolated remnant of wave erosion is a _____.
    A) spit
    B) jetty
    C) groin
    D) sea stack

Answer: D
Diff: 1

15) A sand ridge connecting an island to the mainland or to another island is a _____.
    A) jetty
    B) tombolo
    C) breakwater
    D) sea stack

Answer: B
Diff: 1

16) A flat, bench–like surface cut in rock along a coast is a _____.
    A) sea stack
    B) tombolo
    C) wave–cut platform
    D) spit

Answer: C
Diff: 1

17) Fetch is _____.
    A) a method of shoreline erosion control
    B) the distance between the trough of a wave and the still water level
    C) the circular pattern made by water particles when a wave passes
    D) none of these

Answer: D
Diff: 1

18) Which one of the following structures is built to protect boats from large breaking waves?
    A) jetty
    B) groin
    C) breakwater
    D) seawall
    Answer: C
    Diff: 1

19) Which of the following is designed to prevent or retard shoreline erosion?
    A) groin
    B) beach nourishment
    C) seawall
    D) all of these
    Answer: D
    Diff: 1

20) Which of the following is a tidal current?
    A) spring tide
    B) flood tide
    C) ebb tide
    D) both flood and ebb tide
    Answer: D
    Diff: 1

21) The energy that drives surface ocean currents such as the Gulf Stream comes from _____.
    A) salinity variations
    B) Coriolis effect
    C) prevailing winds
    D) density differences
    Answer: C
    Diff: 1

22) A poleward-moving ocean current is _____.
    A) warm
    B) cold
    C) warm only in the Northern Hemisphere
    D) warm only in the Southern Hemisphere
    Answer: A
    Diff: 1

23) Because of the Coriolis effect, surface ocean currents are deflected to the _____ of their path of motion in the Northern Hemisphere.
    A) right
    B) left
    C) west
    D) east
    Answer: A
    Diff: 1

24) Because of the Coriolis effect, surface ocean currents are deflected to the _____ of their path of motion in the Southern Hemisphere.
   A) right
   B) left
   C) west
   D) east

   Answer: B
   Diff: 1

25) The daily tidal range is GREATEST during _____ tide.
   A) spring
   B) ebb
   C) neap
   D) none of these

   Answer: A
   Diff: 1

26) The daily tidal range is LEAST during _____ tide.
   A) spring
   B) ebb
   C) neap
   D) none of these

   Answer: C
   Diff: 1

27) Fetch refers to _____.
   A) the beachfront area where rapid erosion is taking place
   B) a large expanse of open water over which the wind blows and generates waves
   C) the rotational movements of water particles beneath a passing surface wave
   D) ocean currents moving parallel to the beach

   Answer: B
   Diff: 1

28) How can crashing, collapsing storm waves generate explosive forces and stresses on rocky outcrops and manmade structures?
   A) Oscillating, refractive waves shake the hard materials into small fragments.
   B) Pressurized water and compressed air are driven into cracks and fissures.
   C) Backwash breaks out blocks of rock or concrete and carries them out to deeper water.
   D) all of the above

   Answer: B
   Diff: 1

29) Erosional retreat of a _____ leads to enlargement and extension of a wave-cut platform in the inland direction.
   A) wave-cut tombolo
   B) wave-cut cliff
   C) wave-cut barrier beach
   D) offshore, wave-cut, breakwater bar

   Answer: B
   Diff: 1

30) Large estuaries are more common on a _____ coastline.
   A) submergent
   B) emergent
   C) stable
   D) retreating
   Answer: A
   Diff: 1

31) A _____ is an isolated remnant of bedrock standing above a wave-cut platform.
   A) sea spit
   B) sea rampart
   C) sea span
   D) sea stack
   Answer: D
   Diff: 1

32) _____ is a strong, parallel alignment of different mineral bands in a metamorphic rock.
   A) Rock cleavage
   B) Foliation
   C) Stress streaking
   D) Marbleizing
   Answer: B
   Diff: 1

Match the tide with the appropriate description.
   a. neap tides   b. spring tides

33) Sun, Moon, and Earth form a right triangle in space
   Answer: a
   Diff: 1

34) lowest high tides and highest low tides of the month
   Answer: a
   Diff: 1

35) highest high tides and lowest low tides of the month
   Answer: b
   Diff: 1

36) Sun, Moon, and Earth lie on a straight line in space
   Answer: b
   Diff: 1

Word Analysis. Examine the words and/or phrases for each question below and determine the relationship among the majority of words/phrases. Choose the option which does not fit the pattern.

37) a. wave height   b. wave period   c. wave refraction   d. fetch
   Answer: C
   Diff: 2

38) a. wave-cut cliff   b. wave-cut platform   c. sea arch   d. spit
     Answer: B
     Diff: 1

39) a. sea stack   b. bar   c. tombolo   d. barrier island
     Answer: A
     Diff: 1

40) a. breakwater   b. groin   c. seawall   d. beach nourishment
     Answer: D
     Diff: 1

41) a. spring tide   b. flood tide   c. neap tide   d. tidal flat
     Answer: D
     Diff: 1

42) The horizontal distance separating successive wave crests is called the wave period.
     Answer: FALSE
     Diff: 1

43) Tidal flats are submerged during ebb tide.
     Answer: FALSE
     Diff: 1

44) The turbulent water created by breaking waves is called surf.
     Answer: TRUE
     Diff: 1

45) A baymouth bar is a manmade feature designed to control wave erosion.
     Answer: FALSE
     Diff: 1

46) Although the Sun influences the tides, its effect is considerably less than the effect of the Moon.
     Answer: TRUE
     Diff: 1

47) The energy that creates surface ocean currents comes from prevailing winds.
     Answer: TRUE
     Diff: 1

48) Waves in the open ocean are called waves of oscillation.
     Answer: TRUE
     Diff: 1

49) The addition of sand to a beach has proven to be an economical solution to beach erosion problems.
     Answer: FALSE
     Diff: 1

50) Elevated wave-cut platforms in Southern California are evidence that this coastal area is emergent.

Answer: TRUE
Diff: 1

51) The Gulf Coast lacks barrier islands.

Answer: FALSE
Diff: 1

52) Groins are constructed for the purpose of maintaining or widening beaches that are losing sand.

Answer: TRUE
Diff: 1

53) The largest daily tidal range occurs in association with spring tides.

Answer: TRUE
Diff: 1

54) Neap tides occur about the time of the first quarter and third quarter phases of the Moon.

Answer: TRUE
Diff: 1

55) As the tide rises, water flows in toward the shore as the ebb tide.

Answer: FALSE
Diff: 1

56) A poleward-moving ocean current is considered a warm current.

Answer: TRUE
Diff: 1

57) The Coriolis effect causes ocean currents in the Southern Hemisphere to be deflected to the right of their path of motion.

Answer: FALSE
Diff: 1

58) The Coriolis effect is greatest at high latitudes and diminishes toward the equator.

Answer: TRUE
Diff: 1

59) Surface ocean circulation is also called thermohaline circulation.

Answer: FALSE
Diff: 1

60) Longshore sand transport and longshore currents depend on waves impinging parallel to a shoreline.

Answer: FALSE
Diff: 1

61) The _____ is the distance the wind has traveled across open water.

Answer: fetch
Diff: 1

62) Large circular-moving currents of water within an ocean basin are called _____.

Answer: gyres
Diff: 1

63) When a wave breaks it changes from being a wave of oscillation to being a wave of _____.

Answer: translation
Diff: 1

64) As a deep-water wave enters shallow water, the wave slows down and rotates toward being parallel with the shoreline. This process is known as _____.

Answer: refraction
Diff: 1

65) Currents within the surf zone that flow parallel to the shore are known as _____ currents.

Answer: longshore
Diff: 1

66) A ridge of sand that connects an island to the mainland or to another island is a _____.

Answer: tombolo
Diff: 1

67) Low and narrow offshore ridges of sand that parallel the coast are called _____.

Answer: barrier islands
Diff: 1

68) Structures called _____ are built parallel to the shoreline to protect boats from the force of large breaking waves.

Answer: breakwaters
Diff: 1

69) A barrier built at a right angle to the beach for the purpose of trapping sand that is moving parallel to the shore is called a _____.

Answer: groin
Diff: 1

70) When caves on opposite sides of a headland unite, a _____ results.

Answer: sea arch
Diff: 1

71) What term denotes a sand bar built across the former mouth of an estuary, separating it from the open sea?

Answer: baymouth bar
Diff: 1

72) The rising of cold water from deeper layers to replace warmer surface water is called _____.

Answer: upwelling
Diff: 1

73) Because deep ocean circulation is driven largely by variations in water temperature and salinity, it is also called _____ circulation.

Answer: thermohaline
Diff: 1

74) The low-lying zones that are alternately covered by water during flood tide and exposed following ebb tide are called _____.

Answer: tidal flats
Diff: 1

75) The _____ effect causes ocean currents to be deflected to the right of their path of motion in the Northern Hemisphere.

Answer: Coriolis
Diff: 1

Critical thinking and discussion questions. Use complete sentences, correct spelling, and the information presented in Chapter 13 to answer the questions below.

76) Shorelines are temporary geologic and topographic features. Explain this statement.
Diff: 2

77) Briefly discuss the movement of sand on a beach environment. Include those factors, both natural and human-induced, that affect sand movement.
Diff: 3

78) A variety of techniques and efforts are used to stabilize shorelines throughout the world. Are all of
these efforts only temporary measures or are any of them permanent? Also, does urbanization and development of coastal areas always contribute to shoreline erosion? Explain.
Diff: 3

79) Label the basic parts of a wave on the diagram below.

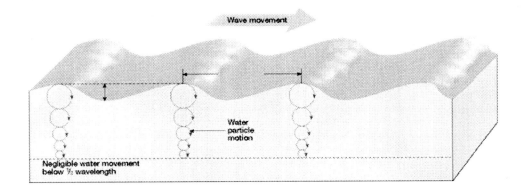

Answer: See Figure 13.3 in the Essentials of Geology, 10e textbook.
Diff: 1

80) What type of current is illustrated in the diagram below?

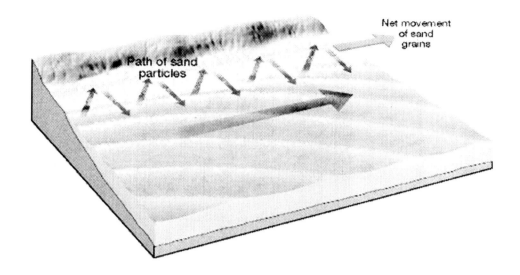

Answer: longshore current
Diff: 1

81) Match the features on the illustration below with the correct answer for each one.
A. tombolo   B. wave–cut cliff   C. spit   D. baymouth bar

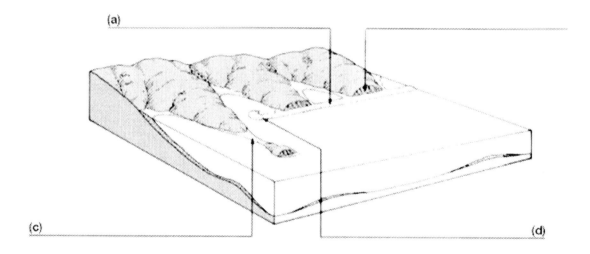

Answer: (a) D (b) B (c) A (d) C
Diff: 2

Chapter 14 Earthquakes and Earth's Interior

1) The elastic rebound theory for the origin of earthquakes was first proposed by _____
   following the _____ earthquake.
   A) Reid; 1906, San Francisco
   B) Giuseppe; 1925, Pizza Lake
   C) Richter; 1989, Loma Prieta
   D) Mohorovicic; 1964, Anchorage

   Answer: A
   Diff: 1

2) When an earthquake occurs, energy radiates in all directions from its source. The source is also
   referred to as the _____.
   A) inertial point
   B) epicenter
   C) focus
   D) seismic zone

   Answer: C
   Diff: 1

3) Which one of the following statements is correct?
   A) P waves travel through solids; S waves do not.
   B) P and S waves travel through liquids, but P waves do not travel through solids.
   C) S waves travel through solids and P waves travel through liquids.
   D) P and S waves travel through liquids, but S waves do not travel through solids.

   Answer: C
   Diff: 1

4) _____ have the highest velocities.
   A) Primary waves
   B) Secondary waves
   C) Surface waves
   D) Refracted S waves

   Answer: A
   Diff: 1

5) Which one of the following is true regarding tsunamis?
   A) They travel as deep–water waves at speeds greater than surface seismic waves but
      slower than S waves.
   B) Their wave heights decrease and wavelengths increase as they move into shallower
      water.
   C) They are started by fault–induced, horizontal shifts in the seafloor that suddenly propel
      great masses of water in opposite directions.
   D) They occur in the open ocean, wavelengths are many miles or kilometers and wave
      heights are only a few feet.

   Answer: D
   Diff: 1

6) The amount of destruction caused by earthquake vibrations is affected by _____.
   A) design of structures
   B) intensity and duration of the vibrations
   C) nature of the surface material
   D) all of these

   Answer: D
   Diff: 1

7) On a typical seismogram, _____ will show the highest amplitudes.
   A) P waves
   B) S waves
   C) surface waves
   D) body waves

   Answer: C
   Diff: 1

8) Major earthquakes are often followed by somewhat smaller events known as _____.
   A) aftershocks
   B) foreshocks
   C) tremors
   D) hyposhocks

   Answer: A
   Diff: 1

9) The _____ magnitude scale is a measure of the energy released. It does not directly measure the extent of building damage.
   A) Gutenberg
   B) Reid
   C) Mercalli
   D) Richter

   Answer: D
   Diff: 1

10) The instrument that records earthquake events is termed a _____.
    A) polygraph
    B) thermograph
    C) seismograph
    D) barograph

    Answer: C
    Diff: 1

11) _____ is the maximum possible damage designation on the Mercalli scale.
    A) XII
    B) 12
    C) X
    D) 10

    Answer: A
    Diff: 1

12) The position on Earth's surface directly above the earthquake source is called the _____.
   A) epicenter
   B) inertial point
   C) focus
   D) seismic zone
   Answer: A
   Diff: 1

13) The mechanism by which rocks store and eventually release energy in the form of an earthquake is termed _____.
   A) elastic rebound
   B) seismic rebound
   C) fault displacement
   D) stress fracture
   Answer: A
   Diff: 1

14) Overall, this type of seismic wave is the most destructive.
   A) P wave
   B) S wave
   C) surface wave
   D) tsunami
   Answer: C
   Diff: 1

15) Approximately how much more energy is released in a 6.5 Richter magnitude earthquake than in one with magnitude 5.5?
   A) 3000 times
   B) 3 times
   C) 300 times
   D) 30 times
   Answer: D
   Diff: 1

16) P waves _____.
   A) propagate only in solids
   B) are faster than S waves and surface waves
   C) have higher amplitudes than do S waves
   D) produce the strongest ground shaking
   Answer: B
   Diff: 1

17) The Mercalli Scale is a scale from _____.
   A) 1 to 12 that rates the energy required for faulting to occur
   B) 1 to 10 that rates the energy released by an earthquake
   C) I to XII that rates the structural damage due to an earthquake
   D) I to X that rates the total energy released during the main quake and all aftershocks
   Answer: C
   Diff: 1

18) The distance between a seismological recording station and the earthquake source is determined from the _____.
   A) earthquake magnitude
   B) intensity of the earthquake
   C) length of the seismic record
   D) arrival times of P and S waves

Answer: D
Diff: 1

19) The Richter magnitude of an earthquake is determined from the _____.
   A) duration of the earthquake
   B) intensity of the earthquake
   C) arrival time of P and S waves
   D) amplitude of the surface waves

Answer: C
Diff: 1

20) Which one of the following best characterizes tsunamis?
   A) They cause the land to ripple and oscillate.
   B) They are faster than seismic surface waves.
   C) They have relatively small amplitudes compared to their very long wavelengths.
   D) They are easily seen at sea but are lost in the swell and breaking waves along a coast.

Answer: C
Diff: 1

21) The _____ earthquake was accompanied by extensive fire damage.
   A) Anchorage, 1964
   B) San Francisco, 1906
   C) Mexico City, 1985
   D) Yerevan, Armenia, 1988

Answer: B
Diff: 1

22) _____ refers to the tendency for a foundation material to lose its internal cohesion and fail mechanically during earthquake shaking.
   A) Slurrying
   B) Liquefaction
   C) Motion slip
   D) Seismoflowage

Answer: B
Diff: 1

23) The record of an earthquake obtained from a seismic instrument is a(n) _____.
   A) seismograph
   B) seismogram
   C) time–travel graph
   D) epigraph

Answer: B
Diff: 1

24) Most of our knowledge about Earth's interior comes from _____.
  A) drill holes
  B) volcanic eruptions
  C) seismic waves
  D) examination of deep mine shafts
  Answer: C
  Diff: 1

25) Which one of the following statements about the crust is NOT true?
  A) It is the thinnest of the major subdivisions.
  B) It is thickest where prominent mountains exist.
  C) Oceanic crust is enriched in potassium, sodium, and silicon.
  D) Continental rocks are compositionally different than oceanic rocks.
  Answer: C
  Diff: 1

26) The dense core of Earth is thought to consist predominantly of _____.
  A) nickel
  B) lead
  C) iron
  D) copper
  Answer: C
  Diff: 1

27) The lithosphere is defined as _____.
  A) a rocky layer having a relatively uniform chemical composition
  B) a rigid layer of crustal and mantle material
  C) a rocky layer composed mainly of crustal rocks
  D) a plastic layer composed mainly of mantle material
  Answer: B
  Diff: 1

28) The average composition of the oceanic crust is thought to approximate that of _____.
  A) granite
  B) basalt
  C) peridotite
  D) iron
  Answer: B
  Diff: 1

29) The average composition of the continental crust most closely approximates that of _____.
  A) granite
  B) basalt
  C) peridotite
  D) iron
  Answer: A
  Diff: 1

30) The Earth's magnetic field originates by _____.
   A) weak electrical currents associated with hot, rising, mantle plumes
   B) magnetic mineral grains in the inner core
   C) weak electrical currents associated with fluid motions in the outer core
   D) magnetization of oxygen and nitrogen atoms in the atmospheric ozone layer by solar radiation

Answer: C
Diff: 1

31) The asthenosphere is located _____.
   A) within the crust
   B) in the upper mantle
   C) between the mantle and outer core
   D) within the outer core

Answer: B
Diff: 1

Word Analysis. Examine the words and/or phrases for each question below and determine the relationship among the majority of words/phrases. Choose the option which does not fit the pattern.

32) a. P wave   b. S wave   c. surface wave   d. body wave

Answer: C
Diff: 1

33) a. focus   b. seismograph   c. epicenter   d. fault

Answer: B
Diff: 1

34) a. tsunami   b. fire   c. liquefaction   d. seiches

Answer: B
Diff: 2

35) a. Modified Mercalli   b. energy   c. Richter   d. amplitude

Answer: A
Diff: 1

36) a. crust   b. lithosphere   c. core   d. mantle

Answer: B
Diff: 1

37) a. core   b. asthenosphere   c. mesosphere   d. lithosphere

Answer: A
Diff: 1

38) S waves can travel through solid and liquid media.

Answer: FALSE
Diff: 1

39) The time between the first P–wave and S–wave arrivals is a measure of the distance from a receiving station to the epicenter of the earthquake.

Answer: TRUE
Diff: 1

40) Earthquakes result from the sudden release of elastic strain energy previously stored in rocks surrounding a zone of fault movement.

Answer: TRUE
Diff: 1

41) Tsunamis are caused by sudden displacement of large volumes of seawater.

Answer: TRUE
Diff: 1

42) The Richter earthquake magnitude scale is based on the total amount of energy released by the earthquake.

Answer: TRUE
Diff: 1

43) The epicenter of an earthquake is on the surface of the Earth directly above the focus.

Answer: TRUE
Diff: 1

44) Unconsolidated, water–saturated soils or sediments provide good foundation materials for buildings and other structures.

Answer: FALSE
Diff: 1

45) Oceanic crust is mainly basaltic in composition; the mantle is more like the igneous rock peridotite in chemical composition.

Answer: TRUE
Diff: 1

46) Continental crust is generally thicker than oceanic crust.

Answer: TRUE
Diff: 1

47) The crust and mantle are solids; the inner core is thought to be solid.

Answer: TRUE
Diff: 1

48) The mantle is composed mainly of metallic iron with small amounts of magnesium silicate minerals.

Answer: FALSE
Diff: 1

49) What instrument is used to record earthquake vibrations?

Answer: seismograph
Diff: 1

50) _____ is the name of the earthquake-magnitude scale based on the amount of seismic energy released during the event.

Answer: Richter
Diff: 1

51) _____ is another name commonly used by scientists to denote seismic sea waves induced by earthquakes.

Answer: Tsunami
Diff: 1

52) An earthquake of magnitude 7.5 releases about how much more energy than one of magnitude 5.5?

Answer: 900 times more
Diff: 2

53) The _____ is the site of initial rupturing associated with an earthquake.

Answer: focus
Diff: 1

54) What is thought to be the material state (liquid, solid, gas) and elemental composition of Earth's outer core?

Answer: liquid iron
Diff: 1

55) _____ is the cool, brittle, outer layer of Earth that includes the crust and uppermost mantle.

Answer: Lithosphere
Diff: 1

56) _____ is the layer of warm rock below the crust and uppermost mantle that readily deforms and
flows plastically.

Answer: Asthenosphere
Diff: 1

57) The _____ core is probably solidified.

Answer: inner
Diff: 1

58) The upper mantle is very close in chemical and mineralogical composition to _____.

Answer: peridotite
Diff: 1

Critical thinking and discussion questions. Use complete sentences, correct spelling, and the information presented in Chapter 14 to answer the questions below.

59) Would earthquakes of similar magnitudes in different regions of the Earth cause approximately the same levels of damage necessarily? In your explanation, consider both geologic and human-induced factors.

Diff: 3

60) Since much of our knowledge of Earth's interior is inferred from the behavior of seismic waves and not actual samples, what are some of the assumptions that are made in order for our models to be correct? (Hint: Think of earth materials, physical and chemical parameters, etc.)
Diff: 3

61) Label the focus and epicenter on the diagram below.

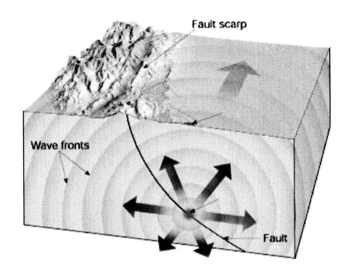

Answer: See Figure 7.2 in Chapter 7 of *Earth Science*, 11e.
Diff: 1

62) Using the time-travel graph below, how long does it take a P wave to travel 2000 km?

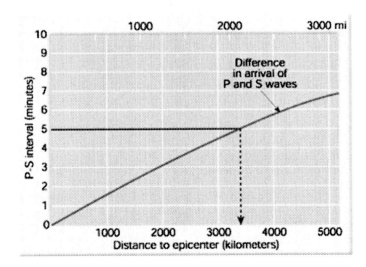

Answer: four minutes
Diff: 1

63) On the blank spaces provided in the illustration below, fill in the names of the layers of Earth's interior that are labeled.

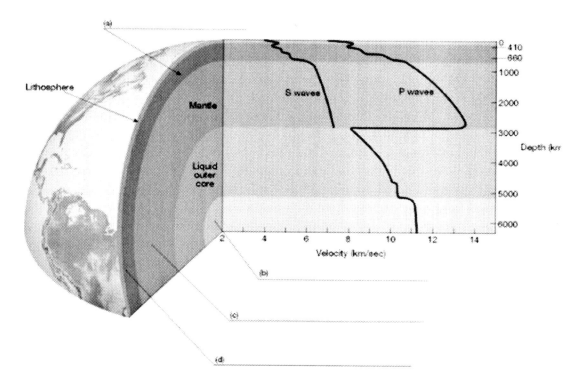

Answer: (a) base of lithosphere or top of asthenosphere (top of low velocity zone)
(b) inner core (c) lower mantle (mesosphere) (d) asthenosphere
Diff: 1

Chapter 15 Plate Tectonics: A Scientific Theory Unfolds

1) _____ was an ancient reptile that lived in South America and Africa during the late Paleozoic.
   A) Granopteris
   B) Monastarious
   C) Glossopteris
   D) Mesosaurus
   Answer: D
   Diff: 1

2) In the early part of the 20th century, _____ argued forcefully for continental drift.
   A) Karl Wagner
   B) Peter Rommel
   C) Alfred Wegener
   D) Bill Kohl
   Answer: C
   Diff: 1

3) The former late Paleozoic super continent is known as _____.
   A) Pandomonia
   B) Pancakea
   C) Pangaea
   D) Panatopia
   Answer: C
   Diff: 1

4) Today, _____ is in about the same geographic position as during late Paleozoic time.
   A) India
   B) South America
   C) Australia
   D) Antarctica
   Answer: D
   Diff: 1

5) Which of the following paleoclimatic evidence supports the idea of the late Paleozoic supercontinent in the Southern Hemisphere?
   A) lithified loess (wind–blown) deposits in the deserts of Chile, Australia, and Africa
   B) tillites (rocks formed by glaciers) in South Africa and South America
   C) thick sediments in the Amazon and Congo deltas of South America and Africa
   D) cold water fossils in the deep–water sediments of the South Atlantic abyssal plain
   Answer: B
   Diff: 1

6) The _____ is an example of an active, continent–continent collision.
    A) Arabian Peninsula slamming into North Africa under the Red Sea
    B) westward movement of the South American plate over the Nazca plate
    C) northern movement of Baja California and a sliver of western California toward the Hawaiian Islands
    D) northward movement of India into Eurasia
    Answer: D
    Diff: 1

7) Pull–apart rift zones are generally associated with a _____ plate boundary.
    A) transform
    B) divergent
    C) convergent
    D) all plate boundaries
    Answer: B
    Diff: 1

8) The temperature below which magnetic material can retain a permanent magnetization is called the _____.
    A) Darcy temperature
    B) Vine temperature
    C) Bullard point
    D) Curie point
    Answer: D
    Diff: 1

9) A very long-lived magma source located deep in the mantle is called a _____.
    A) magma welt
    B) basalt spout
    C) melt well
    D) hot spot
    Answer: D
    Diff: 1

10) Linear, magnetic patterns associated with mid–ocean ridges are configured as _____.
    A) concentric circles about a rising plume of hot mantle rocks and magma
    B) reversed magnetizations along the rift valleys and normal magnetizations along the ridge
    C) normal and reversed magnetized strips roughly parallel to the ridge
    D) normal and reversed magnetized strips roughly perpendicular to the ridge axis
    Answer: C
    Diff: 1

11) The _____ is (are) a logical evolutionary analog of the African Rift Valleys ten million years from now.
    A) Ural Mountains
    B) San Andreas fault
    C) Peru–Chile trench
    D) Red Sea
    Answer: D
    Diff: 2

12) A typical rate of seafloor spreading in the Atlantic Ocean is _____.
   A) 2 feet per year
   B) 0.1 inches per year
   C) 20 feet per year
   D) 2 centimeters per year

Answer: D
Diff: 1

13) Which of the following energy sources is thought to drive the lateral motions of Earth's lithospheric plates?
   A) gravitational attractive forces of the Sun and Moon
   B) electrical and magnetic fields localized in the inner core
   C) export of heat from deep in the mantle to the top of the asthenosphere
   D) swirling movements of the molten iron particles in the outer core

Answer: C
Diff: 1

14) The continental drift hypothesis was rejected primarily because Alfred Wegener could not _____.
   A) find geologic similarities on different continents
   B) disprove competing theories that were more accepted by scientists
   C) identify a mechanism capable of moving continents
   D) all of the above

Answer: C
Diff: 1

15) All of the following are evidence supporting the theory of plate tectonics except for _____.
   A) changes in the Moon's orbit due to shifting plates
   B) ocean floor drilling
   C) hot spots
   D) paleomagnetism

Answer: A
Diff: 1

16) _____ was never proposed as evidence supporting the existence of Pangaea.
   A) Geometrical fit between South America and Africa
   B) Islands of Precambrian rocks along the Mid–Atlantic Ridge
   C) Late Paleozoic glacial features
   D) Similar fossils on different continents

Answer: B
Diff: 1

17) Which one of the following most accurately describes the volcanoes of the Hawaiian Islands?
   A) stratovolcanoes associated with subduction and a convergent plate boundary
   B) shield volcanoes fed by a long–lived hot spot below the Pacific lithospheric plate
   C) shield volcanoes associated with a mid–Pacific ridge and spreading center
   D) stratovolcanoes associated with a mid–Pacific transform fault

Answer: B
Diff: 1

18) Which of the following statements apply to the asthenosphere, but not the lithosphere?
    A) zone in the upper mantle that deforms by plastic flowage
    B) cool, rigid layer of crust and upper mantle that forms the tectonic plates
    C) deforms mainly by brittle fracturing and faulting
    D) partial melting of rising granitic plumes produces huge volumes of basaltic magma
    Answer: A
    Diff: 1

19) New oceanic crust and lithosphere are formed at _____.
    A) divergent boundaries by submarine eruptions and intrusions of rhyolitic magma
    B) convergent boundaries by submarine eruptions and intrusions of rhyolitic magma
    C) divergent boundaries by submarine eruptions and intrusions of basaltic magma
    D) convergent boundaries by submarine eruptions and intrusions of basaltic magma
    Answer: C
    Diff: 1

20) Cooler, older, oceanic lithosphere sinks into the mantle at _____.
    A) subduction zones along convergent plate boundaries
    B) transform fault zones along divergent plate boundaries
    C) rift zones along mid-ocean ridges
    D) sites of long-lived, hot spot volcanism in the ocean basins
    Answer: A
    Diff: 1

21) Deep ocean trenches are surficial evidence for _____.
    A) rifting beneath a continental plate and the beginning of continental drift
    B) sinking of oceanic lithosphere into the mantle at a subduction zone
    C) rising of hot asthenosphere from deep in the mantle
    D) transform faulting between an oceanic plate and a continental plate
    Answer: B
    Diff: 1

22) A transform plate boundary is characterized by _____.
    A) stratovolcanoes on the edge of a plate and shield volcanoes on the adjacent plate
    B) two converging oceanic plates meeting head-on and piling up into a mid-ocean ridge
    C) a divergent boundary where the continental plate changes to an oceanic plate
    D) a deep, vertical fault along which two plates slide past one another in opposite directions
    Answer: D
    Diff: 1

23) Which one of the following is an important fundamental assumption underlying the plate
    tectonic theory?
    A) Earth's magnetic field originates in the outer core
    B) Earth's diameter has been essentially constant over time
    C) radioactive decay slows down at the extreme pressures of the inner core
    D) Earth's ocean basins are very old and stable features
    Answer: B
    Diff: 2

24) The modern-day Red Sea is explained by plate tectonics theory because it is _____.
   A) a tiny remnant of a once immense ocean that was closed as Africa moved Asia
   B) the site of a transform fault along which Arabia is moving away from Africa
   C) a rift zone that may eventually open into a major ocean if Arabia and Africa continue to separate
   D) a rare example of a two-continent subduction zone where the African continental plate is sinking under the Arabian continental plate

   Answer: C
   Diff: 1

25) Mount St. Helens and the other Cascade volcanoes are _____.
   A) young, active stratovolcanoes built on a continental margin above a sinking slab of oceanic lithosphere
   B) a row of young, active, shield volcanoes built as western North America moved over a hot spot deep in the mantle
   C) old, deeply eroded stratovolcanoes built before the Pacific Ocean existed
   D) old, deeply eroded, basaltic shield volcanoes built when western North America was over the present-day site of the Hawaiian hot spot

   Answer: A
   Diff: 1

26) The volcanoes and deep valleys of east Africa are related to a _____.
   A) continental rift along which parts of the African continent are beginning to slowly separate
   B) fault allowing Arabia to slip westward past east Africa and penetrate into Turkey
   C) transform fault aligned with the Red Sea carrying the Arabian and African blocks in opposite directions
   D) continental collision zone between Africa and the Zagros Mountains along the southern margin of Eurasia

   Answer: A
   Diff: 1

27) The Aleutian Islands occur at a _____.
   A) convergent boundary on a volcanic arc above a northward-subducting Pacific plate
   B) transform boundary where North America has moved towards Alaska
   C) divergent boundary where shield volcanoes are forming
   D) convergent, continental margin with uplifted fault blocks, much like those of the Basin and Range Province

   Answer: A
   Diff: 1

28) _____ most effectively outline the edges of the lithospheric plates.
   A) Lines of active stratovolcanoes
   B) Margins of the continental shelves
   C) The locations of deep mantle hot spots
   D) Lines of earthquake epicenters

   Answer: D
   Diff: 1

29) Deep-oceanic trenches are most abundant around the rim of the _____ ocean basin.
   A) Atlantic
   B) Indian
   C) Arctic
   D) Pacific

   Answer: D
   Diff: 1

30) Where would you drill to recover samples of the oldest basalts of the oceanic crust, which are Jurassic in age?
   A) crest of the East Pacific, mid-ocean ridge
   B) oceanic side of the Aleutian trench
   C) just offshore from the Hawaiian Islands
   D) Mid-Atlantic Ridge under Iceland

   Answer: B
   Diff: 2

31) _____ first related the symmetrical magnetic patterns in seafloor basalts to seafloor spreading at a mid-ocean ridge.
   A) Evans and Novak
   B) Vine and Matthews
   C) Matthews and Marks
   D) Wegener and Wilson

   Answer: B
   Diff: 1

32) Early results of the Deep Sea Drilling Project clearly justified the conclusion that _____.
   A) the oceans have not always contained most of Earth's water
   B) the ocean basins are relatively young; most ocean basin rocks and sediments are Cretaceous or younger in age
   C) Proterozoic rocks are found only as seamounts in the deepest parts of the ocean basins
   D) the youngest sediments were deposited directly on the oldest seafloor basalts

   Answer: B
   Diff: 1

Word Analysis. Examine the words and/or phrases for each question below and determine the relationship among the majority of words/phrases. Choose the option which does not fit the pattern.

33) a. fossil evidence   b. fit of the continents   c. paleomagnetism   d. paleoclimates

   Answer: C
   Diff: 1

34) a. Curie point   b. paleomagnetism   c. magnetic poles   d. polar wandering

   Answer: D
   Diff: 2

35) a. oceanic ridge   b. seafloor spreading   c. arc volcanoes   d. divergent

   Answer: C
   Diff: 1

36) a. Hawaii   b. island arc   c. volcanic arc   d. subduction

Answer: A
Diff: 1

37) a. slab pull   b. mantle drag   c. ridge push   d. slab suction

Answer: B
Diff: 1

Match the plate boundary with the appropriate phrase.
   a. convergent   b. transform   c. divergent

38) plates are moving apart from one another

Answer: a
Diff: 1

39) plates are sliding past one another horizontally

Answer: b
Diff: 1

40) this boundary is normally devoid of volcanism

Answer: b
Diff: 1

41) where lithosphere is sinking into the mantle

Answer: a
Diff: 1

42) characterized by basaltic volcanism and seafloor spreading

Answer: c
Diff: 1

43) characterized by arcs of stratovolcanoes and deep-ocean trenches

Answer: a
Diff: 1

44) the Mid-Atlantic Ridge

Answer: c
Diff: 1

45) where subduction zones occur

Answer: a
Diff: 1

46) the San Andreas fault

Answer: b
Diff: 1

47) the west coast of South America

Answer: a
Diff: 1

48) The oldest rocks on the seafloor are much younger than the oldest rocks on the continents.
Answer: TRUE
Diff: 1

49) Earth's radius and surface area are slowly increasing to accommodate the new oceanic crust being formed at mid-ocean ridges.
Answer: FALSE
Diff: 1

50) Hawaii is the oldest island of the Hawaiian Island chain.
Answer: FALSE
Diff: 1

51) The oldest rocks of the oceanic crust are found in deep ocean trenches far away from active, mid-ocean ridges.
Answer: TRUE
Diff: 1

52) As the South Atlantic basin widens by seafloor spreading, Africa and South America are moving closer together.
Answer: FALSE
Diff: 1

53) In general, rocks of the continental crust are less dense than rocks of the oceanic crust.
Answer: TRUE
Diff: 1

54) During various times in the geologic past, the polarity of Earth's magnetic field has been reversed.
Answer: TRUE
Diff: 1

55) The rate of seafloor spreading is, on the average, about one meter per year.
Answer: FALSE
Diff: 1

56) Wegener's continental drift hypothesis was weakened because a viable mechanism for moving the continents was lacking.
Answer: TRUE
Diff: 1

57) During the geologic past, the magnetic field poles have generally been very close to Earth's rotational poles.
Answer: TRUE
Diff: 1

58) Seafloor spreading rates can be estimated if the geologic ages of the magnetic field reversals are independently known.
Answer: TRUE
Diff: 2

59) The volcanoes of Hawaii are localized above a deep mantle hot spot; they are not part of the East Pacific oceanic ridge.

Answer: TRUE
Diff: 1

60) Iceland is a good example of an island arc, formed from an oceanic–oceanic plate collision.

Answer: FALSE
Diff: 1

61) An extensive, late Paleozoic glaciation affected southern India, southern Africa and southeastern South America.

Answer: TRUE
Diff: 1

62) The Himalayan Mountains are the tectonic product of a collision between India and Eurasia that began in Eocene time and still continues.

Answer: TRUE
Diff: 1

63) During the first two decades of the twentieth century, _____ was a vigorous proponent of continental drift.

Answer: Alfred Wegener
Diff: 1

64) A _____ is a long-lived, stationary magma source deep in the mantle, well below the base of the lithosphere.

Answer: hot spot
Diff: 1

65) The _____ today marks the location of the rift along which Africa separated from South America.

Answer: Mid–Atlantic Ridge
Diff: 1

66) Japan and the Aleutian Islands have formed from an _____ to _____ convergent boundary.

Answer: ocean; ocean
Diff: 1

67) The San Andreas fault in California is a good example of a _____ plate boundary.

Answer: transform
Diff: 1

68) _____, in the north Atlantic Ocean, is a volcanic island formed over a hot spot on a divergent plate boundary.

Answer: Iceland
Diff: 1

69) Rifting and normal faulting are characteristic of a _____ plate boundary.

Answer: divergent
Diff: 1

Critical thinking and discussion questions. Use complete sentences, correct spelling, and the information presented in Chapter 15 to answer the questions below.

70) Although Alfred Wegener presented compelling evidence for his continental drift hypothesis (despite lacking a mechanism), why was the true nature of plate boundaries not determined until the 1960s? (Hint: Don't think of historical scientific developments, but rather the scope and rate of geological processes involved in plate tectonics.)
Diff: 2

71) If you could time travel back to the 1920s and meet Alfred Wegener, who was the original proponent of the continental drift hypothesis, what could you tell him about our modern idea of plate tectonics? What would you tell him regarding the structure of the Earth's interior, what evidence exists for plate tectonics, what is the relationship between volcanoes and earthquakes to plate tectonics (specifics), and what are some (if any) of the problems we still have in explaining certain features of plate tectonics?
Diff: 3

72) In the diagram below, match the letter of each illustration to the correct type of plate boundary.

a) transform   b) divergent   c) convergent

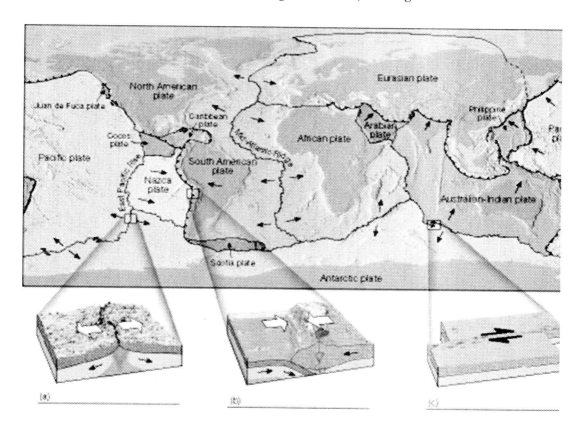

Answer: (a) = b, (b) = c, (c) = a
Diff: 1

73) On the blanks provided below, write the names of the features that are labeled.

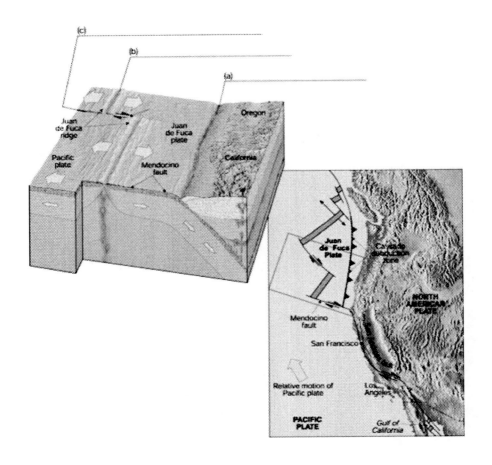

Answer: (a) deep-ocean trench   (b) ridge   (c) transform fault
Diff: 1

74) What is the name of the volcanic mountain chain shown in the diagram below?

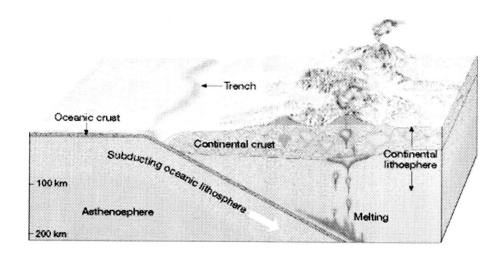

Answer: continental volcanic arc
Diff: 1

75) What is the name of the chain of volcanic islands shown in the diagram below?

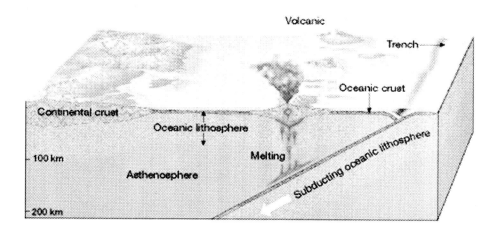

Answer: volcanic island arc
Diff: 1

76) Describe exactly what type of plate boundary is illustrated below and explain your answer.

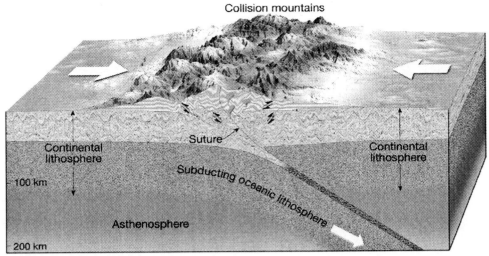

C. Continental-continental

Copyright © 2006 Pearson Prentice Hall, Inc.

Answer: This is an example of a continental–to–continental convergent plate boundary. The continental lithosphere is too buoyant for subduction to occur; therefore, the two plates collide and the crust is buckled, fractured, and thickened. Major mountain systems including the Alps, Himalayas, Appalachians, and the Urals formed during continental collisions.

Diff: 2

Chapter 16 Origin and Evolution of the Ocean Floor

1) In the 1870s, the _____ was involved in the first far-reaching, comprehensive study of Earth's oceans.
    A) H.M.S. Moonbeam
    B) H.M.S. Bismarck
    C) H.M.S. Challenger
    D) H.M.S. Brit
Answer: C
Diff: 1

2) Water depths and seafloor topography are now routinely determined by _____.
    A) ship-mounted, optical-fiber satellite uplink systems
    B) computerized, satellite-mounted, parallel transponder systems
    C) ship-mounted echo sounders
    D) by satellite-linked, laser reflector systems
Answer: C
Diff: 1

3) Geologically, _____ are actually submerged parts of the continents.
    A) coastal guyots
    B) continental shelves
    C) continental trenches
    D) abyssal plains
Answer: B
Diff: 1

4) The _____ lies at the base of the continental slope.
    A) offshore shelf
    B) off-slope reef
    C) continental rift
    D) continental rise
Answer: D
Diff: 1

5) Submarine canyons found on the continental slope and rise are believed to have been created _____.
    A) by rivers during the ice age
    B) by faulting
    C) because of a plate plunging into the mantle
    D) none of these
Answer: D
Diff: 1

6) Which one of the following would most likely be covered with thick turbidite layers?
   A) axial rift zone of an active mid-ocean spreading center
   B) upper part of a steep, narrow, submarine canyon
   C) deep-sea fan at the base of a continental slope
   D) ocean floor around a conical-shaped seamount

   Answer: C
   Diff: 1

7) Which of the following is NOT true of deep ocean trenches?
   A) they are long and narrow depressions
   B) they are sites where plates plunge back into the mantle
   C) they are geologically very stable
   D) they may act as sediment traps

   Answer: C
   Diff: 1

8) Seamounts _____.
   A) are a special type of oceanic trench
   B) are volcanoes that form on the ocean floor
   C) form only in the Pacific Ocean basin
   D) are submarine canyons found near Australia

   Answer: B
   Diff: 1

9) "Black smokers" are associated with _____.
   A) oceanic ridges
   B) metal-rich sulfide deposits
   C) hot water
   D) all of these

   Answer: D
   Diff: 1

10) _____ marks the edge of a continent.
    A) An offshore, barrier island system
    B) The lowest part of the continental slope
    C) The center of an abyssal plain
    D) The highest part of the continental shelf

    Answer: B
    Diff: 1

11) The gently sloping submerged surface extending from the shoreline toward the deep ocean is termed the _____.
    A) continental shelf
    B) continental slope
    C) continental rise
    D) submarine canyon

    Answer: A
    Diff: 1

12) Which one of the following is not connected in any way with submarine, hot spring vents?
    A) sediment rich in metallic sulfides
    B) ecological communities living without photosynthesis
    C) thick turbidites on the continental rise
    D) black smokers on a mid-ocean ridge
Answer: C
Diff: 1

13) Which one of the following would typically have the widest continental shelf?
    A) a tectonically passive, trailing continental margin
    B) a tectonically passive, mid-ocean ridge and trench system
    C) a tectonically active continental margin next to a deep ocean trench
    D) all of the above would roughly equal continental shelves
Answer: A
Diff: 1

14) _____ are not associated with a mid-ocean ridge.
    A) Very thin, ocean floor, sediment layer
    B) Submarine basaltic lava eruptions
    C) Shallower depths than abyssal plains
    D) Deep ocean trenches
Answer: D
Diff: 1

15) Which one of the following did not accompany the 1929 Newfoundland earthquake?
    A) submarine cables on the floor of the North Atlantic were broken
    B) a giant tsunami struck the coasts of Newfoundland and Nova Scotia
    C) submarine landslides moved down the continental slope
    D) turbidity currents moved down the continental rise to the edges of the North Atlantic
       abyssal plain
Answer: C
Diff: 1

16) How do calcareous oozes form?
    A) the particles are precipitated in warm, surface waters and sink to the bottom
    B) the particles are precipitated by bottom-dwelling organisms
    C) the particles are precipitated in the water column below the depth of sunlight
       penetration and then sink to the bottom
    D) the particles settle out from calcite-rich turbidity currents at depths greater than 15,000
       feet
Answer: A
Diff: 1

17) _____ is/are not part of an ophiolite complex.
    A) Basaltic lavas and pillow lavas
    B) Residual, unmelted, crustal lithosphere
    C) Intrusive, coarse-grained gabbro
    D) Steeply inclined, basaltic dikes
Answer: B
Diff: 1

18) Where in the oceans are biological communities thriving without sunlight?
    A) in shallow water, coral reefs
    B) in muds of deep-ocean trenches
    C) around seafloor, hot spring vents
    D) around fissure vents for flood basalts

Answer: C
Diff: 1

19) Which one of the following is not typical of sandy turbidite deposits?
    A) contain land-derived and shallow-water fossil materials, even though deposited in deep waters
    B) form very gently sloping fans or submarine deltas at the mouths of submarine canyons
    C) within a depositional layer, show graded bedding but little stratification
    D) occur in cross-stratified dunes with very low silt and clay contents

Answer: D
Diff: 1

20) A(n) _____ is a low lying, coral reef island perched above a sunken, truncated volcano.
    A) guyot
    B) seamount
    C) fringing reef
    D) atoll

Answer: C
Diff: 1

21) Graded bedding is _____.
    A) a quality-rating scale for different brands of mattresses
    B) an upward decrease in clastic particle size within a single sediment layer
    C) an accumulation of sedimentary beds beginning with sand layers at the bottom and ending with clay layers at the top
    D) the layering in coral limestone produced by the combined chemical action of living coral animals and submarine, hot spring emissions

Answer: B
Diff: 1

22) Which one of the following statements concerning submarine canyons is not true?
    A) they extend from the continental shelf to the base of the continental slope
    B) they channel turbidity currents down the continental slope to deeper waters
    C) they generally conned across the continental shelf to specific river valleys on land
    D) they were cut by streams and rivers during the Pleistocene when sea level had dropped

Answer: C
Diff: 1

23) _____ proposed a correct theory of how atolls formed.
    A) Isaac Newton
    B) Charles Darwin
    C) James Hutton
    D) Charles Lyell

Answer: D
Diff: 1

24) _____ develop where oceanic lithosphere bends downward and sinks into the mantle.
    A) Submarine canyons
    B) Abyssal seamounts
    C) Deep ocean trenches
    D) Rift valleys on mid-ocean ridges

Answer: A
Diff: 1

25) Calcareous ooze is composed of _____ sediment.
    A) androgynous
    B) terrigenous
    C) biogenous
    D) hydrogenous

Answer: D
Diff: 1

26) _____ are highly detrimental to healthy growth of coral reefs.
    A) Clear, sunlit waters
    B) Nutrient-rich waters with luxuriant algae growth
    C) Warm water temperatures
    D) Vigorous wave action and water circulation

Answer: C
Diff: 1

27) _____ is the oceanward edge of a continental shelf.
    A) The deepest portion of a deep-ocean trench
    B) The top of the abyssal plain
    C) The base of the continental rise
    D) The top of the continental slope

Answer: D
Diff: 1

28) _____ sediments represent weathered rock and mineral particles eroded mainly from land areas.
    A) Exogenous
    B) Hydrogenous
    C) Terrigenous
    D) Biogenous

Answer: C
Diff: 1

29) Manganese nodules represent _____ sediment on the seafloor.
    A) biogenous
    B) hydrogenous
    C) androgynous
    D) terrigenous

Answer: D
Diff: 1

30) Geologically, what is the best way to explain the thousands of feet of coral limestone beneath most atolls?
   A) sea level has fallen thousands of feet since the reef began to grow
   B) an eroded volcanic seamount rose thousands of feet after the limestone formed
   C) the eroded volcano slowly sank as sea level remained steady or rose gradually
   D) the volcano never reached the surface, allowing a very thick cap of coral limestones to accumulate

Answer: D
Diff: 1

31) The continental rise is located _____.
   A) at the top of a mid-ocean ridge
   B) at the top of the continental slope
   C) between an abyssal plain and continental slope
   D) at the seaward edge of a deep ocean trench

Answer: D
Diff: 1

32) An echo sounder operates by measuring the time required for a _____.
   A) light beam to travel from a satellite at a known altitude to the sea bottom and back
   B) radar beam to travel from a harbor patrol boat to a fuzz-buster on a speeding yacht
   C) radar beam to travel from a ship to the seafloor and back
   D) sound pulse travels from a ship to the seafloor and back

Answer: D
Diff: 1

33) Which one of the following concerning mid-ocean ridges is false?
   A) are sites for submarine eruptions of basaltic lava
   B) are where young lithosphere is added to the edges of spreading, oceanic plates
   C) terrigenous sediment coverings are very thin or absent
   D) sediments include thick siliceous ooze deposits and sandy turbidite beds

Answer: D
Diff: 1

34) Oceans cover approximately _____ of Earth's surface area?
   A) 10%
   B) 90%
   C) 50%
   D) 70%

Answer: D
Diff: 1

Match the ocean floor sediment with each phrase.
   a. biogenous   b. terrigenous   c. hydrogenous

35) manganese nodule

Answer: b
Diff: 1

36) calcareous ooze

    Answer: c
    Diff: 1

37) quartz sand

    Answer: b
    Diff: 1

38) diatom ooze

    Answer: a
    Diff: 1

39) turbidite deposits

    Answer: b
    Diff: 1

40) abyssal plain clay

    Answer: b
    Diff: 1

Word Analysis. Examine the words and/or phrases for each question below and determine the relationship among the majority of words/phrases. Choose the option which does not fit the pattern.

41) a. continental slope   b. continental rise   c. active continental margin d. continental shelf

    Answer: C
    Diff: 1

42) a. trench   b. submarine canyon   c. abyssal plain   d. seamount

    Answer: B
    Diff: 1

43) a. manganese nodules b. pillow basalts   c. sheeted dikes   d. gabbro

    Answer: A
    Diff: 1

44) a. East African Rift   b. Basin & Range c. Red Sea   d. Baikal Rift

    Answer: C
    Diff: 2

45) The west coast of South America and the east coast of North America have very different continental margins.

    Answer: TRUE
    Diff: 1

46) Abyssal plains with sediments covering the seafloor igneous rocks are more extensive in the central Pacific basin than in the North Atlantic.

    Answer: FALSE
    Diff: 1

47) Submerged, flat-topped seamounts are known as guyots.

Answer: TRUE
Diff: 1

48) The Atlantic and Pacific basins have oceanic ridges; the Indian Ocean has no oceanic ridge.

Answer: FALSE
Diff: 1

49) Manganese nodules do not accumulate below 4500 meters depth because the manganese minerals are highly soluble in seawater below that depth.

Answer: FALSE
Diff: 1

50) Turbidites and siliceous oozes are both biogenous sediments.

Answer: FALSE
Diff: 1

51) In the oceans, calcium carbonate is more soluble in warm, surface waters than in deeper, colder waters.

Answer: TRUE
Diff: 1

52) An atoll is a low, coral reef island typically surrounding an interior lagoon.

Answer: TRUE
Diff: 1

53) Submarine canyons form the deepest parts of the ocean basins.

Answer: FALSE
Diff: 1

54) Compared to the Southern Hemisphere, a higher percentage of the Northern Hemisphere is water covered.

Answer: FALSE
Diff: 1

55) The average height of the continents above sea level is greater than the average depth of the ocean basins below sea level.

Answer: FALSE
Diff: 1

56) The continental rise lies at the top of the continental slope.

Answer: FALSE
Diff: 1

57) Seafloor hot springs occur mainly in oceanic, abyssal plains.

Answer: FALSE
Diff: 1

58) Sand, silt, and clays deposited on the ocean floor are described as terrigenous sediments.

Answer: TRUE
Diff: 1

59) _____ is a characteristic, internal structure exhibited by turbidite sediment layers.
Answer: Graded bedding
Diff: 1

60) _____ correctly formulated a basic theory concerning the formation of atolls in the 1800s.
Answer: Charles Darwin
Diff: 1

61) Submerged, flat-topped volcanoes that rise from the deep ocean floor are called _____.
Answer: guyots
Diff: 1

62) Valleys that lead from the continental shelf into deeper waters are known as _____.
Answer: submarine canyons
Diff: 1

63) _____ continental margins typically exhibit wide, extensive, continental shelves.
Answer: Passive
Diff: 1

64) A(n) _____ is a volcanic mountain, built up from the seafloor, that never reached the sea surface.
Answer: seamount
Diff: 1

65) A low lying, coral limestone island with a central lagoon is called an _____.
Answer: atoll
Diff: 1

66) A(n) _____ is the vast, relatively deep, flat, sediment-covered portion of the deep-ocean basin.
Answer: abyssal plain
Diff: 1

67) A(n) _____ marks the site where old, oceanic lithosphere begins its descent into a subduction zone.
Answer: trench
Diff: 1

Critical thinking and discussion questions. Use complete sentences, correct spelling, and the information presented in Chapter 16 to answer the questions below.

68) Where are most of the current active continental margins located on Earth today? Why? What is the relationship of the age of rocks on the ocean floor to the location of these active margins?
Diff: 2

69) Briefly discuss the formation and structure of oceanic crust. What rock compositions are involved and how do these compositions change as a result of interaction with seawater?
Diff: 3

70) List several areas on Earth where continental rifting is occurring today. Eventually, what will happen to these areas as rifting continues? Finally, how is continental rifting similar to seafloor spreading and how is it different?

Diff: 3

71) The illustration below is a topographic profile of a passive continental margin. Fill in the blanks with the correct name of the feature labeled.

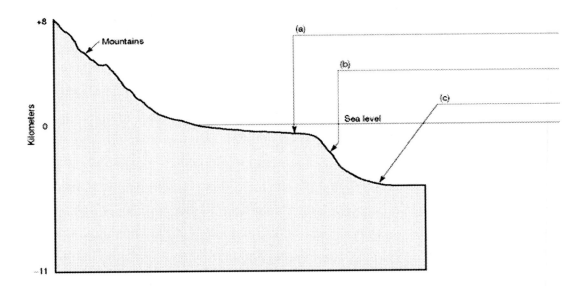

Answer: (a) continental shelf (b) continental slope (c) continental rise

Diff: 1

72) What is the name of the valley in the central portion of the diagram below?

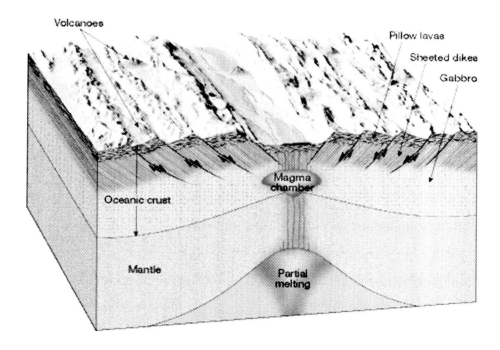

Answer: rift valley
Diff: 1

73) Label the layers that make up the oceanic crust on the diagram below.

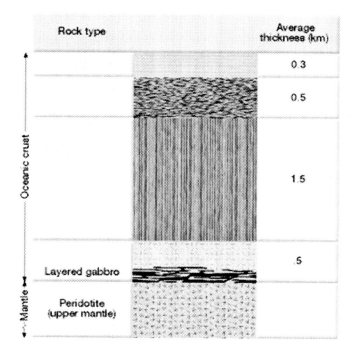

Answer: See Figure 16.13 in Essentials 10e.
Diff: 2

74) On the diagram below, match the features to the correct answer for each one.

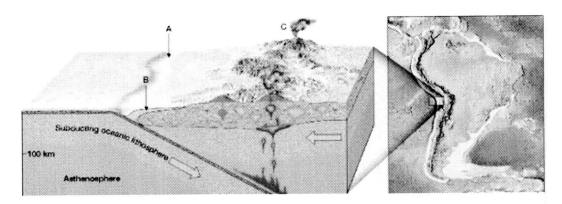

a = continental volcanic arc
b = trench
c = accretionary wedge

Answer: A = b, B = c, C= a
Diff: 2

Chapter 17 Crustal Deformation and Mountain Building

1) A _____ fault has little or no vertical movements of the two blocks.
   A) stick slip
   B) oblique slip
   C) strike slip
   D) dip slip
   Answer: C
   Diff: 1

2) In a _____ fault, the hanging wall block moves up with respect to the footwall block.
   A) normal
   B) inverse
   C) reverse
   D) abnormal
   Answer: B
   Diff: 1

3) In thrust faulting, _____.
   A) grabens develop on the footwall block
   B) the crust is shortened and thickened
   C) horizontal, tensional stresses drive the deformation
   D) the hanging wall block slips downward along the thrust fault
   Answer: B
   Diff: 1

4) Which one of the following stress situations results in folding of flat–lying, sedimentary strata?
   A) horizontally directed; compressive stresses
   B) vertically directed; extensional or stretching stresses
   C) horizontally directed; extensional stresses
   D) vertically directed; compressional stresses
   Answer: A
   Diff: 1

5) A graben is characterized by _____.
   A) a hanging wall block that has moved up between two reverse faults
   B) a footwall block that has moved up between two normal faults
   C) a hanging wall block that has moved down between two normal faults
   D) a footwall block that has moved down between two reverse faults
   Answer: C
   Diff: 1

6) The mountains and valleys of the Basin and Range Province of the western United States formed in response to _____.
   A) strike–slip faulting and hanging wall block uplifts
   B) reverse faults and large displacement, thrust faulting
   C) tensional stresses and normal–fault movements
   D) normal faulting and horizontal compression

   Answer: C
   Diff: 1

7) In a normal fault _____.
   A) the hanging wall block below an inclined fault plane moves downward relative to the other block
   B) the footwall block below an inclined fault plane moves downward relative to the other block
   C) the hanging wall block above an inclined fault plane moves downward relative to the other block
   D) the footwall block above an inclined fault plane moves upward relative to the other block

   Answer: C
   Diff: 1

8) A transform fault is _____.
   A) a strike–slip fault that forms the boundary between tectonic plates
   B) a dip–slip fault connecting an anticline with a syncline
   C) a reverse fault that steepens into a thrust fault
   D) the rift bounding faults on a mid–ocean ridge

   Answer: A
   Diff: 1

9) Brittle deformation would be favored over plastic deformation in which of the following conditions?
   A) high confining pressures
   B) warmer temperatures
   C) cooler temperatures
   D) shallow depths

   Answer: C
   Diff: 2

10) A thrust fault is best described as _____.
    A) a steeply inclined, oblique–slip fault
    B) a low–angle, reverse fault
    C) a vertical, normal fault
    D) a near vertical, strike–slip fault

    Answer: B
    Diff: 1

11) A horst is _____.
   A) an uplifted block bounded by two normal faults
   B) a downdropped block bounded by two reverse faults
   C) an uplifted block bounded by two reverse faults
   D) a downdropped block bounded by two normal faults

Answer: A
Diff: 1

12) A syncline is _____.
   A) a fold in which the strata dip away from the axis
   B) a fold with only one limb
   C) a fold in which the strata dip toward the axis
   D) a fold characterized by recumbent limbs

Answer: C
Diff: 1

13) The Black Hills of South Dakota are a good example of a(n) _____.
   A) anticline
   B) syncline
   C) basin
   D) dome

Answer: D
Diff: 1

14) Large circular downwarped structures are called _____.
   A) anticlines
   B) synclines
   C) basins
   D) domes

Answer: C
Diff: 1

15) Which of the following combinations should favor folding rather than faulting?
   A) high temperature and low confining pressure
   B) low confining pressure and low temperature
   C) high confining pressure and low temperature
   D) high temperature and high confining pressure

Answer: D
Diff: 1

16) Tensional forces normally cause which one of the following?
   A) strike–slip faults
   B) reverse faults
   C) normal faults
   D) thrust faults

Answer: C
Diff: 1

17) The _____ in California is the boundary between the North American and Pacific plates.
   A) Sierra Nevada frontal fault
   B) San Andreas strike-slip fault
   C) San Luis Obispo thrust fault
   D) San Francisco normal fault

   Answer: B
   Diff: 1

18) A(n) _____ is a thick accumulation of sediments and small, tectonic blocks formed of material scraped off a descending, lithospheric plate.
   A) mass movement complex
   B) continental shelf, terrain complex
   C) accretionary-wedge complex
   D) subterranean-accumulation complex

   Answer: C
   Diff: 1

19) The Sierra Nevada, California, and Teton, Wyoming, ranges are examples of _____.
   A) fault blocks uplifted by late Tertiary to Quaternary normal faulting
   B) folding, compression, and thickening of Paleozoic strata in Jurassic time
   C) isostatic uplift of crust overthickened in early Paleozoic time
   D) uplifted blocks bounded by Quaternary reverse faults

   Answer: A
   Diff: 1

20) A good example of a present-day, passive continental margin is the _____.
   A) north flank of the East Pacific Rise
   B) west coast of South America
   C) east coast of the Japanese Islands
   D) east coast of North America

   Answer: D
   Diff: 1

21) The _____ are a geologically old mountain range folded and deformed during the Paleozoic.
   A) Cascades in the northwestern United States
   B) Rockies in the western United States
   C) Appalachians in the eastern United States
   D) Alps in Europe

   Answer: C
   Diff: 1

22) The term _____ refers specifically to geologic mountain building.
   A) orogneisses
   B) orogenesis
   C) orthogeny
   D) orthogonal

   Answer: B
   Diff: 1

23) The _____ is (are) characterized by terrane accretion that has been active throughout most of Mesozoic and Cenozoic time.
    A) western margin of Africa
    B) southern margins of India and Australia
    C) western margin of North America
    D) western margin of the Mid–Atlantic Ridge
Answer: C
Diff: 1

24) Folded limestones that occur high in the Himalayas were originally deposited as sediments in a _____.
    A) marine basin between India and Eurasia
    B) Cenozoic fault basin between Africa and Arabia
    C) deep ocean trench along the southern margin of India
    D) late Paleozoic syncline north of the Tibetan Plateau
Answer: A
Diff: 1

25) The concept that rocks of the crust and upper mantle are floating in gravitational balance is known as _____.
    A) isotropy
    B) isostasy
    C) isobration
    D) isomonism
Answer: B
Diff: 1

26) A(n) _____ is a thick accumulation of sediments and small, tectonic blocks formed of material scraped off a descending, lithospheric plate.
    A) mass movement complex
    B) continental shelf, terrain complex
    C) accretionary–wedge complex
    D) subterranean–accumulation complex
Answer: C
Diff: 1

27) Which one of the following is an example of an isostatic movement?
    A) stream downcutting following a drop in sea level
    B) arching of strata at the center of a dome
    C) numerous aftershocks associated with deep–focus earthquakes
    D) uplift of areas recently covered by thick, continental ice sheets
Answer: D
Diff: 1

Word Analysis. Examine the words and/or phrases for each question below and determine the relationship among the majority of words/phrases. Choose the option which does not fit the pattern.

28) a. elastic   b. ductile   c. folding   d. compression
Answer: D
Diff: 1

29) a. dome   b. anticline   c. monocline   d. basin

Answer: C
Diff: 2

30) a. normal fault   b. reverse fault   c. thrust fault   d. strike–slip fault

Answer: D
Diff: 1

31) a. Himalayas   b. Andes   c. Appalachians   d. Alps

Answer: B
Diff: 1

32) High rock temperatures enhance plastic deformation and flow in the asthenosphere and inhibit brittle fracturing.

Answer: TRUE
Diff: 1

33) In a reverse fault, the hanging wall block moves up relative to the footwall block.

Answer: TRUE
Diff: 1

34) Normal faults form in response to horizontal, tensional stresses that stretch or elongate the rocks.

Answer: TRUE
Diff: 1

35) Basin and range topography, like that in the western and southwestern United States, indicates that compressive folding is active today or was active very recently, geologically speaking.

Answer: FALSE
Diff: 1

36) Plastic deformation occurs more readily in warm rock than in cool rock.

Answer: TRUE
Diff: 1

37) A graben is an upraised block bounded by two reverse faults.

Answer: FALSE
Diff: 1

38) Horizontal, compressive deformation involves shortening and thickening of the crust.

Answer: TRUE
Diff: 1

39) The Himalayan Mountains and Tibetan Plateau are still rising today as Eurasia slides beneath the Indian subcontinent.

Answer: FALSE
Diff: 1

40) Terrane accretion generally occurs along a divergent boundary between a continental plate and an oceanic plate.

Answer: FALSE
Diff: 1

41) Accretionary wedges develop along subduction zones where sediments and other rocks are scraped off a descending plate and piled against the leading edge of the overriding plate.

Answer: TRUE
Diff: 1

42) Fold-and-thrust belts are commonly associated with fault-block mountains.

Answer: FALSE
Diff: 1

43) Fractures in rock that have not involved any fault slippage are called joints.

Answer: TRUE
Diff: 1

44) Are horsts and grabens bounded by normal or reverse faults?

Answer: normal
Diff: 1

45) A(n) _____ has strata on both limbs dipping inward toward the axis.

Answer: syncline
Diff: 1

46) A circular to elliptical structure developed by upward arching of the central strata is a _____.

Answer: dome
Diff: 1

47) In a thrust fault, the hanging wall moves _____ relative to the footwall, and the fault plane is oriented at a _____ angle.

Answer: up; low
Diff: 1

48) A(n) _____ fault develops in response to horizontal, tensional stresses in crustal rocks.

Answer: normal
Diff: 1

49) A circular to elliptical structure developed by downwarping of the central strata is a _____.

Answer: basin
Diff: 1

50) The east coast of North America is a good example of a _____ tectonic margin.

Answer: passive
Diff: 1

51) The _____ mountains in North America were formed by a continent–continent collision in the Paleozoic.

Answer: Appalachian
Diff: 1

52) Fault–block mountains occur in regions dominated by _____ faulting.

Answer: normal
Diff: 1

53) Any accreted crustal fragment that has a geologic history distinct from that of the adjoining fragments is termed a _____.

Answer: terrane
Diff: 1

54) _____ are fractures showing little or no movement of the rocks on either side.

Answer: Joints
Diff: 1

Critical thinking and discussion questions. Use complete sentences, correct spelling, and the information presented in Chapter 17 to answer the questions below.

55) A fault is observed in a road cut, but there are no obvious rocks units to correlate on either side of the fault to determine relative movement. How else might you determine or even infer whether the hanging wall has moved up or down relative to the footwall? (Hint: Think of fossils, tectonic setting, etc.)

Diff: 2

56) A region is characterized by numerous anticlines and synclines. There are also several faults present that appear to have formed at the same time as the folding. Without looking at any details, what type of faults would you assume them to be? Why?

Diff: 2

57) Describe the characteristics of regions dominated by fault–block mountains such as the Basin & Range. What is their relationship to plate tectonics and why don't they create large–scale areas of orogenesis like Andean–Type margins or continental collisions?

Diff: 3

58) Carefully study each illustration below to determine the type(s) of geologic structure(s) it contains. Match each one to the correct answers listed.

A. reverse fault   B. monocline   C. normal fault

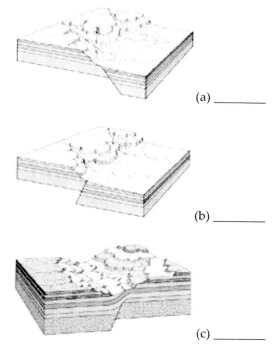

(a) _____

(b) _____

(c) _____

Answer: (a) C (b) A (c) B
Diff: 1

59) On the blanks provided below, fill in the name of the specific type of geologic features that have been labeled.

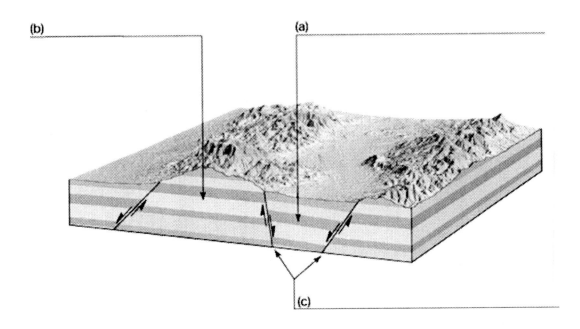

Answer: (a) graben (b) horst (c) normal faults
Diff: 1

60) What kind of geologic structure is present in the photograph below? Explain your answer.

Answer: Normal fault. The hanging wall on the left has moved down relative to the footwall.
Diff: 2

61) Each of the block diagrams below portrays a specific kind of geologic structure. Write the name of the
structure on the blank provided beside each block diagram.

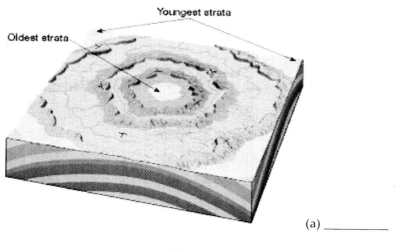

(a) _____

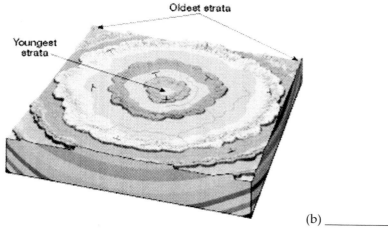

(b) _____

Answer: (a) dome (b) basin
Diff: 1

Chapter 18 Geologic Time

1) An unconformity is a buried _____.
   A) fault or fracture with older rocks above and younger rocks below
   B) surface of erosion separating younger strata above from older strata below
   C) fault or fracture with younger strata above and older strata below
   D) surface of erosion with older strata above and younger strata below

Answer: B
Diff: 1

2) Which of the following best characterizes an angular unconformity?
   A) Tilted strata lie below the unconformity; bedding in younger strata above is parallel to the unconformity.
   B) Horizontal lava flows lie below the unconformity and horizontal, sedimentary strata lie above.
   C) The discordant boundary between older strata and an intrusive body of granite.
   D) Tilted strata lie below the unconformity with loose, unconsolidated soil above.

Answer: A
Diff: 1

3) In the late 1700s James Hutton published his important work titled _____.
   A) *Catastrophism*
   B) *Principles of Geology*
   C) *Modern Earth Science*
   D) *Theory of the Earth*

Answer: D
Diff: 1

4) Which of the following is not a very long-lived, radioactive isotope?
   A) U-238
   B) K-40
   C) Rb-87
   D) C-14

Answer: D
Diff: 1

5) Catastrophism _____.
   A) was a philosophy that was first expounded by the early Greeks
   B) was based upon the belief that Earth was millions of years old
   C) helped man understand the true nature of the forces that shaped the Grand Canyon
   D) is a modern term used to describe earthquakes and volcanic activity

Answer: A
Diff: 1

6) The subdivision of the geologic time scale that represents the longest time span is called a(n)
_____.
   A) epoch
   B) era
   C) period
   D) stage
Answer: A
Diff: 1

7) The ratio of parent to daughter isotopes in a radioactive decay process is 0.40. How many half-lives have elapsed since the material was 100% parent atoms?
   A) less than 1
   B) more than 3
   C) between 1 and 2
   D) between 2 and 3
Answer: C
Diff: 2

8) Consider the names of the eras in the geologic time scale. What is meant by "zoic"?
   A) life; living things
   B) rocks; lithified strata
   C) time; recording of events
   D) places; geographic references
Answer: A
Diff: 1

9) Who is credited with formulating the doctrine of uniformitarianism?
   A) Aristotle
   B) Lyell
   C) Hutton
   D) Playfair
Answer: C
Diff: 1

10) Which of the following geologic observations would not bear directly on working out the sequence of geologic events in an area?
   A) inclusions of sandstone in a granite pluton
   B) a well-exposed dike of basalt in sandstone
   C) the feldspar and quartz contents of a granite
   D) an unconformity between a granite and sandstone
Answer: C
Diff: 2

11) What fundamental concept states that in a horizontal sequence of conformable sedimentary strata, each higher bed is younger than the bed below it?
   A) law of original correlation
   B) theory of correlative deposition
   C) law of superposition
   D) theory of superstition
Answer: C
Diff: 1

12) What of the following refers to the investigative process by which geologists identify and match sedimentary strata and other rocks of the same ages in different areas?
  A) super matching
  B) correlation
  C) strata indexing
  D) cross–access dating

Answer: B
Diff: 1

13) The _____ is the idea or concept that ancient life forms succeeded each other in a definite, evolutionary pattern and that the contained assemblage of fossils can determine geologic ages of strata?
  A) principle of cross correlation
  B) law of fossil regression
  C) law of correlative indexing
  D) principle of faunal succession

Answer: D
Diff: 1

14) Which of the following is an essential characteristic of an index fossil?
  A) the organism lived only in specific environments such as beaches or estuaries
  B) the organism only lived for a short period of geologic time
  C) the fossils are exceptionally abundant and well preserved
  D) the fossils occur in deep–water marine sediments, but the organism actually lived in the sunlit, surface layer of the ocean

Answer: B
Diff: 2

15) By applying the law of superposition _____ dates can be determined.
  A) conventional
  B) radiometric
  C) relative
  D) both relative and radiometric

Answer: C
Diff: 1

16) The era of "ancient life" is the _____ era.
  A) Cenozoic
  B) Paleozoic
  C) Mesozoic
  D) Precambrian

Answer: B
Diff: 1

17) About 88 percent of geologic time is represented by the time span called the _____.
  A) Paleozoic
  B) Precambrian
  C) Mesozoic
  D) Phanerozoic

Answer: B
Diff: 1

18) What is the age of the Earth accepted by most scientists today?
   A) 6.4 billion years
   B) 4.5 million years
   C) 4.5 billion years
   D) 6.4 million years

Answer: C
Diff: 1

19) Which of the following describes radioactive decay by beta particle emission?
   A) The atomic number of the daughter isotope is one more than the parent; the mass numbers are the same.
   B) The mass number of the daughter isotope is one more than the parent, and both isotopes have the same atomic number.
   C) The daughter isotope has an atomic number two less than the parent and a mass number four less
   D) The daughter isotope has an atomic number one less than the parent and a mass number two less.

Answer: A
Diff: 1

20) The half-life of carbon-14 is about 6000 years. Assume that a sample of charcoal formed by burning of living wood 15,000 years ago. How much of the original carbon-14 would remain today?
   A) more than one-half
   B) between one-fourth and one-eighth
   C) between one-half and one-fourth
   D) between one-half and one-third

Answer: B
Diff: 2

21) Visualize five horizontal sedimentary strata exposed in a cliff or canyon wall identified by consecutive numbers, 1 being the lowest bed and 5 being the highest. Which of the following statements concerning the strata are true?
   A) Bed 5 is the oldest.
   B) Beds 1 and 3 are older than bed 4.
   C) Bed 4 is older than bed 2.
   D) Bed 3 is older than beds 2 and 4.

Answer: B
Diff: 2

22) Which of the following denotes the divisions of the geologic time scale in correct order of decreasing lengths of time beginning with the longest time interval and ending with the shortest?
   A) eon, era, epoch, period
   B) era, period, epoch, eon
   C) eon, epoch, period, era
   D) eon, era, period, epoch

Answer: D
Diff: 1

23) Assume that man's recorded history can be stretched back to 4600 years before the present. This is approximately what fraction of geologic time?
   A) one ten-thousandth
   B) one millionth
   C) one billionth
   D) one hundred-thousandth

Answer: B
Diff: 1

24) When a radioactive isotope decays by electron capture, the electron _____.
   A) combines with a neutron in the nucleus, raising the mass number of the daughter isotope by one
   B) combines with a proton in the nucleus; the atomic number of the daughter is one less than the parent
   C) makes the parent isotope into an ion with a charge of negative one
   D) makes the daughter isotope into an ion with a charge of positive one

Answer: B
Diff: 1

25) _____ is an erosional contact between tilted, older strata below and horizontal, younger strata above.
   A) Inverse bedding
   B) An angular unconformity
   C) A disconformity
   D) Cross cutting

Answer: B
Diff: 1

26) Who made the first clear statement of the law of superposition? When?
   A) John Wesley Powell, 19th century
   B) William Smith, 18th century
   C) John Stuart Priestly, 19th century
   D) Nicolaus Steno, 17th century

Answer: D
Diff: 1

27) Sandstone strata and a mass of granite are observed to be in contact. Which of the following statements is correct geologically?
   A) The sandstone is younger if the granite contains sandstone inclusions.
   B) The sandstone is younger if it shows evidence of contact metamorphism.
   C) The granite is older if the sandstone contains pebbles of the granite.
   D) The granite is older if it contains inclusions of sandstone.

Answer: C
Diff: 2

28) Assume that you have just examined several flat-lying sedimentary layers. After much study you determine that there is a considerable span of time for which no sedimentary rock layer exists at this site. You have just discovered a(n) _____.
   A) angular unconformity
   B) series of conformable strata
   C) disconformity
   D) example of cross-cutting relationships
   Answer: C
   Diff: 2

29) A worm would stand a poor chance of being fossilized because _____.
   A) worms have been rare during the geologic past
   B) worms have no hard parts
   C) worms contain no carbon-14
   D) all of these
   Answer: B
   Diff: 1

30) The era known as the "age of mammals" is the _____.
   A) Precambrian
   B) Paleozoic
   C) Mesozoic
   D) Cenozoic
   Answer: B
   Diff: 1

Word Analysis. Examine the words and/or phrases for each question below and determine the relationship among the majority of words/phrases. Choose the option which does not fit the pattern.

31) a. electron capture   b. alpha emission   c. delta capture   d. beta emission
   Answer: C
   Diff: 2

32) a. Paleozoic   b. Mesozoic   c. Phanerozoic   d. Cenozoic
   Answer: B
   Diff: 1

33) a. superposition   b. correlation   c. original horizontality   d. inclusions
   Answer: B
   Diff: 1

34) a. Uranium-238   b. Rubidium-87   c. Carbon-14   d. Potassium-40
   Answer: C
   Diff: 1

35) The geologic time scale was devised before numerical dating using radioactivity was invented.
   Answer: TRUE
   Diff: 1

36) Numerical age dates based on radioactivity are very important for studying Precambrian geologic history because fossils are rare or absent.

Answer: TRUE
Diff: 1

37) The term Mesozoic refers to life forms intermediate in complexity between early and much later, more modern–looking life forms.

Answer: TRUE
Diff: 1

38) Most sedimentary rocks are readily dated by radiometric methods.

Answer: FALSE
Diff: 1

39) After three half–lives, one–ninth of an original, radioactive parent isotope remains and eight–ninths has decayed into the daughter isotope.

Answer: FALSE
Diff: 1

40) A disconformity is an erosional unconformity with parallel beds or strata above and below.

Answer: TRUE
Diff: 1

41) Phanerozoic, marine, sedimentary strata of the same age on different continents can usually be correlated by their fossil assemblages.

Answer: TRUE
Diff: 1

42) The radioactive isotope, potassium–40, has argon–40 as a daughter product.

Answer: TRUE
Diff: 1

43) The term Paleozoic describes the era of ancient life forms.

Answer: TRUE
Diff: 1

44) Pebbles of granite in sandstone and conglomerate resting on the granite suggest that the granite intruded the sedimentary beds.

Answer: FALSE
Diff: 2

45) Radiometric dating means placing events in their proper sequence.

Answer: FALSE
Diff: 1

46) The percentage of radioactive atoms that decay during one half–life is always the same.

Answer: TRUE
Diff: 1

47) An unconformity involving older metamorphic rocks and younger sedimentary strata is termed a nonconformity.

Answer: TRUE
Diff: 1

48) Strata above an angular unconformity were tilted before the older strata were eroded.

Answer: FALSE
Diff: 1

49) Correlation of rock units between continents or widely separated areas is accomplished by using physical features such as color, texture, and thickness of units.

Answer: FALSE
Diff: 1

50) Rapid burial and possession of hard parts are necessary conditions for the preservation of plant or animal remains as fossils.

Answer: TRUE
Diff: 1

51) The Paleozoic is the era of "ancient life."

Answer: TRUE
Diff: 1

52) All of geologic time prior to the beginning of the Paleozoic era is termed the Phanerozoic eon.

Answer: FALSE
Diff: 1

53) When a beta particle is emitted, the mass number of the isotope remains unchanged.

Answer: TRUE
Diff: 1

54) When a beta particle is emitted, the mass number of the isotope remains unchanged.

Answer: TRUE
Diff: 1

55) After two half-lives there is no longer any of the original radioactive material remaining.

Answer: FALSE
Diff: 1

56) What are the mass and charge of an alpha particle?

Answer: 4, +2
Diff: 1

57) The phrase, "The present is the key to the past," refers to the doctrine of _____.

Answer: uniformitarianism
Diff: 1

58) What is the inert gas, daughter product of the radioactive isotope, K-40?

Answer: argon
Diff: 1

59) For a radioactive isotope like Uranium–235, what does the 235 indicate?

Answer: atomic mass
Diff: 1

60) Isotopes of what element are the stable, end products of both uranium decay series?

Answer: lead
Diff: 1

61) If the ratio of radioactive parent to stable daughter isotope is 1:3, how many half–lives have elapsed?

Answer: two
Diff: 1

62) What term denotes blocks of older rock enclosed in a body of younger igneous rock?

Answer: inclusions
Diff: 1

63) What general term denotes a buried, erosional surface where rock layers are missing?

Answer: unconformity
Diff: 1

64) What kind of unconformity is produced when tilted, older strata are eroded and buried by younger strata?

Answer: angular unconformity
Diff: 1

65) What process involves identifying and matching rocks of similar ages in different areas?

Answer: correlation
Diff: 1

66) What is the name of a Phanerozoic era that means ancient life?

Answer: Paleozoic
Diff: 1

67) The remains or traces of prehistoric life are called _____.

Answer: fossils
Diff: 1

68) We now live in the _____ era.

Answer: Cenozoic
Diff: 1

69) In an undeformed sequence of sedimentary rocks, each bed is older than the one above and younger than the one below. The preceding is a statement of the law of _____.

Answer: superposition
Diff: 1

70) All of geologic time prior to the beginning of the Paleozoic era is commonly referred to as the _____.

Answer: Precambrian
Diff: 1

71) An unconformity in which the strata on either side are essentially parallel is termed a(n) _____.

Answer: disconformity
Diff: 1

Critical thinking and discussion questions. Use complete sentences, correct spelling, and the information presented in Chapter 18 to answer the questions below.

72) Compare and contrast relative age dating with radiometric age dating. What is a limitation (if any) of each?

Diff: 2

73) In a given area where you have little knowledge of the local geology (rocks types, fossils, etc.), what type of unconformity would be the most difficult to recognize in an exposed sequence of rocks? Why?

Diff: 2

74) You are asked to interpret the geologic history of a county in California where the geology is quite complex. Aside from visiting various sites in the county for observing geologic sites firsthand, you are permitted to request five different pieces of information or data to aid in your interpretation. List the five that you would choose and explain why each is important for your study.

Diff: 3

75) On the blank provided beside each geologic cross section below, write the name of the specific type of unconformity that is labeled with an arrow. The v–pattern indicates igneous rocks. All other patterns are different types of sedimentary rocks.

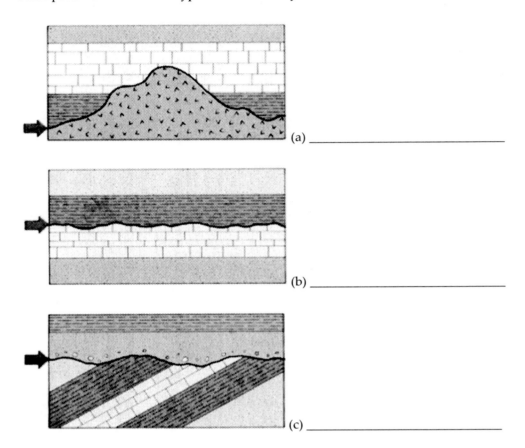

(a) _____

(b) _____

(c) _____

Answer: (a) nonconformity (b) disconformity (c) angular unconformity
Diff: 1

76) In the chart of radioactive decay shown below, how many half–lives have elapsed by time? (a) _____

How many half–lives have elapsed by time? (b) _____

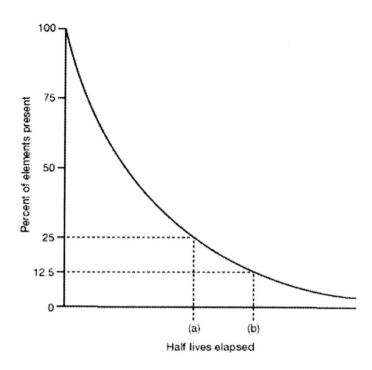

Answer: (a) two (b) three
Diff: 2

77) Examine the geologic cross section below.

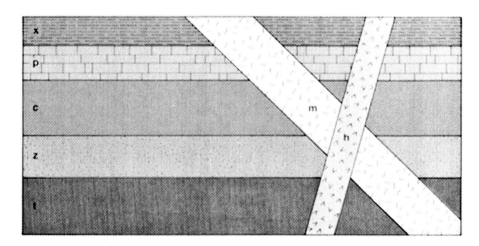

Which feature is the youngest? (a) _____
Which feature is the oldest? (b) _____

Answer: (a) h (b) t
Diff: 2

78) Examine the illustration below (a cross section through the Earth as you might observe on the wall of a quarry or a road cut). Give two reasons why the granite must be older than the sedimentary layers.

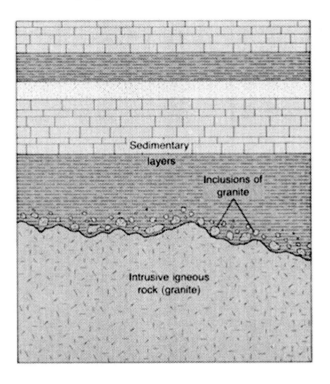

Answer: The sedimentary layers are deposited on top of the granite (principle of superposition). Also, inclusions of the granite in the sedimentary layer indicate that the granite is older using the principle of inclusions.

Diff: 2

Chapter 19   Earth's Evolution through Geologic Time

1) Which of the following gases was NOT part of Earth's original atmosphere?
   A) water vapor
   B) carbon dioxide
   C) nitrogen
   D) oxygen
   E) both A and C

   Answer: D
   Diff: 1

2) The most common Precambrian fossils are _____, layered mounds of calcium carbonate.
   A) prokaryotes
   B) chert
   C) trilobites
   D) stromatolites
   E) none of the above

   Answer: D
   Diff: 1

3) The _____ era is known as the "age of flowering plants."
   A) Precambrian
   B) Paleozoic
   C) Cenozoic
   D) Devonian
   E) Silurian

   Answer: C
   Diff: 1

4) _____ are among the most widespread Paleozoic fossils.
   A) Stromatolites
   B) Birds
   C) Dinosaurs
   D) Salamanders
   E) Brachiopods

   Answer: E
   Diff: 1

5) As the solar system began forming, the first materials to condense into small particles were _____ and nickel.
   A) oxygen
   B) silicon
   C) nitrogen
   D) carbon
   E) none of the above

   Answer: E
   Diff: 1

6) Which one of the following represents the greatest expanse of geological time?
   A) Mesozoic
   B) Cenozoic
   C) Precambrian
   D) Paleozoic
   Answer: C
   Diff: 1

7) During the early Paleozoic era, the current continents of South America, Africa, Australia, Antarctica, India, and perhaps China comprised the vast southern continent of _____.
   A) Europe
   B) Laurasia
   C) Gondwanaland
   D) Antindia
   E) Pangaea
   Answer: C
   Diff: 1

8) Which type of bacteria thrives in environments that lack free oxygen?
   A) aerobic
   B) placental
   C) anaerobic
   D) foraminifera
   E) photosynthetic
   Answer: C
   Diff: 1

9) Which era of geologic time spans about 88% of Earth's history?
   A) Precambrian
   B) Paleozoic
   C) Mesozoic
   D) Cenozoic
   E) none of the above
   Answer: A
   Diff: 1

10) The _____ means "the sun in the making."
    A) solar disk
    B) presun
    C) nebular sun
    D) sol
    E) protosun
    Answer: E
    Diff: 1

11) Mammals became the dominant land animals during the _____ era.
   A) Pleistocene
   B) Cenozoic
   C) Cretaceous
   D) Mesozoic
   E) Paleozoic

Answer: B
Diff: 1

12) The _____ period was a time of major extinctions, including 75 percent of amphibian families.
   A) Jurassic
   B) Mississippian
   C) Permian
   D) Pennsylvanian
   E) Devonian

Answer: C
Diff: 1

13) The beginning of the Cambrian Period marks an important event in animal evolution — the appearance of organisms with _____.
   A) wings
   B) cells
   C) hard parts
   D) vertebrae
   E) none of the above

Answer: C
Diff: 1

14) The era of "ancient life" is the _____ era.
   A) Cenozoic
   B) Precambrian
   C) Neolithic
   D) Mesozoic
   E) none of the above

Answer: E
Diff: 1

15) Due to a virtual absence of land plants and certain animals, fossil fuels are notably absent in _____ rocks.
   A) Precambrian
   B) Paleozoic
   C) Mesozoic
   D) Cenozoic
   E) Paleozoic and Mesozoic

Answer: A
Diff: 1

16) The major source of free oxygen in the atmosphere is from _____.
   A) molten rock
   B) water
   C) green plants
   D) silicate minerals
   E) glaciers
   Answer: C
   Diff: 1

17) The age of Earth is about _____.
   A) 2 billion years
   B) 4.5 million years
   C) 16 million years
   D) 4.5 billion years
   E) 195 million years
   Answer: D
   Diff: 1

18) The Precambrian rock record indicates that much of Earth's first free oxygen combined with _____ dissolved in water.
   A) potassium
   B) silicon
   C) iron
   D) carbon
   E) none of the above
   Answer: C
   Diff: 1

19) Which one of the following does NOT characterize the early development and specialization of the primitive mammals?
   A) increase in size
   B) increase in stomach capacity
   C) increase in brain capacity
   D) specialization of limbs
   E) specialization of teeth
   Answer: B
   Diff: 1

20) As they formed, due to their high temperatures and comparatively weak gravitational fields, which planets were unable to retain appreciable amounts of hydrogen, helium, and ammonia?
   A) Jupiter and Neptune
   B) Mercury and Earth
   C) Uranus and Pluto
   D) Jupiter and Uranus
   E) Neptune and Uranus
   Answer: B
   Diff: 1

21) Abundant fossil evidence did not appear in the geologic record until about _____.
   A) 5 billion years ago
   B) 6 million years ago
   C) 550 million years ago
   D) 300 million years ago
   E) 3 billion years ago
   Answer: C
   Diff: 1

22) During the late Paleozoic, the present–day North America, Europe, western Asia, Siberia, and perhaps China formed the northern continent of _____.
   A) Gondwanaland
   B) Laurasia
   C) Greenland
   D) Africa
   E) none of the above
   Answer: B
   Diff: 1

23) Most _____ rocks are devoid of fossils, which hinders correlation of rocks.
   A) Precambrian
   B) Paleozoic
   C) Mesozoic
   D) Cenozoic
   E) Mesozoic and Cenozoic
   Answer: A
   Diff: 1

24) The _____ period is sometimes called the "golden age of trilobites."
   A) Cambrian
   B) Silurian
   C) Pennsylvanian
   D) Devonian
   E) Triassic
   Answer: A
   Diff: 1

25) _____ means "planets in the making."
   A) Jovian
   B) Asteroids
   C) Terrestrial
   D) Protoplanets
   E) none of the above
   Answer: D
   Diff: 1

26) The process in which plants use light energy to synthesize food sugars from carbon dioxide is called _____.
   A) photosynthesis
   B) hydration
   C) oxidation
   D) fusion
   E) none of the above

Answer: A
Diff: 1

27) The beginning of the _____ era is marked by the appearance of the first life forms with hard parts.
   A) Precambrian
   B) Paleozoic
   C) Mesozoic
   D) Cenozoic

Answer: B
Diff: 1

28) Each continent contains large "core areas" of Precambrian rocks referred to as _____.
   A) rifts
   B) plates
   C) plateaus
   D) shields
   E) none of the above

Answer: D
Diff: 1

29) By the close of the Paleozoic, all the continents had fused into the single super continent of _____.
   A) Laurasia
   B) Pangaea
   C) Appalachia
   D) Gondwanaland
   E) Europa

Answer: B
Diff: 1

30) Earth's primitive atmosphere evolved from gases _____.
   A) produced by radioactive decay
   B) collected from the nebula
   C) escaping from water
   D) from the sun
   E) expelled from within

Answer: E
Diff: 1

31) The most economically important resource in Cenozoic strata of the Gulf Coast is _____.
   A) petroleum
   B) carbon
   C) coal
   D) fresh water
   E) iron

   Answer: A
   Diff: 1

32) The waste gas released by plants as they synthesize food sugars from carbon dioxide and water is _____.
   A) oxygen
   B) methane
   C) nitrogen
   D) carbon dioxide
   E) none of the above

   Answer: A
   Diff: 1

33) Most of Earth's iron ore occurs in middle _____ rocks.
   A) Precambrian
   B) Paleozoic
   C) Mesozoic
   D) Cenozoic

   Answer: A
   Diff: 1

34) The first true terrestrial animals were the _____.
   A) mammals
   B) reptiles
   C) lobe-finned fish
   D) trilobites
   E) marsupials

   Answer: B
   Diff: 1

35) This least understood era of Earth's history has not been subdivided into briefer time units.
   A) Precambrian
   B) Paleozoic
   C) Mesozoic
   D) Cenozoic

   Answer: A
   Diff: 1

36) During the _____ Period, large evaporite deposits of rock salt and gypsum formed in North America.
   A) Cambrian
   B) Silurian
   C) Pennsylvanian
   D) Jurassic
   E) Tertiary

Answer: B
Diff: 1

37) The supercontinent of Pangaea began to breakup during the _____ Era.
   A) Precambrian
   B) Paleozoic
   C) Mesozoic
   D) Cenozoic

Answer: C
Diff: 1

38) Which era is sometimes called the "age of dinosaurs"?
   A) Pleistocene
   B) Cenozoic
   C) Cretaceous
   D) Mesozoic
   E) none of the above

Answer: D
Diff: 1

39) During the _____ Era, the westward–moving North American plate began to override the Pacific plate, eventually causing the tectonic activity that formed the mountains of western North America.
   A) Precambrian
   B) Paleozoic
   C) Mesozoic
   D) Cenozoic
   E) none of the above

Answer: C
Diff: 1

40) By the _____ period, large tropical swamps extended across North America, eventually becoming the vast coal deposits of today.
   A) Cambrian
   B) Silurian
   C) Pennsylvanian
   D) Devonian
   E) Triassic

Answer: C
Diff: 1

41) One group of reptiles, exemplified by the fossil *Archaeopteryx*, led to the evolution of _____.
   A) dinosaurs
   B) mammals
   C) cephalopods
   D) birds
   E) horses
   Answer: D
   Diff: 1

42) Which period is known as the "age of fishes"?
   A) Jurassic
   B) Mississippian
   C) Permian
   D) Pennsylvanian
   E) Devonian
   Answer: E
   Diff: 1

43) During the Cenozoic, plate interactions gave rise to many events of mountain building, volcanism, and earthquakes in _____ North America.
   A) western
   B) central
   C) eastern
   D) southern
   E) northern
   Answer: A
   Diff: 1

44) The cells of these primitive organisms lack organized nuclei and they reproduce asexually.
   A) trilobites
   B) eukaryotes
   C) prokaryotes
   D) brachiopods
   E) none of the above
   Answer: C
   Diff: 1

45) Following the reptilian extinctions at the close of the Mesozoic, two groups of mammals, the marsupials and _____, evolved.
   A) eukaryotes
   B) cephalopods
   C) trilobites
   D) placentals
   E) stromatolites
   Answer: D
   Diff: 1

46) The theory for the origin of the solar system is known as the _____ hypothesis.
    A) Big Bang
    B) nebular
    C) terrestrial
    D) solar
    E) none of the above
Answer: B
Diff: 1

Word Analysis. Examine the words and/or phrases for each question below and determine the relationship among the majority of words/phrases. Choose the option which does not fit the pattern.

47) a. Cambrian   b. Mississippian   c. Jurassic   d. Devonian
    Answer: C
    Diff: 1

48) a. trilobites   b. brachiopods   c. fish   d. dinosaurs
    Answer: D
    Diff: 1

49) a. Cenozoic   b. Phanerozoic   c. Mesozoic   d. Paleozoic
    Answer: B
    Diff: 1

50) a. placental   b. eukaryote   c. marsupial   d. mammal
    Answer: B
    Diff: 1

51) a. oxygen   b. nitrogen   c. carbon dioxide d. photosynthesis
    Answer: B
    Diff: 2

52) The decay of radioactive atoms, coupled with heat released by colliding particles, produced at least some melting of Earth's early interior.
    Answer: TRUE
    Diff: 1

53) We are now living in the Mesozoic era.
    Answer: FALSE
    Diff: 1

54) Most Mesozoic rocks are devoid of fossils, consequently this is the least understood span of Earth's history.
    Answer: FALSE
    Diff: 1

55) Probably the single most characteristic feature of the Precambrian is its great abundance of fossil evidence.
    Answer: FALSE
    Diff: 1

56) Due to differentiation, the lighter, gaseous materials escaped Earth's interior and became the primitive atmosphere.
Answer: TRUE
Diff: 1

57) During the early Paleozoic Era, the continent of Gondwanaland included North and South America.
Answer: FALSE
Diff: 1

58) The bodies of our solar system began forming about 5 billion years ago from an enormous cloud of minute rocky fragments and gases.
Answer: TRUE
Diff: 1

59) The first true terrestrial land animals were the mammals.
Answer: FALSE
Diff: 1

60) Earth's original atmosphere, several billion years ago, was similar to the present atmosphere.
Answer: FALSE
Diff: 1

61) The Cenozoic Era is the age of mammals.
Answer: TRUE
Diff: 1

62) The major source of oxygen in Earth's atmosphere is from the decay of plants.
Answer: FALSE
Diff: 1

63) The supercontinent of Pangaea formed during the late Mesozoic Era.
Answer: FALSE
Diff: 1

64) Much of the original free oxygen in the atmosphere combined with iron dissolved in water to become iron oxide.
Answer: TRUE
Diff: 1

65) With the perfection of the shelled egg, reptiles quickly became the dominant land animals of the Mesozoic Era.
Answer: TRUE
Diff: 1

66) Because of their high surface temperatures and comparatively weak gravitational fields, during their formation, the inner planets retained appreciable amounts of hydrogen, helium, and ammonia as part of their composition.
Answer: FALSE
Diff: 1

67) During the Cenozoic Era, the eastern and western margins of North America experienced similar geologic events.

Answer: FALSE
Diff: 1

68) Altered climatic conditions at the end of the Paleozoic Era caused one of the most dramatic biological declines in all Earth history.

Answer: TRUE
Diff: 1

69) Evidence indicates that some dinosaurs were warm blooded.

Answer: TRUE
Diff: 1

70) The large outer planets (Jupiter, Saturn, Uranus, and Neptune) contain huge amounts of hydrogen and other light materials as part of their composition.

Answer: TRUE
Diff: 1

71) Fossil fuels are abundant in Precambrian rocks.

Answer: FALSE
Diff: 1

72) A major event of the Mesozoic Era was the breakup of the supercontinent called Pangaea.

Answer: TRUE
Diff: 1

73) The fault–block mountains of Nevada and Mexico formed during the Cenozoic Era.

Answer: TRUE
Diff: 1

74) When Earth's primitive surface cooled below water's boiling point, torrential rains slowly filled low areas, forming oceans.

Answer: TRUE
Diff: 1

75) Volcanic activity was common in the West during much of Cenozoic time.

Answer: TRUE
Diff: 1

76) The earliest land plants had large, broad leafs to efficiently intercept sunlight.

Answer: FALSE
Diff: 1

77) Mammals replaced reptiles as the dominant land animals in the Cenozoic Era.

Answer: TRUE
Diff: 1

78) Well preserved remains of many tiny organisms extend the record of life back beyond 5 billion years.

Answer: FALSE
Diff: 1

79) A wave of late Pleistocene extinctions rapidly eliminated many large mammals.

Answer: TRUE
Diff: 1

80) The fossil record supports the hypothesis that the hard parts of organisms evolved for survival.

Answer: FALSE
Diff: 1

81) The evolution of both birds and mammals was strongly influenced by the development of flowering plants.

Answer: TRUE
Diff: 1

82) The beginning of the Precambrian Era is marked by the appearance of the first life forms with hard parts.

Answer: FALSE
Diff: 1

83) Many reptile groups became extinct at the close of the Cenozoic Era.

Answer: FALSE
Diff: 1

84) During the Cenozoic Era, a great wedge of sediments from the eroding Rockies created the Great Plains.

level: 1

Answer: TRUE
Diff: 1

85) Evidence of an extensive glaciation places western Africa near the South Pole during the early Paleozoic Era.

Answer: TRUE
Diff: 1

86) Bacteria that thrive in oxygen free environments are called _____ bacteria.

Answer: anaerobic
Diff: 1

87) The theory for the formation of the solar system is known as the _____.

Answer: nebular hypothesis
Diff: 1

88) During the early Paleozoic Era, the _____ orogeny affected eastern North America from the present-day central Appalachians to Newfoundland.

Answer: Taconic
Diff: 1

89) What were the three gases that made up Earth's original atmosphere?

Answer: water vapor, carbon dioxide, nitrogen
Diff: 1

90) The rock formations of the _____ Era are more widespread and less disturbed than those of any other time.

Answer: Cenozoic
Diff: 1

91) During the process of _____, plants release the gas _____.

Answer: photosynthesis; oxygen
Diff: 1

92) By the late _____ Period, true air-breathing amphibians with fish-like heads and tails had evolved.

Answer: Devonian
Diff: 1

93) The _____ Era spans about 88% of Earth's history.

Answer: Precambrian
Diff: 1

94) The most economically important resource in Cenozoic strata of the Gulf Coast is _____.

Answer: petroleum (natural gas)
Diff: 1

95) Planets in the making are referred to as _____.

Answer: protoplanets
Diff: 1

96) The most common Precambrian rock type is _____ rock.

Answer: metamorphic
Diff: 1

97) The Cenozoic Era is often called the "age of _____."

Answer: mammals
Diff: 1

98) On continents, large "core areas" of Precambrian rocks, called _____, dominate the surface.

Answer: shields
Diff: 1

99) The _____ Period was the "golden age of trilobites."

Answer: Cambrian
Diff: 1

100) The time of the great extinction that took place at the end of the Mesozoic Era is called the _____ or KT boundary.

Answer: Cretaceous-Tertiary
Diff: 1

101) The sun in the making is known as the _____.

Answer: protosun
Diff: 1

102) Western North America is the leading edge of the _____ plate.

Answer: North America
Diff: 1

103) Extensive deposits of _____ ore are found worldwide in Precambrian rocks.

Answer: iron
Diff: 1

104) In North America (including Greenland), the vast exposure of Precambrian rocks, called the _____ Shield, encompasses 2.8 million square miles.

Answer: Canadian
Diff: 1

105) The development of _____, organisms that reproduce sexually and have cells that contain nuclei, may have increased dramatically the rate of evolutionary change.

Answer: eukaryotes
Diff: 1

106) Human evolution takes place during the _____ Period of the _____ Era.

Answer: Quaternary; Cenozoic
Diff: 1

107) Fossils that are not of the animals themselves, but of their activities, such as trails and wormholes, are referred to as _____ fossils.

Answer: trace
Diff: 1

108) The _____ were the dominant trees of the Mesozoic Era.

Answer: gymnosperms
Diff: 1

109) Following the reptilian extinctions at the close of the Mesozoic Era, two groups of mammals, the marsupials and _____, evolved and expanded.

Answer: placentals
Diff: 1

110) Many of the most ancient fossils are found in a hard, dense, chemical rock called _____.

Answer: chert
Diff: 1

111) The late _____ Era extinction was the greatest of at least five mass extinctions to occur over the past 600 million years.

Answer: Paleozoic
Diff: 1

112) _____ are the dominant land plants of the Cenozoic Era.

Answer: Angiosperms

Diff: 1

113) Primitive organisms, called _____, reproduce asexually and contain cells that lack organized nuclei.

Answer: prokaryotes

Diff: 1

114) Toward the end of the Mesozoic Era, the _____ orogeny formed the southern ranges of the Rocky Mountains.

Answer: Laramide

Diff: 1

115) One hypothesis for the extinction that took place at the end of the Mesozoic is that a large _____ collided with Earth.

Answer: asteroid

Diff: 1

Critical thinking and discussion questions. Use complete sentences, correct spelling, and the information presented in Chapter 19 to answer the questions below.

116) Compare and contrast the patterns of life in the Paleozoic Era to the Mesozoic Era. What are the major differences between these two eras? Are there similarities or similar trends?

Diff: 2

117) Why is it so difficult to interpret the geology of the Precambrian? How are these difficulties or limitations different in the younger eras of the Phanerozoic Eon? Finally, are there unique rocks or events in the Precambrian that are not present in younger rocks?

Diff: 2

118) Briefly discuss the origin of Earth's atmosphere and oceans. Are the two related to on another? Also, has the atmosphere remained constant over time or has it changed? And if so then how has it changed?

Diff: 2

119) Examine the figure below, which illustrates the distribution of shields, stable platforms, and younger mountain belts on Earth today. Briefly discuss how have these regions have developed over time using the concept of plate tectonics. Include the relationship between specific types of plate boundaries to the various regions if possible.

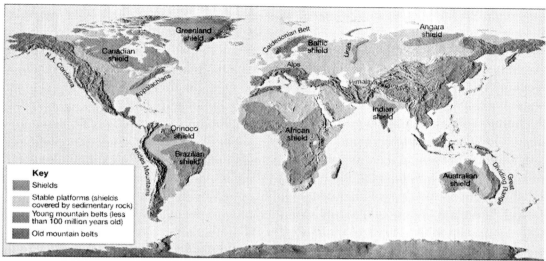

Copyright © 2006 Pearson Prentice Hall, Inc.

Diff: 3